The

BIG
CRYPTIC
CROSSWORDS

Over 200 cryptic crosswords

hamlyn

An Hachette UK Company
www.hachette.co.uk

First published in Great Britain in 2019 by Hamlyn,
an imprint of Octopus Publishing Group Ltd
Carmelite House
50 Victoria Embankment
London EC4Y 0DZ
www.octopusbooks.co.uk

ISBN 9-780-60063-631-1

A CIP catalogue record for this book is available from the British Library.

Printed and bound in the UK

10 9 8 7 6 5 4 3 2

The material in this book has previously been published in
Daily Mail All New Cryptic Crosswords 4, *Daily Mail All New Cryptic
Crosswords 5* and *Daily Mail All New Cryptic Crosswords 6*

ACKNOWLEDGEMENTS

Editorial Director: Trevor Davies
Editor: Abi Waters
Editorial Assistant: Mireille Harper
Designer: Jack Storey
Senior Production Manager: Peter Hunt
Production Assistant: Serena Savini
Page make-up: Dorchester Typesetting Group Ltd

1 Capital. **5** Sample. **9** Project. **10** Monocle. **11** End. **12** Constrained. **13** Sisal. **14** Universal. **16** Repenting. **17** Timid. **19** Blameworthy. **22** Nag. **23** Egotism. **24** Palette. **26** Skinny. **27** Secures.

Down

1 Cypress. **2** Proud as a peacock. **3** Tie. **4** Latin. **5** Something. **6** Mania. **7** Loch Ness monster. **8** Feudal. **12** Colon. **14** Uniformly. **15** Entry. **16** Rubber. **18** Digress. **20** Evian. **21** Tapes. **25** Lac.

Puzzles

26

Across

1 Frankincense. **8** Evasion. **9** Bungled. **11** Matchmaker. **12** Hall. **14** Furbelow. **16** Estate. **17** Oaf. **19** Frolic. **21** Rekindle. **24** Iota. **25** Descendant. **27** Edition. **28** Inertia. **29** Short-sighted.

Down

1 Flatter. **2** Arithmetic. **3** Kangaroo. **4** Nabbed. **5** Erne. **6** Sultana. **7** Term of office. **10** Differential. **13** Assignment. **15** War. **18** Fetching. **20** Ostrich. **22** Drafted. **23** Tennis. **26** Liar.

27

Across

6 Elizabethan age. **9** Stance. **10** Courting. **11** Carriage. **13** Hilary. **15** Ambush. **17** Israel. **19** Weasel. **20** Emission. **22** Hiawatha. **24** Onrush. **26** Tatterdemalion.

Down

1 Central America. **2** Finn. **3** Camera. **4** Thoughts. **5** Gnat. **7** Etched. **8** General consent. **12** Rebus. **14** Loads. **16** Solitary. **18** Legate. **21** Isobar. **23** Wits. **25** Ruin.

Across

6 Cheeky youngster with more fashionable paparazzo (14)
9 Consumable belied its unusual source (6)
10 Hence 16 avoided it on way up to get spouse (4,4)
11 Artist Tracey in French church for cardinal's 14 (8)
13 Torrid heat in middle of valley causing death (6)
15 Businessmen unexpectedly leave Essen in cloud (6)
17 Funny story about English mollusc (6)
19 I'm upset by this awfully poor stroke (6)
20 E.g. flu I'd caught in gym among infected mice (8)
22 Told to find out about ruins of Rome (8)
24 Daniel's embarrassed saying no (6)
26 Fine elegant wind instrument in black box (6,8)

Down

1 Woman's edition designed on line, lacking depth (3-11)
2 Mike's recruited into Liberal branch (4)
3 Anger noticed around Poland (6)
4 Every year supporter welcomes a nun in trouble (8)
5 Special American tinned food (4)
7 Like autumn leaves right across central Sussex? (6)
8 An arid exterior maybe, but outstanding (14)
12 Compose hymn about origin of pretty young woman (5)
14 E.g. Lord or Lady let it out (5)
16 University team lit up final (8)
18 Drop the French church official (6)
21 Like games at home at party or … (6)
23 … unseemly revelry or extremes of gluttony? (4)
25 It's somewhat redundant climbing with no clothes on (4)

Across

1 Class influence exerted by the Lords? (4,8)
8 Like West Berlin once, or Valence after revolution (7)
9 Shake and tumble dry cloth (7)
11 US property price includes English ornate slate (4,6)
12 Almost perfect concept (4)
14 Loafer or yob taking a horse back (8)
16 Frank also blocks detectives (6)
17 Endlessly manufactured crackers (3)
19 I get a cocktail at close of play in theatre (6)
21 Hazy intelligence about blue compound (8)
24 Put back, say, a criminal leader in prison (4)
25 Shocker, remake of "Hall of Mirrors"? Al's not in it (6,4)
27 Be careful in crow's nest for instance (7)
28 Advanced alone, adrift round island due to wind action (7)
29 Harry keeps blocking new sponsor's mouthpiece (12)

Down

1 Going north, some martyr accepts S. American mammal (7)
2 To make things worse, Rex beat ace controversially (10)
3 Guitarist uses it mixed with woad to make talcum powder (8)
4 They live abroad in Portugal crushed by absurd taxes … (6)
5 … or in Sussex, say, suffering pain (4)
6 Curved like some figures approximately (7)
7 Nervous US soldier in pub supports new currency (12)
10 Flattery blinds the man in a mess (12)
13 Our lab is refurbished by us so it's healthy (10)
15 Brown tried acting nonchalantly at first (3)
18 Reduce iron? (8)
20 Pouring liquid for clique (2-5)
22 View old shackle (7)
23 It's fine to use unusually young mammal (6)
26 Pawn white wine (4)

Across

1 What the country owes is notable and it needs sorting! (8,4)
8 News agency's treasure ruined after losing article (7)
9 One of a variety of blooms surrounding square (7)
11 It shows speech pattern in weird moving picture (no mug) (10)
12 It's just a travelling show (4)
14 Worked up silver I'd positioned outside gallery (8)
16 Cycling non-stop, I go round private areas only (6)
17 Organise race (3)
19 New recruits content to appoint a keeper (6)
21 Friendly and sociable, having recently retired (8)
24 The instant Jack leaves it's risky (4)
25 Mellors was Lawrence's willing guy in goal (10)
27 On a quest to meet 13 (all or part of) (7)
28 A loser's up the creek without a paddle (7)
29 She had bra repaired at Rye working with this? (12)

Down

1 Tuna cooked by writer, followed by 51 molluscs (7)
2 The old ships captivate MEP in leisure attractions (5,5)
3 Witness finished describing Serb in distress (8)
4 Person with pigment defect harassed on Bali (6)
5 Piece of old rope in sink (4)
6 Type of rice: sampan regularly brought in a bit perhaps (7)
7 I visit retail complex to get trifles (12)
10 Dinners go badly with RSM in formal wear (7,5)
13 Crazy Greek going for crazy monarch (4,6)
15 Pair perform round university (3)
18 A lot of miners love to protect union (8)
20 Send up plump cheese in flimsy material (7)
22 Writer's sympathy masks English irreverence (7)
23 Shabby colour covering a child's horse (6)
26 Sunny start to fortnight in Spain (4)

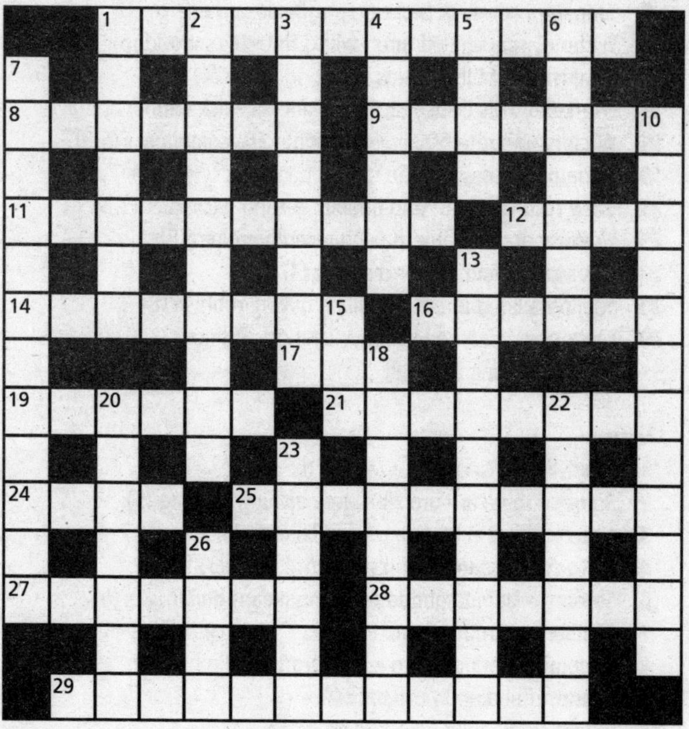

Across

1 Short skirts go in government department (8)
5 Mike's unwisely beginning to tempt fate (6)
9 Teenaged solver gets the flu maybe, losing energy (8)
10 Water nymph almost lures sailors in Lewis's world (6)
12 Final trumpet blow needs no introduction (4)
13 These days Ms Dench and Ms Blanchett pick winners (10)
15 What magistrate has, adjudicating noise complaint? (5,8)
19 No minor routes confine radical people in wetlands (7,6)
23 Ladybird flies over heart of Deal getting basic diet (5,5)
25 Loafer in Head Office in Sussex perhaps? (4)
28 Attempt to hold 16 ounces in hat (6)
29 Film boss cried uncontrollably recalling rubbish (8)
30 Doctor reversed Conservative's fungal problem (3,3)
31 Omit 25 mixing drink (8)

Down

1 Short-lived insect might take to the air (6)
2 Some of them are proper sisters owning nothing (5)
3 Note nothing in area of central London (4)
4 Full editor supports drinks bought in pub (7)
6 Someone from Baghdad put Republicans on TV quiz (5)
7 Mothers guard northeastern area tigers, typically (3-6)
8 Vary test, turning it into a parody (8)
11 Expert turned up in Uruguay (4)
14 In France the road back has no money (4)
15 Condition of slaves? It's very bad round Illinois (9)
16 Sail starts in Jamaica in middle of Caribbean (3)
17 Seize Greek sailor (4)
18 It's in Dundee, damaged but as originally written (8)
20 Where to park in stockbroker belt (4)
21 Natural style is protected by kingdom (7)
22 E.g. caviar government sent up for king (6)
24 Lout upended old boy carrying book (5)
26 Where does rabbit live? In shed at church (5)
27 Some provide money for public meeting (4)

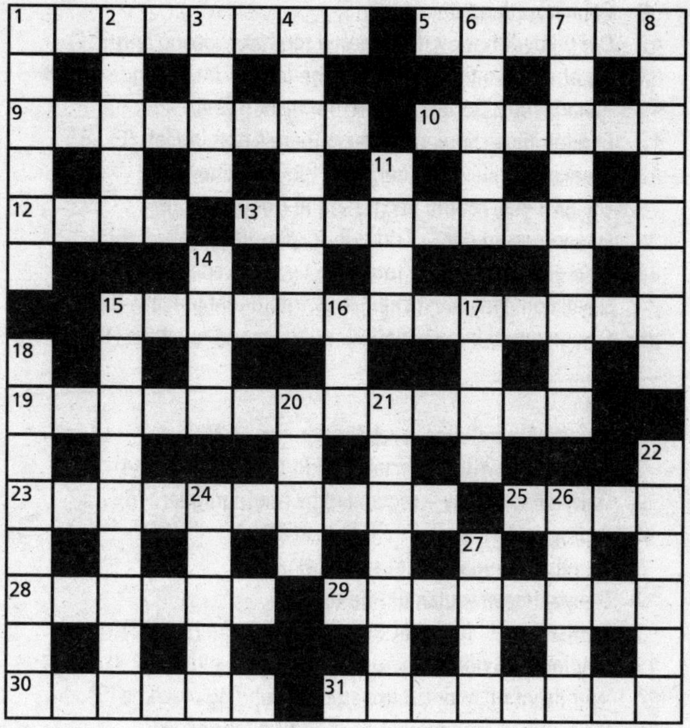
1
2
3
4
5
6
7
8
9
10
11
12
13
14
15
16
17
18
19
20
21
22
23
24
25
26
27
28
29
30
31

Across

6 Log temperatures etc. here in Wales working in hottest area (7,7)

9 Counsel a daughter on sin (6)

10 Old fellow's back with battered top hat, walking here? (8)

11 It's about two thousand and nine maybe, happening soon (8)

13 Billiard shots boffins played, not bishop (2-4)

15 Enough time clipping borders! There's nothing left (6)

17 Breaking the law can generate lots of money (6)

19 US spies nab retired people in the Odeon, say (6)

20 Dangerous amount of drug in surplus does spread (8)

22 He'd entered working total exactly when specified (2,3,3)

24 Small company must change its traditional practice (6)

26 Design mural in a chapel using letters and numbers (14)

Down

1 A pair of mandolines I repaired in flat (3-11)

2 Short-story writer entertains a kid to some extent (4)

3 Dairy product, say – requested by photographer? (6)

4 A protein converted into a poison (8)

5 Domestic animals upset stage (4)

7 Deny referee regular cup tie (6)

8 Foolish word "tut", but it can be delightful (3,2,4,5)

12 Employed at home, energy supports you and me (2,3)

14 With front off, worked like smooth-running machine (5)

16 It's tough in government to keep ring fencing (8)

18 Lowest part in Shakespeare? (6)

21 Extra piece once irritated engineers (6)

23 Hidden boundary that's twice out of bounds (2-2)

25 How you feel after portion of classic kebab? (4)

Across

6 Immature, like dull photographs (14)
9 Pain in side made by knitting needle? (6)
10 British soldiers once broke code kept by deserters (8)
11 Spooky places scattered across Turkey (8)
13 Writer's left to bring goods in (6)
15 Relatives spoilt the majority of Swanlinbar (2-4)
17 Less attractive gruel is stirred with one (6)
19 Cuba soon acquires new powerful weapon (6)
20 Top of seat sheared off at junction (8)
22 Wide hotel includes odd gaps the width of a bird (8)
24 Wild excitement when Stephen tours east New Zealand (6)
26 Pertinent ratio needs analysis and elucidation (14)

Down

1 Mark heads new political unit: it creates a product (14)
2 What newspapermen do every day in their leaders (4)
3 A king badly hurt another king (6)
4 Small plant in Leeds built in Garforth originally (8)
5 US TV channel covers old vagrant (4)
7 In a strange way anger's rising in cathedral city (6)
8 Join unit receiving fancy prizes in favoured business area (10,4)
12 Mark appears in Co. Londonderry … (5)
14 … before deputy head of monastery (5)
16 Date stone swallowed in drink may block this (8)
18 Risk removing end of eastern part of church (6)
21 Public disturbance caused by a very strong beam (6)
23 IT nerd runs out of language (4)
25 Leave team in borders of Egypt (4)

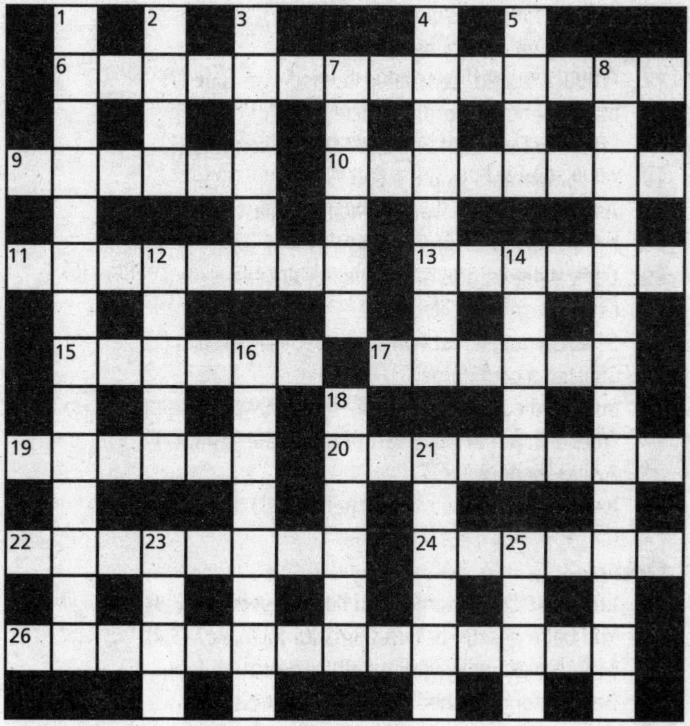
1
2
3
4
5
6
7
8
9
10
11
12
13
14
15
16
17
18
19
20
21
22
23
24
25
26

Across

1 Give up after rough net play? Goal should result (7,4)
9 Former lovers welcome it after constant thrills (7)
10 College for priests cut study group (7)
11 Student returns to river in France (3)
12 Produce eggs of zero value, addled over time (7)
13 Make money importing article made of clay (7)
14 Primarily friends of England? On the contrary (3)
15 All competitors stop the ball (5)
17 Avoid centre of Nevada, heading to east (5)
18 He's resigned to interrupting this way (5)
20 Carry a pet on odd occasions in vault (5)
22 Label teaspoon "Silver" (3)
24 Swedish queen met earl on horseback perhaps (7)
25 Shorten a card game (7)
26 Some did equation backwards, which was to be proved (3)
27 Gold dish put at front part of range that's flat (7)
28 Artists' underwear (7)
29 Identical twins like muffled bells? (4,7)

Down

1 Imagine PC sent home from holiday perhaps (7,8)
2 You bet a quarter or two-thirds for instance? (3,4)
3 Man, for example, underneath large cotton fabric (5)
4 Beatles song finished at 12 last night (9)
5 I'm on river in Liverpool finally going for dip (7)
6 Send 13 kids abroad, showing generosity (4-11)
7 Start golf match chewing toffee (3,3)
8 Brown gets medal (6)
16 Chancellor's office in former PM's home (unfinished) (9)
18 Seafood is served up outside tents (6)
19 Fabulous creature, a rich eccentric hosting writer (7)
21 Le Carré turned up describing row of houses (7)
23 Well-oiled Greek's no problem (6)
25 Notice fellow's extra feature (3-2)

Across

1 "That's a pitiful excuse!" cries Conservative (3,5)
5 Manage OK with mead, blended (4,2)
9 Radical changes fish during drinks (5-3)
10 Cryptic clues hide short answer in part of sentence (6)
12 Vessel's a cutter with bow removed? (4)
13 Ramshackle joint tiler repaired round Bury complex (5-5)
15 Art style has to make mark on leaderless Jewish movement (13)
19 What's in one's mind before taking job? (13)
23 Antiviral protein represents almost new frontier (10)
25 Stay away from former vandals close to front (4)
28 Element found in American's pocket (6)
29 Order nothing for special soldier (8)
30 Fifty-one stories told in flowers (6)
31 First of young mares key in African nation's riding event (8)

Down

1 Abbess is terrifying, confining one of her charges (6)
2 Native American bachelor party (5)
3 Long walk to reach east Kimberley first (4)
4 Peter stupidly gets the Parisian full (7)
6 Unscripted remark by a Dutch politician? (2,3)
7 Learning issue involves sport at Murrayfield (9)
8 Working at night, say, finished redesigning item (8)
11 Cut Hibernian flower (4)
14 Huge photograph attached to email? (4)
15 Exactly like personal papers a client mislaid (9)
16 Liquid essential to plants apparently (3)
17 Exclude circle at US technical university (4)
18 Left to personal choice, old mate got into trouble (8)
20 Second-hand American edition (4)
21 Words of regret from a heartless guy bagging game (7)
22 Hair from orang-outang or alpaca? No, maybe goat (6)
24 Old law officer's always promoted round end of June (5)
26 Stainer's two numbers defended by male alto (5)
27 A donkey's nearly wild (4)

Across

1 Unknown individual's nuts about sharp weapons (8)
5 People on slope injured kisser (6)
9 Former lover's in fold sadly, and weak (3,5)
10 Mouse frightened queue, say, inside place of worship (6)
12 I like occasionally following small QC (4)
13 Nothing in cardboard box; it's stuffed in funny drawer (10)
15 Detailed plan pacifist once devised to control India (13)
19 I'm shown after PM in good wise all-embracing TV satire (8,5)
23 Taking over power, Unionist nervously put on airs (10)
25 Expert gave up reading *Ulysses* at the start (4)
28 Irish question is baffling adult people in Baghdad (6)
29 Choir etc. in poor form? It always bounces back (8)
30 Chap in hot water, say? (6)
31 Small fish oddly seen ashore in distress (3,5)

Down

1 Read through lines in revolutionary English book (6)
2 Sing falsetto verse in outskirts of Yeovil (5)
3 New university students are worth nothing (4)
4 Their heads get beaten by awful nameless man in pit (7)
6 It's not very different (or very far) from Tokyo (5)
7 Beautiful 9 is in quiet form (9)
8 Perspiring? Have a meal during jazz music (8)
11 Small decorated box displayed in the Tuileries (4)
14 Message for tenor outside (4)
15 Mimic keeping time and cause some excitement (9)
16 Game over – rookie's lost in mist (3)
17 The first man not to have one! (4)
18 Given a quantity of money, confess having taken it (8)
20 E.g. A sharp memorandum? (4)
21 Revere wedding declaration on exotic isle (7)
22 First of all release relative (6)
24 I sit for artist outside, showing composure (5)
26 Woman's supporting you and me as escort (5)
27 Scrub middle of toothbrush? Nonsense (4)

1
2
3
4
5
6
7
8
9
10
11
12
13
14
15
16
17
18
19
20
21
22
23
24
25
26
27
28
29
30
31

Across

1 Halt Marilyn Monroe film (3,4)
5 Old writer's bed in Kent, say (6)
9 About start of nineties a dunce amazingly graduated (7)
10 It helps TV presenter in traffic hold-up, say (7)
11 Old churchman's rum (3)
12 Smart student doctor in Lewes sadly spends regularly (4,7)
13 Collars thugs by the sound of it (5)
14 Natural result of firm recalling all men on line (9)
16 Outer layer of crushed spider mite lacking tension (9)
17 Dizzy Gillespie's intro did move Yankee (5)
19 Chap with radio is excited, having swallowed this? (11)
22 It's cold, especially at the start (3)
23 Steeped in trouble at extreme level (7)
24 Delay American writer in South Dakota (7)
26 Big car in Maryland, for instance (6)
27 Supernatural power in valley returned and went by (7)

Down

1 Nice greeting makes our job awkward around north (7)
2 Reserve stall of cod, say, on headland (15)
3 Twitch in odd places (3)
4 Reportedly sell bicycle part (5)
5 They're probably upheld in military parades (9)
6 I cut rotten tree, but what to do with loose knot? (5)
7 Annoying passengers support advertisers abroad (4-4,7)
8 Germany delay training? That's fatal (6)
12 Washington set broadcast rubbish (5)
14 Discussion group arrive welcoming German with note (9)
15 Reason heads of LEAs offer grants in college (5)
16 Large antelopes in eastern countries (6)
18 Bore conceded (7)
20 Last character from Athens to appear in Rome games (5)
21 Publication is to take action (5)
25 Circuit in Belgium or Spain (3)

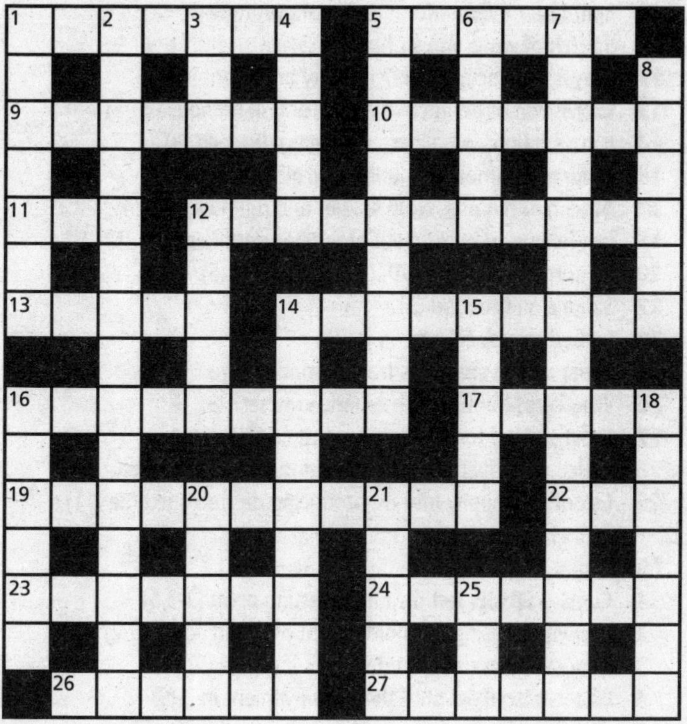

Across

1 Carroll's poem irritated Roy and Jack Webb (11)
9 Harbour master trained pet (7)
10 Spilt bitter over uniform as act of gratitude (7)
11 Stretch of water in La Chapelle (3)
12 Why 8's replacing hotel? It's very important (7)
13 Expression of boredom by most of 8 in hothouse (5-2)
14 It covers floor in ballgame by being dropped (3)
15 Turkish governor has bubbly secretary in front (5)
17 African ruminants avoid soldier and run away (5)
18 Old fellows in back street are upper-class gents … (5)
20 … some nobles, say? Ah, the poor dears (5)
22 Sailor's on the road (3)
24 Embed money scheme in it (7)
25 Spots almost seamless transformation (7)
26 Who cares about South American tuber? (3)
27 Leaves space for small restaurant (3,4)
28 Welcome arrival goes wild about duke and loses head (7)
29 CIA office happily met us, producing desired outcome (11)

Down

1 Coming up alp, Jeff disputed starting point (7-3,5)
2 Awful job raising bar holding hot and cold liquid (5-2)
3 Almost doesn't start at dawn for instance (5)
4 Observe legal action – there's movement in it (9)
5 Posh food is nice for a change around university (7)
6 Shy Ulster hotel sadly keeps nothing for casual travellers (5,10)
7 Person who demonstrates one way to wash (6)
8 Grow into suit (6)
16 Extremely tiny nuclear U-boat parts exchanged (9)
18 Number needing a drink avoiding sun (6)
19 Speak abusively of flags not in correct order (4,3)
21 Whatshisname repeated notes (2-3-2)
23 Live and die tragically after short rest (6)
25 Scotsman welcomes Joe's conjuring (5)

Across

1 As supplier of fertiliser busy shop came top (7,4)
9 A new lunar formation in the shape of a circle (7)
10 Where conductor stands or turns to play banjo, say (7)
11 It's lovely to finish somewhere in Cambridgeshire (3)
12 River birds – they introduce records (7)
13 Sozzled, i.e. deeply drunk, left abandoned (3-4)
14 Some people invested in European currency (3)
15 Exclude book with expensive jacket (5)
17 Queen's consort in colony agreed to host king (5)
18 Dance company never got accepted at first (5)
20 Way of painting perhaps bears a stigma (5)
22 Hide 4 with no oxygen (3)
24 How to smash a ball past a magistrate (7)
25 Answer in nasty murder is crucial for hearing (7)
26 Watch group of 13 (3)
27 What man trod on roughly, ignoring both names (7)
28 Feels bitter about unopened gifts (7)
29 Sexy top of French non-U colleague taking tea, say (11)

Down

1 Novice once fed on cooked frozen meals, for example (11,4)
2 Exciting drama about two students and a duck (7)
3 Harry goes across river to find monsters (5)
4 Conservatives try to keep old role at start of year (4,5)
5 Soap location's English and set abroad? Yes and no (4,3)
6 4 event in Tory France sadly with little cash about (5,10)
7 Footwear worn in Tunis and Algiers (6)
8 E.g. mud's scattered, making dirty mark (6)
16 Fixed table, inlaying same crude zinc or tin, say (4,5)
18 Skies like this could upset youth leader (6)
19 Weak CIA man managed to conserve energy (7)
21 Turbulent sea-air over Uruguay's vast land mass (7)
23 Forgetful Bible studies teacher? (6)
25 Ghostly eastern lake (5)

Across

1 Leave people to talk endlessly about branch (12)
8 In recession firm imports wild grain grown naturally (7)
9 Ghost metamorphoses a month after priest (7)
11 Beef up horribly thin teenagers (not i.e. adult) (10)
12 One needing to exercise without female in centre (4)
14 Convert honestly but without anyone knowing (2,3,3)
16 Silly article, not the leader, analysed cake (6)
17 Put scenery on stage (3)
19 Persuade and regularly coax GI to hold line (6)
21 Conspicuously indicate supporter in war (8)
24 A drink upset Indian ruler (4)
25 He's put in steel mat shaped out of this? (5,5)
27 17s are not well, so leave port (3,4)
28 Tolkien's monsters have concealed flowers (7)
29 Unexpectedly like painter's incomplete colour range? (3,2,3,4)

Down

1 Pursue Communist riding at a gentle pace (7)
2 One of many produced by evergreen – nine peeled off (4,6)
3 Solo performances could be realistic if I got involved (8)
4 E.g. Miss Piggy met up comically with Prince (6)
5 Close section of the Thirty-nine Articles (4)
6 Dish girl on volcano going up (7)
7 Unstable edifice Kings and Queens etc. built? (5,2,5)
10 TT entrant spreads cost with Tom and Cyril (12)
13 Thrifty English stand-up Murray keeps working (10)
15 The old soprano's positive reply (3)
18 Newspaper picked up single 15° strip of earth (4,4)
20 African charm retains its form of self-defence (7)
22 I learnt at sea where to go in the services (7)
23 Small house in Switzerland American rented (6)
26 Starch has a good taste (4)

Across

1 Research assistant secures support for body (7)
5 Floral display in stock, mostly English originally (6)
9 Barbecue topside of beef and more nuts (avoiding first) (7)
10 Women rise angrily when office machine's put out (4,3)
11 Green area that's illegal in places (3)
12 Wild pine marten crosses motorway, doesn't stay long … (11)
13 … its cousin's surprisingly alert (5)
14 In GB, he worried our man next door (9)
16 Place in Texas, or two nearly in Scottish inlet (4,5)
17 Republican is monarch? It's certainly a step up (5)
19 Not working in church, he returns to river café (6,5)
22 One fellow's heart's not healthy (3)
23 It's fashionable to arrange a deal involving doctor (1,2,4)
24 Sort of 15 has left one load of rubbish (7)
26 Theatre staff keep still (2,4)
27 Designed ideal PR for what some deaf people do (3-4)

Down

1 He works with last Australian friend guarding lake (7)
2 In reality, after Mao, fat cats flourished (2,1,6,2,4)
3 One of a pair in winter sports kit (3)
4 Take clothes off in band (5)
5 Decorate again after wreckage of brush fire (9)
6 Group of Dutch in Africa or somewhere further east (5)
7 A degree of complex facts and ceremonies (6,2,7)
8 Crown of every tenth tree diseased in English city (6)
12 Family member at home with the French woman (2-3)
14 It could be worth staying in comfy home in Lancs, say (9)
15 Possibly Arab king wears stockings (5)
16 One group of agents in Florida offer beauty treatment (6)
18 Transmitted early broadcast by newspaper chief (7)
20 Call up first woman to receive fine (5)
21 Floral top's medium with sort of blue border (5)
25 6's up for one circuit of track (3)

Across

1 American priest is in Southend for stay (7)
5 Omit passage from speech rector overlooked (6)
9 Total wipe-out's bound to come after many years (7)
10 Mitchell's bust, having dumped lines in shop (7)
11 Napoleon's sign (3)
12 Rampart 11 built round unit gives tank protection (6,5)
13 Sailor's knocked about? It's established practice (5)
14 Poet's staggered in drunk, as it were (2,2,5)
16 Disabled transport's hatch I repaired in 22 (4,5)
17 Match takes place over in beer garden (5)
19 Good claret's spoiled if kept here (4,7)
22 Bar oil company stocking uranium in recession (3)
23 Tire that's unknown in the USA strangely (7)
24 Napoleon, say, overthrew theatre in Rome completely (7)
26 Stallone accepts Gibson's rank (6)
27 Shout to all galloping, including leaders of York hunt (5-2)

Down

1 The last condemned burglar needed more of this! (7)
2 Lily's a leading light (4,2,9)
3 It's plumed but not all over (3)
4 King made broadcast about his ultimate ambition? (5)
5 Run into meeting (9)
6 He tucked into mushroom and chicken, I hear? (5)
7 It's owned by busy Tipperary vet with professional input (7,8)
8 Sudden display by nude skater doing acrobatics? (6)
12 *Room at the Top* – fantastic work fan's forgotten (5)
14 Able to sail but nervous about duck in rough water (9)
15 The sort of bread that's left at the end in market? (5)
16 Pour water in it typically (6)
18 Ban English doctor getting on old ship (7)
20 What craniologist studies in a row, say (5)
21 Spy's a polite man (5)
25 Friend's mixed up in 12 Across (3)

Across

6 Cleaner which manages somehow to keep fashionable (7,7)
9 French author in stupor, drunk (6)
10 What engravers do at home with former writer (8)
11 Adopting old-fashioned marriage (8)
13 Hide missing drug in soap (6)
15 Girl oddly unable to find yearbook (6)
17 Smashing feast includes recipe for pudding (6)
19 Circle funny man in church (6)
20 Person who connects you to a rope thrown over river (8)
22 Celebrate round water hole, getting louder (8)
24 Outcome of Ulster's new assembly (6)
26 Job of QC going over to engage former African despot (5-9)

Down

1 Risky performer promises wife to concede during series (5-9)
2 Jacob's brother covered in apple sauce (4)
3 Break adversely affected us touring America (6)
4 Sign on staff to compose scales in B and F (4,4)
5 Fish daily (4)
7 Nearly cooked in front of radiator (6)
8 Special Bible lesson about love, say, upheld peer's duty (8,6)
12 Proprietor's fit of depression, missing daughter (5)
14 Character in Greek theatre's no good without note (5)
16 Historical documents I've bound in different 5s (8)
18 Old governor general's in trouble up in balcony (6)
21 I grew alarmed clutching a creepy-crawly (6)
23 Rich heavy drinker (4)
25 British rugby team's upset, lacking new ground (4)

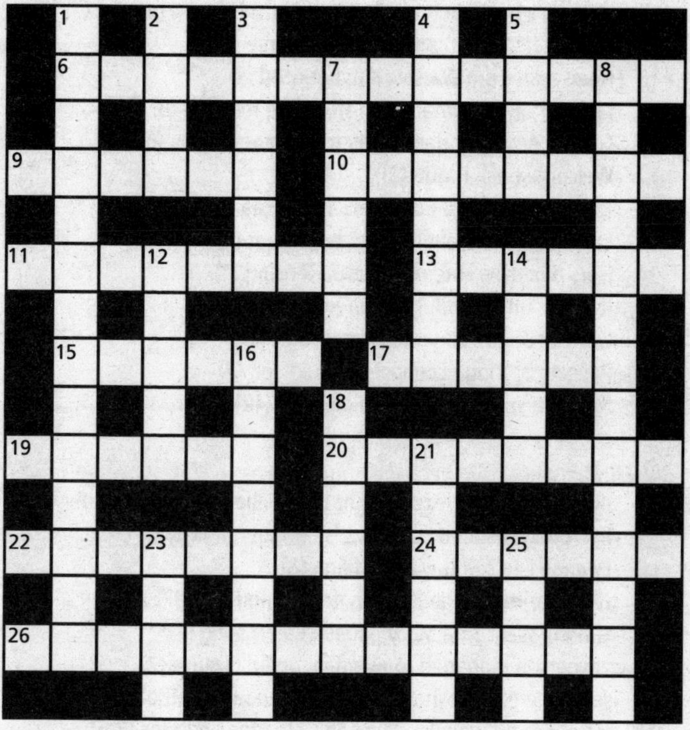
1
2
3
4
5
6
7
8
9
10
11
12
13
14
15
16
17
18
19
20
21
22
23
24
25
26

Across

1 I'd admitted to putting stress on mate, not meaning to (12)
8 Occupants of zoo in Milan complex like cages (7)
9 Woman's hesitation about new hips? It's just a rumour (7)
11 Child stars need managing to a degree (5,5)
12 Head man from Warsaw's announced (4)
14 I leave Italy in container to stimulate reaction (8)
16 Greek one has variable jetty to prevent erosion (6)
17 Welcome back Braun (3)
19 Funny story about European aphrodisiac perhaps (6)
21 Letters record dreadful lies about saint (8)
24 Hors d'oeuvre eaten by Sherpa Tensing (4)
25 It could kill beautiful lady in Rome (10)
27 Crochet doilies to put on a pedestal (7)
28 Reports of fringe collapsing round you (7)
29 Mascara stain ruined cloth on chair (12)

Down

1 I'm impressed by exotic saint but I believe in nature's soul (7)
2 Eric oddly inspired composer's "Bringer of Light"? (10)
3 Divulge Leo's dodgy record first (8)
4 It's quite fresh when distributed around island (6)
5 Girl in "West Side Story" doesn't start song (4)
6 Layperson managed to avoid an awful disease (7)
7 Job done editing short topical film about a Catholic (4,8)
10 He glides on wheels, waves to Catherine and runs (6,6)
13 I'd carried in gifts for heads of state (10)
15 First woman in heart of 7 (3)
18 Formal defence in a game I had in Georgia (8)
20 Take a seat – it's plastic with soft hair (3,4)
22 Ran like liquid, longer and thinner (7)
23 Information on 17 somewhere in Switzerland (6)
26 Suitable dress for this car? (4)

Across

1 Top surgery? It's blooming awful without oxygen (12)
8 Fruit with date wrapped in handkerchief (7)
9 Another male's partly a help when balloon goes up (7)
11 It stops flow to vessel quite dramatically (10)
12 Leaders in Worcester sent back bird (4)
14 A city abroad hosts a king and duke (supporting figure) (8)
16 In Paris she's arrested by trustee and bank official (6)
17 Top and bottom missing from low-cost supermarket (3)
19 Give off when river swamps hall nearly (6)
21 It gets chipped in dance at St. Andrews (4,4)
24 Taking the wrong course can be a worry 29 (4)
25 Sleep here about noon would be risky for drivers (6,4)
27 It involves guts dethroning king (7)
28 Old 11 side sadly get rusty (7)
29 Calais colony dispersed now and then (12)

Down

1 Monkey swallows duck in dreamy relaxed state (7)
2 Flower appearing in war-torn Libya cut twice a year (10)
3 Serene translation of Quran with lit-up binding (8)
4 Glove's dry in appearance (6)
5 Noticed what sounds like part of play (4)
6 Cast learn about 29 dummy figure (7)
7 A celeb co-star collapsed in 400m hurdles, say (8,4)
10 Topless flower girls catch cold; they're looked down on (5,7)
13 What ascetic practises Linda feels is wrong (4-6)
15 29 doing a bit of archaeology (3)
18 Almost distrust fool's gold coin (8)
20 He disputed rite with Catholic (7)
22 E.g. local library could be scuppered any time (7)
23 Stunted tree in Lisbon's ailing at its core (6)
26 Permit is needed to enter London museum (4)

Across

1 Board's not backing fish food (8)
5 Fines put in money box (6)
9 Animal and insect go to Gretna maybe (8)
10 Order nine at random to swallow demijohn (6)
12 Nobleman nearly stripped (4)
13 Polish penalise writer with rent outstanding (10)
15 Girls' neat beds arranged in same room as this (8,5)
19 Overwhelmed by grief re death possibly? (6-7)
23 In Thailand (Bangkok suburbs) one's tea is best cut (1-4,5)
25 Slight imperfection in speech (4)
28 Turn Gabon and Austria into one nation (6)
29 Energy and speed, unchanged, create stress (8)
30 They teach you French to reach standard primarily (6)
31 Worst case, best case or iron case, perhaps? (8)

Down

1 Fowl, one with male in cage (6)
2 Eccentric 12 has time to change (5)
3 Clothing hiding top of legs in Edinburgh (4)
4 Ban leaders from latest news? It's what tyrants do (7)
6 Cat on one occasion captivated youth centre (5)
7 Where plants escaped over tangled bower? (9)
8 Score -1, getting broken-hearted (see above) (8)
11 3, changing time to noon for oven (4)
14 Yield grain, say (4)
15 Underarm ball gets one dotard out (9)
16 There's anger in this if upset (3)
17 Thanks and cheerio (4)
18 Criminal burst into old court to halt proceedings (8)
20 Take them off going into Chatsworth (4)
21 A cinema that's untidy and lacking vitality (7)
22 Painting on wall in Corfe's vandalised (6)
24 Bush senior (5)
26 He fails to win dramatic roles (5)
27 Lower leg uncovered in sunshine (4)

Across

6 I replaced nib he damaged but result's illegible (14)
9 Harry tried to acquire old film cutter (6)
10 Much ink wasted describing head of pale squirrel (8)
11 E.g. emblem of firm involved in petrology's not right (8)
13 Cloth found in Hindu's territory (6)
15 Cost of accepting new member of royal family (6)
17 Old firm receives tax return for special book size (6)
19 Dozing – disturb please! (6)
20 RC priest managed to write another version of play (8)
22 Final letters call for 8 etc. to retire (4,4)
24 Underdeveloped European bear (6)
26 Risk funding new lucrative patent? Not all of it (7,7)

Down

1 Doctor forbids sea journey for migrants (5,2,7)
2 Section of traditional access to mine (4)
3 Second tandoori, say? You'll have to move fast! (6)
4 Intermittent price changes take in Institute of Directors (8)
5 Tree within your grasp? (4)
7 Pinch one of six hanging round snooker table (6)
8 NCOs Carol and Pearl possibly? (5,9)
12 1 goes round 6, looking sheepish (5)
14 Top celebrity takes one step (5)
16 Storage unit and trophy table (8)
18 Judge and councillor in charge touring Italy (6)
21 Plain 14 gym (6)
23 Toodle-oo! Thanks and thanks again (2-2)
25 Establish age of fruit (4)

Across

6 Capturing artillery, battered Allies race on in NE France (6-8)
9 Restore all except first faulty audio system (6)
10 Put into words what you think of French writer (8)
11 Doctor unable to mask very variable colour (4,4)
13 Small insect that bites cat's tail (6)
15 Feisty girl could get my boot if she misbehaves (6)
17 Backers with devious motives exchanging two letters (6)
19 It's hard to find tin in pig-house (6)
20 Fail to notice old injured lover's fine (8)
22 Stewed apples containing it as soup ingredient (5,3)
24 Pelmet needs fixing in place of worship (6)
26 Anthracite Glen combusted in it? (7,7)

Down

1 Verb form finished small item (about one page) (4,10)
2 Escort gets rid of heroin for addict (4)
3 Train group of marine mammals (6)
4 French names changed to protect hot first-year student (8)
5 Couple appear at intervals in plagiary (4)
7 Large snake used to climb on roof (6)
8 Peer's duty selling OBEs? OBE possibly (8,6)
12 Beefeaters perhaps miss old country (5)
14 You and I will briefly support daughter's stay (5)
16 Top athlete: "I'm only running with a pacemaker at first" (8)
18 Fertiliser container has exploded (6)
21 Snare spouse not quite heading north (6)
23 It's only tiny amount originally (4)
25 Where pirates operated in cinema industry (4)

Across

1 Like drip in hospital with terrible nut aversion (11)
9 I left begonias wilting around Nag's Head (7)
10 Unusual, like retired local bobby? (7)
11 German city in dreadful mess (3)
12 Tenor likes working with choir leader; it's amusing (7)
13 Pub grub cooked in peacetime, not these days (4,3)
14 Girl's father's not plump (3)
15 Fail, whichever way you look at it (5)
17 Dug up retro material (5)
18 Knock back a little cappuccino or tea, more likely (5)
20 Royal contest entailing taking men on board (5)
22 Expert spin doctor (3)
24 Renaissance artist crushed in libel (7)
25 Some people got ripped off in selfish display (3,4)
26 Resistance when odd characters leave Gotham (3)
27 Told story about taking wife for a rest (3-4)
28 Country with prohibition *inter alia* (7)
29 Pioneer in sporty jacket after collapse of trial (11)

Down

1 Scatter pellets in centre? It'll keep flies away (6,9)
2 Like underground? Or Oldfield's bells? (7)
3 Gun goes off inside when Scotsman emerges (5)
4 Trading on-line, English come across German car (1-8)
5 Casual worker supports taking holiday (7)
6 Idle investor makes a mess of representing pal (8,7)
7 Grab lift (6)
8 Old source of power crosses river or brook (6)
16 Made up blend of oil in fact (9)
18 Part of road surface put together roughly (6)
19 An Australian-Irish area over in US state (7)
21 How British blocked reduced amount in entertainment (7)
23 E.g. Annie, whose parents sadly have no sweets (6)
25 By which 4 is conducted by topless female, say? (1-4)

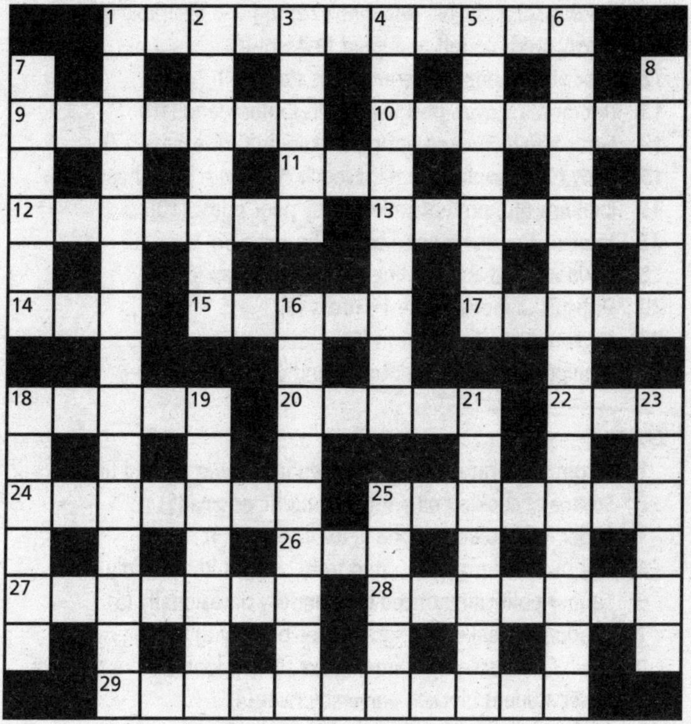

Across

1 Would friend, say, be game? (8)
5 Copper does oddly circulate as old money (6)
9 In Paris she nabs big one who's retired and desirable (8)
10 Newly-wed has left headgear at Ascot (6)
12 Row about computer equipment's over (4)
13 Doctor Marlowe's peculiar day in fantasy land (10)
15 Somehow I'd missed boring trickery in Cruise, say (6,7)
19 Early milk supplier's benefit led to fluid with good heart (7,6)
23 Explains ground rent collected by poor priest (10)
25 Man, say, removing odd bits of lip salve (4)
28 Boris worried about a line on weather map (6)
29 Difficult to move Route 16 rocks (8)
30 Most recent US city exam (6)
31 It helps you stop a park bed being vandalised (5,3)

Down

1 It commemorates those who died in the war abroad (6)
2 Source of cooking oil with very exotic origins (5)
3 Order NCO to accept one 5, for instance (4)
4 Not much energy generated from coal on Rhine oddly (7)
6 Labour politician noticed hosting Tory occasionally (5)
7 Gradually weaken foreign articles belonging to me (9)
8 Fresh Dover sole, not large, cooks for too long (8)
11 Quiet student blocked university river (4)
14 Bird initially kept inside with islanders (4)
15 Heavy outerwear a cottager's worn (9)
16 Hauled up rotten fish (3)
17 It's moved to European location (4)
18 Authorised person, boffin at heart, turned secular (8)
20 Seed's genetically modified? Queen intervenes (4)
21 Boro etc. played for several days in autumn (7)
22 Top 16 stood up to receive English ambassador (6)
24 They're used to travel in Greek island, say (5)
26 Note from small stringed instrument (5)
27 Dodge bird (4)

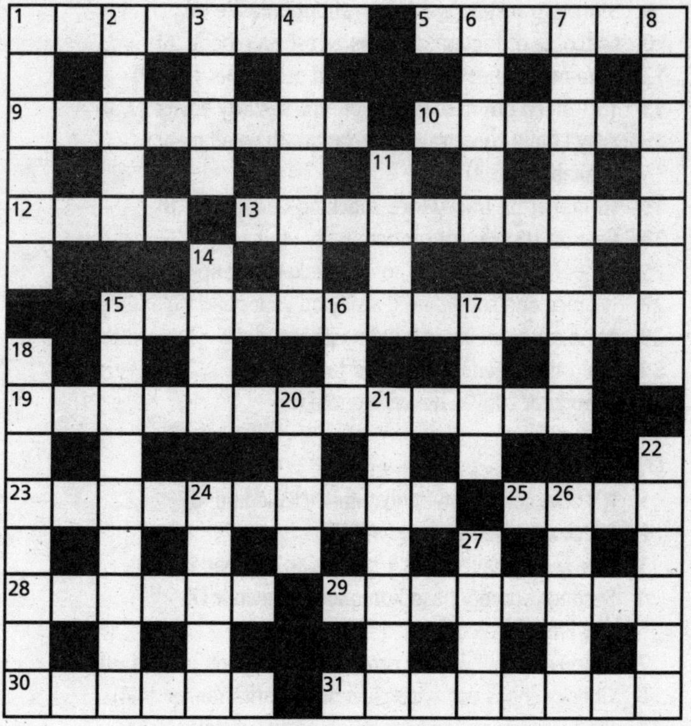

Across

1 Some staff are ordering a permit about end of August (4-4)
5 Meeting prisoner of war? That's amazing! (6)
9 Start to translate war poem about parasite (8)
10 Outcome of friction: coppers arrest everybody (6)
12 Bare necessities usually demand economies first (4)
13 150 sheep got herded into on-line security device (7,3)
15 Why I have crew trained at Yarmouth by all means available (5,5,3)
19 Formal artist Tracey tries shocking Cameron (5,8)
23 Post off US bills for random tests (4,6)
25 School's disorganised, so overlooked lake up north (4)
28 It's nice and small and it's silly on your head (6)
29 Mine refuse delay in building phase (4,4)
30 Plant that needs IT installed for speed (6)
31 Triangular canvas delays trouble (8)

Down

1 It's obvious person in hospital lacks iodine (6)
2 Quick attack to seize power (5)
3 It may be smaller than 17 and won't spread (4)
4 Second recovery based on good behaviour (7)
6 Old English tax collected like eggs (5)
7 Women on pill wore cosmetic, showing self-control (9)
8 Cheeky chaps use wigs cleverly to baffle Yankee (4,4)
11 Do some engraving with some pocket chisels (4)
14 Yield grain, say (4)
15 Leader lied awkwardly about a riot abroad (9)
16 Welsh cricket side came first (3)
17 E.g. Coventry and its outskirts surround it (4)
18 It's in instalments and is copied everywhere (8)
20 Cross after central Tibet to find goat there (4)
21 Blink to decipher it in personality test (3,4)
22 Odd place to host opening to holy place of worship (6)
24 Provide food in wobbly crate (5)
26 Last character contributes to home game (5)
27 Urgently extracting rent is objectionable (4)

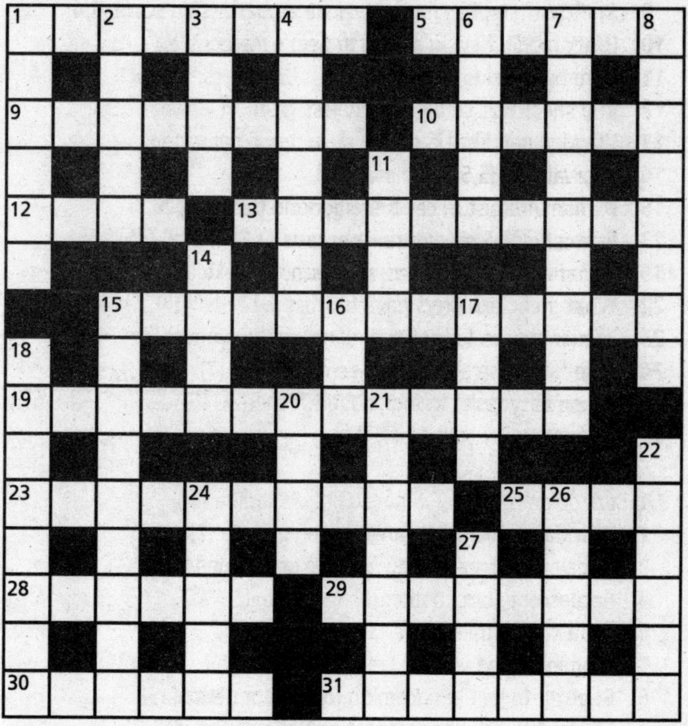

Across

1 Walk beside canal to what perhaps restricts parking (7)
5 Regularly see round odd parts of Vienna (6)
9 An "Owl" stupidly has energy for embarrassing score (3,4)
10 Fancy model having a right to peer's status! (7)
11 Georgia's fuel (3)
12 In early radios, comic acts try less (7,4)
13 Clapped out, like US cars? (5)
14 Poor Aphrodite wasted away (9)
16 Do lilies, withered, need energy from this fuel? (6,3)
17 Indian landowner otherwise known as "bwana"? (5)
19 Social outcasts or victims of punch? (4-3-4)
22 What arctic explorers have to cross (3)
23 Leader chosen for national team, say, in a novel (7)
24 Fake fails miserably to fool youth leaders (7)
26 It's an easy task picking up French cheeses (6)
27 Riot controller split 11 (4,3)

Down

1 Idea that Hugo formulated has no answer (7)
2 Car cleaner inspired new crew to get trained (10,5)
3 Adolescent starts bother (3)
4 50 in sacred tree (5)
5 It's concerning voters? Let oracle loose (9)
6 Register to join in upcoming football or netball (5)
7 Monarch's aides amazingly win Italia design (6-2-7)
8 Hideous Medusa tickled (6)
12 What beggars do to get five notes (5)
14 Keeping away from a video can hurt (9)
15 Underwear's rubbish (5)
16 Work out 2/500? (6)
18 Sleep beside kerb occasionally? Certainly (3-4)
20 Alert in a late party? (5)
21 One has first sign of flab if one's this (5)
25 Grass hopper beginning to disappear (3)

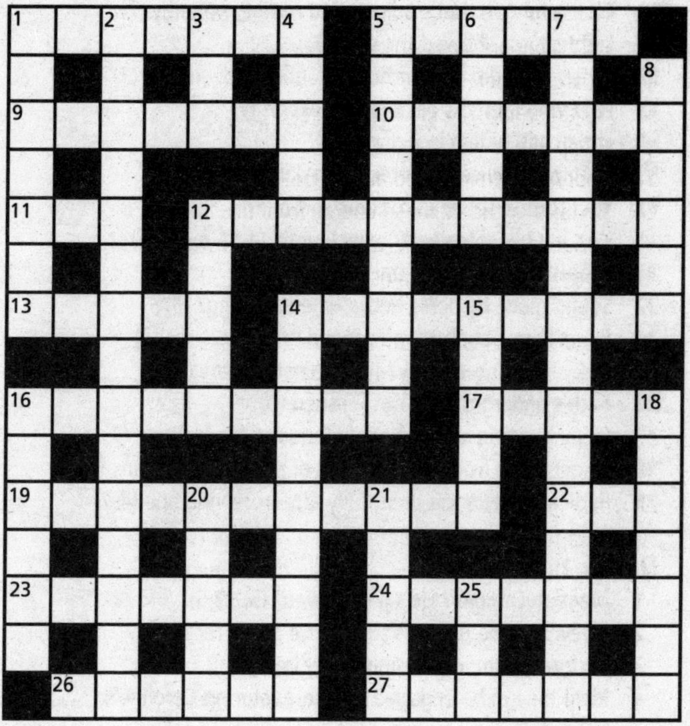

Across

1 New fashion mag covers very early facial application (7,4)
9 Touring S. Africa, this stage décor may be necessary (7)
10 Chaise longue that's adjusted to recline primarily (7)
11 Light source showed the way (3)
12 Writer took dip here at home, sounding overcome (7)
13 Poet who laments eastern law expert (7)
14 Little chap hiding in Belfast (3)
15 S. America twice imported Latin dance music (5)
17 Your former setter's aromatic shrub (5)
18 He's in pub, completely reversing this treatment (5)
20 Spanish golfer grasps one riddle (5)
22 Sound made by horse heard when refusing? (3)
24 Punctilious people stand ground after exercises (7)
25 Sick girl taking ecstasy? It's against the law (7)
26 Bath's underground's not finished (3)
27 Enjoy hugging international lifeguard, for example (7)
28 Singer gains from arrangement of pianos and organs (7)
29 Radicals sweltering dreadfully after receiving fine (4-7)

Down

1 Mention Dickens? He's just arrived! (5,2,3,5)
2 Forever young princess's elegance partly recalled (7)
3 Pastoral poem idly composed by lake (5)
4 Ideal time to be engaged maybe, capturing Caroline's heart (6,3)
5 Wealthy Open University acquires power fast (7)
6 Trouble filming gangs, say? This lens may help (10,5)
7 Hope to become a penny-pinching father? (6)
8 I threw out snake (6)
16 Doctor starts breaking law? That does it! (4,5)
18 Salesman sat out meal (6)
19 Avoid expert who has no knowledge of sources (4,3)
21 Europeans swallow various pills for figure (7)
23 What you do when you're suddenly hurt and afraid? (6)
25 Playwright and children's author came up endlessly (5)

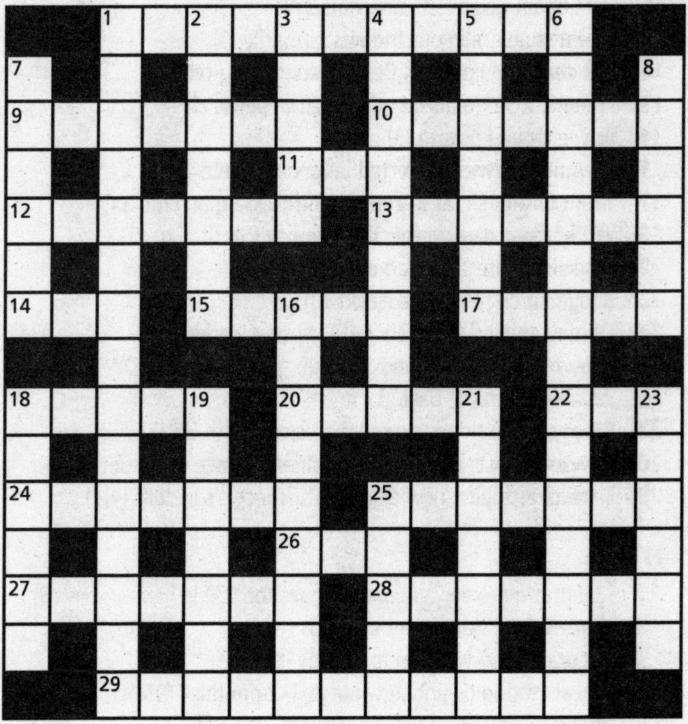

Across

1 Dicky emptied main equipment for expedition (11)
9 Declare once more while others had a meal (7)
10 Tries again when hers are ruined (7)
11 Title of some religious Indians primarily (3)
12 Criticises and harasses Best, taking a long time (7)
13 I phone, worried about black part of pelvis (3,4)
14 Amy chopped potato (3)
15 Mogul's first idea rubbished in press, TV etc. (5)
17 They control horses in centre when a German enters (5)
18 Writer these days makes little money (5)
20 It houses more than half of the horses (5)
22 Body bag carried by Cossacks (3)
24 Oprah's thrilled to host a hot Egyptian leader (7)
25 Showing genuine feelings because Queen's back (7)
26 An attempt in the past (3)
27 Savage restriction is on escaped creature in US (7)
28 New king hosts Queen and cardinal to make new contacts (7)
29 Detectives follow new clue; CIA suspect it's in cells (7,4)

Down

1 Music arrangement meant changes for 100 in instruction (15)
2 Non-existent Hampton novel (7)
3 Decorate shop window to display it? (5)
4 A human stupidly inhales foul air – from this? (9)
5 Phone or otherwise his chances are zero (2-5)
6 In car-boot sale abroad I'd synthetic hormone (8,7)
7 Bad-tempered taxi driver carried rabbi (6)
8 Their leaves tremble softly in a sense non-stop (6)
16 Release record "Argentina" he covered (9)
18 Pope's office's secretaries disheartened clergy (6)
19 Community secures amazing A-list kind of band (7)
21 Crazy guy in a cult needs treatment (7)
23 Controls people in Prague, I hear (6)
25 Lad in charge of producing sound (5)

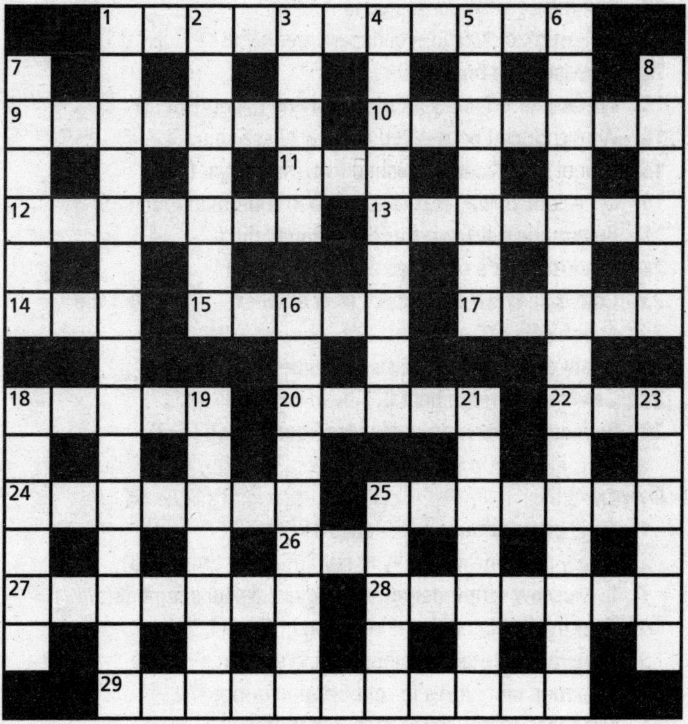

Across

1 Sad, sore old roué drinks cold glasses to improve things? (4-8)
8 Being aloof, nearly offend a king (7)
9 Can has present contained in it (7)
11 Diseased goldenrod – unknown tree expert studies it (10)
12 Movement in prison (4)
14 Writer probed nasty crimes involving hypnotism (8)
16 Wrong U-turn negotiated approaching Spain (6)
17 Policeman returned holding ring? That's him (3)
19 On vessel abroad Rex changes position (6)
21 Rum made with rare ingredients in blend (8)
24 E.g. Bismarck's old empire expelled man (4)
25 Coal is sent out to women (men at weekend), helping the poor (6,4)
27 Again pick Scottish dance etc. to be played (2-5)
28 Celebrated bridge here in Govan is demolished (7)
29 Endorses advertisements in traditional shop? (12)

Down

1 Feels bitter about unopened gifts (7)
2 Salary rose unexpectedly in revolutionary times (5,5)
3 In Moscow script, nervous family circle shuns fame (8)
4 Gets injured in banks of Limpopo in fires (4,2)
5 Unfairly exploited omnibus edition's centrepiece (4)
6 Someone who votes for old German prince (7)
7 Sue made minor changes to minor offence (12)
10 Harrowing, somehow never running out of potassium (5-7)
13 Basic French and German articles not telling the truth (10)
15 Sham fish (3)
18 Birds seen in places at sea (8)
20 Monopoly starts here, very busy (2,3,2)
22 Rubs oil on stain on ground (7)
23 In Paris I got lost, hurt elbow (6)
26 Five on one German vessel (4)

Across

1 She looks after those milling about on liner (7)
5 Keep quiet and secure when driving (4,2)
9 Reported private soldier showing resentment (7)
10 Stood up to work with Edward taking in small 12 Across (7)
11 Single person in polo neck (3)
12 Talks over nasty problem: losing 50 overnight containers (7,4)
13 Fit ground into US city? That's clever (5)
14 Denizen of Borneo finally wasted a UN grant (5-4)
16 Car runs round with terrible racket here (9)
17 Primate's bird captured by both sides (5)
19 Foolishly play with e.g. coins as aerial targets (4,7)
22 Is it given as approval or refusal to director? (3)
23 Grandfather clock for instance, a fabulous thing (7)
24 Inherited item takes you in – it's the real McCoy (7)
26 Was it added by old Queen to house former lover? (6)
27 2011 could be spent anywhere except Hungary (3,4)

Down

1 Prattle away about old whaler's weapon (7)
2 Event organiser's instinct in fiascos one's once botched (5,2,8)
3 Bergson's intermittent self-interest (3)
4 ME country broadcasts rising across Yemen's capital (5)
5 BBC took novel about the French polisher (9)
6 Drive back over to find outcast (5)
7 Drunk Ulsterman's in Kop? It's clearly not cricket (15)
8 Inventor turned up for end of rugby match (6)
12 Conservative party broadcast one missed in vault (5)
14 Grade A-One bubbly refreshment (9)
15 Fools harbour scavengers (5)
16 Ornate style in gold erected by two firms (6)
18 Animals like Rudolph pull up grass (3,4)
20 Exercises the night before cause irritation (5)
21 Instrument built from more than half of either 14 (5)
25 Barn owl's wings get clipped these days (3)

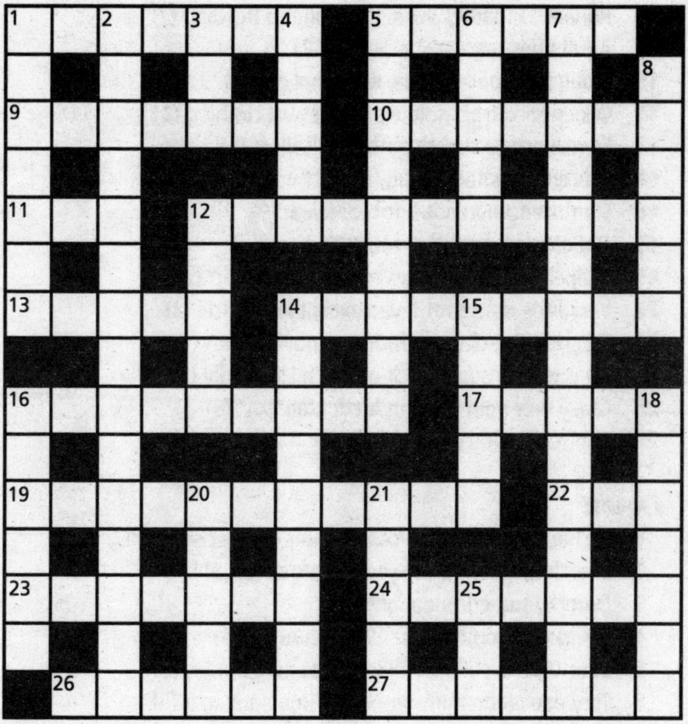

Across

1 Races away round a department's passageways (7)
5 What's left for instance to a charity *in extremis*? (6)
9 Rodent in Thames swims, heading to Reading (7)
10 Adult wins regularly in band (5-2)
11 Indulge in sport in Zürs, Kitzbühel etc. (3)
12 Commanding US soldiers in relevant clothing (11)
13 French article covering help for sailors (5)
14 This crew jostled to bag first of thrushes (9)
16 Slim changes in votes for footwear (9)
17 Old coin one found in tube (5)
19 Output device produces nearly nine per litre (4,7)
22 Very little data's retrieved except last article (3)
23 Extend US preface introducing novel's start (7)
24 Icy conditions for a kick-off in La Liga sadly (7)
26 Crazy oiks hold party in Arctic transport (6)
27 Centre forward downs tools (7)

Down

1 A chap's stupid to welcome writer without speech (7)
2 Search one country to secure safe access (11,4)
3 Dorothy turned to daughter (3)
4 It suggests indifference in Welsh rugby (5)
5 Poor GOC is still not fully maintaining armies (9)
6 Tory education minister has a large hand in it (5)
7 Sting's kind of eccentric arrangement (10,5)
8 Hogwarts study periods (6)
12 Mike has managed to secure time for subject (5)
14 Rebuke ruler during total chaos (7-2)
15 Person sowing crops, say, or tree (5)
16 Small growths in college and primary school heads (6)
18 Roofer has two daughters; one's not much of a catch (7)
20 Haughty, quiet and surprisingly dour (5)
21 Iberian flower in August blossomed after you left (5)
25 Regular helpings of caviare create atmosphere (3)

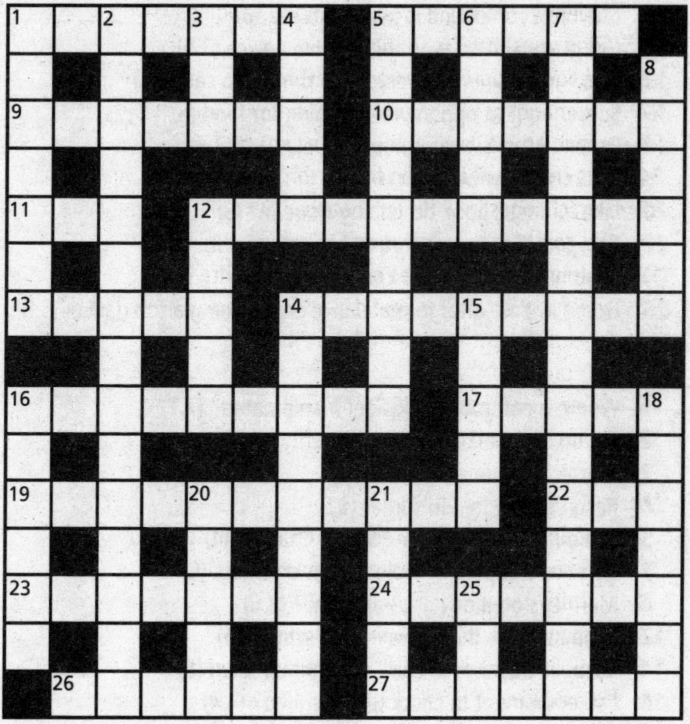

Across

6 TUC holds editor in admiration for what mature students do (5,9)
9 Car's what's left in will (6)
10 Chemical compound is held up at sea (8)
11 Get grime shifted with this kitchen device (3,5)
13 Gap can be seen by everyone in run-down canal (6)
15 Some shoot at opponents returning for food (6)
17 Darling Mary's excited touring Delaware (2,4)
19 RM puts away best suit (6)
20 Like fantastic book describing Houdini? (8)
22 Boy gets ill with rare thrush, for instance (8)
24 Long garment's able to conceal rear (6)
26 Home in time after formal dance entertaining a top dancer (5,9)

Down

1 Where a paramour's legs get manipulated? (7,7)
2 Young dog sits on a young butterfly (4)
3 Master disciplined class (6)
4 Reserve cash for kid's treat (3,5)
5 Cut out an extract from "Sweet Charity" (4)
7 Remove weapons in violent raids on Malta (6)
8 Mariner's on a day out – this one? (8,6)
12 Thomas holds the edges in clan symbol (5)
14 Catholic member of Lords brought up fawn (5)
16 Lab equipment to check underground? (4,4)
18 Nervous, not taking sides, having lost heart (6)
21 Seal hidden store at end of street (6)
23 Some playing American football, say … (4)
25 … weaken its controlling body, nearly causing harm (4)

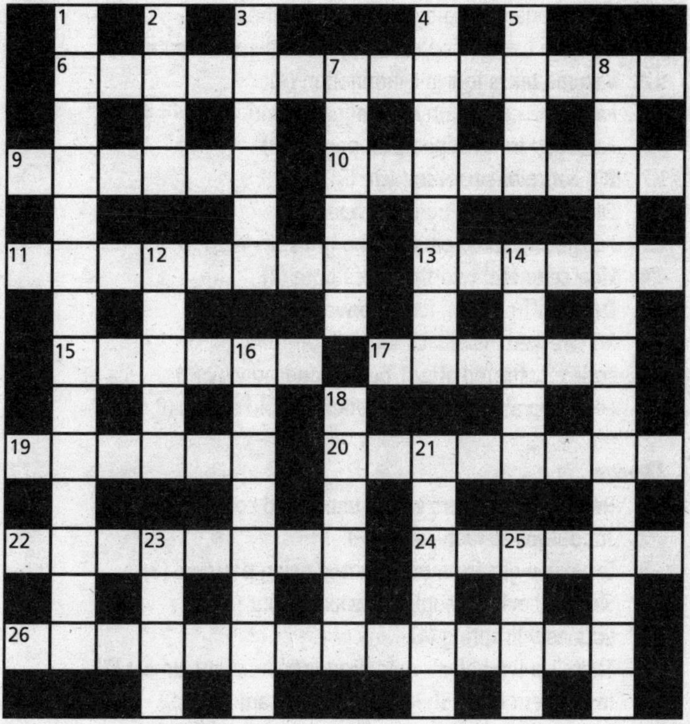
1
2
3
4
5
6
7
8
9
10
11
12
13
14
15
16
17
18
19
20
21
22
23
24
25
26

Across

1 Average flour-manufacturing boss has it (3-2-3-4)
8 Pilot takes a classic route to Russia (7)
9 Sort of energy in old cattle parasite mostly (7)
11 America backs people paying for underwear items (10)
12 Virginia takes fourth examination (4)
14 Large MP carried on broken jug in field event (4,4)
16 Fish food fraud appears on page 1 (6)
17 Big hand for secretary/wife (3)
19 Old widow spilt litre over cape (6)
21 I covered injured person who got separated (8)
24 Unable to feel two-thirds of figure (4)
25 Dodgy off-cut deal for outerwear (6,4)
27 26 wrecked in setback for riot controller (4,3)
28 Tories frustrated after Liberal stands idly by (7)
29 Loyal trip abroad in May generated old drama (8,4)

Down

1 Restrains engineers where unmarried couple live? (5,2)
2 Toad's gossip with sailor (10)
3 Explosive gas from tree created rising pressure (8)
4 Shriek shocked people on walking tour (6)
5 Lots new in spring (4)
6 There's a light element in display of humility almost (7)
7 Instrument Clare Short kept in old pram … (4,8)
10 … played by this person doing a stint with 19 (12)
13 Is she in form to fix oscillograph? Apparently not (10)
15 Odd bits of plaid in shock absorber (3)
18 Sly gets drunk on purpose (8)
20 Posh doctor in Lagos reduced back problem (7)
22 Old king and queen in modest US kitchen (7)
23 Wry smile about university breakfast (6)
26 Less than a paragraph about site of Taj Mahal (4)

33

Across

1 He's maybe solicitous with Gustav Mahler's first pieces (12)
8 Some important Arabs give blast on trumpet (7)
9 Where balloons go in positive hospital rooms (7)
11 Aspect of a church in opposition (4,2,4)
12 It's only a fish (4)
14 Clot damaged mobile and SIM I left (8)
16 Quiet drink outside shed (4,2)
17 Woman's father loses weight (3)
19 Small fruit reportedly delivered after dinner? (6)
21 Snitch allowed back with extremely light beer (8)
24 Retired paediatrician absorbs plan (4)
25 Tidy up this barn and decorate it with this? (10)
27 Wiggled her toe, having cold foot (7)
28 Jeers at some in Paris accepting lift (7)
29 Prepares to sail in a storm – who's in charge? (6,6)

Down

1 CBI man arranged to catch one taxi (7)
2 Clever dick's alert at sea in fishing boat (5,5)
3 Female is strangely chary about crustaceans (8)
4 Start meal about one (6)
5 Formal dress increased in size, except rear end (4)
6 Strong beer bottles soldiers deal with (4,3)
7 This red loose material's first for pompous guy (7,5)
10 19 let out on rough sea for race (12)
13 Happy event left foreign bird in awkward hitch (10)
15 Had a rendezvous with London police (3)
18 Checked progress of a German in new diner (6,2)
20 Eccentric Eeyore's unsightly feature (7)
22 Doctor reads about a French article in parts (7)
23 Ships of the desert arrived last occasionally (6)
26 Heavy, with ugly contents (4)

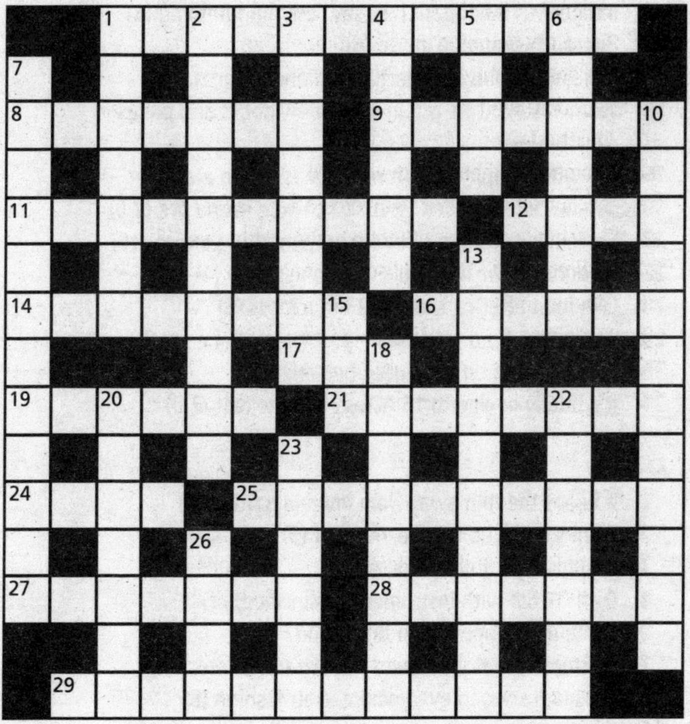

34

Across

1 Opening in a cheeky river (8)
5 An angry sort of clue (6)
9 Indigenous inhabitant has, say, less than nothing (8)
10 Big ranch spared in storm (6)
12 Obsessive hobbyist's partial to dinner dances (4)
13 Women's Institute put in funny new doors and panes in church (4,6)
15 Hip with atrophy? Yes, it needs massaging etc. (13)
19 Maybe cistern boiled, getting hot here round fire (7,6)
23 Vince has tried in a different way, meriting praise (10)
25 It sounds quite like Paul Gascoigne's strip (4)
28 Like food after cart leaves 23 in a mess (6)
29 Dutch RAF fund collapses – problem with head? (8)
30 Burly woman on tram goes berserk (6)
31 It's briefly in clue to 15 Across and the rest (2,6)

Down

1 It keeps the rain away from lawn in garden (6)
2 Keen to take up reggae, not golf (5)
3 Archbishop's frilly dress (4)
4 Dish "Artist with Instrument (unfinished)" (7)
6 Some exotic apricots in this island? (5)
7 Doctor drove right behind – it attracts interest (9)
8 On sea, I swayed everywhere, crab-fashion (8)
11 John entertains some troops primarily for a joke (4)
14 Sacred song for that guy, say (4)
15 Tariff's split awkwardly to cover cereal (5,4)
16 Globe's gold book (3)
17 It's produced over in northern Holland (4)
18 I'm carrying a recce out in freezing course (3,5)
20 Nearly ache for a long time (4)
21 E.g. Robin's new in retail development (7)
22 Fibrous stuff's a tangled affair (6)
24 Arctic house is big-looking inside (5)
26 An attractive accent (5)
27 Cutting tool gives more, they say (4)

1 2 3 4 5 6 7 8
9 10
11
12 13
14
15 16 17
18
19 20 21
22
23 24 25 26
27
28 29
30 31

35

Across

6 Old writers' English story? Claim is based on it (7,7)
9 Waft from French cheeses, say (6)
10 I attempt to secure new cooler for soldiers (8)
11 Jailbird priest is working here, stripped (8)
13 Can't stand Liberal pledge on energy (6)
15 Ruffian fetched up getting long time inside (6)
17 A few trapped in Irish compound (6)
19 Twice Kent opener's out on this (6)
20 Cook ready to grasp nettle now and then with passion (8)
22 Framework in which keel's wobbly, not vertical (8)
24 River seen in shimmering image? (6)
26 Mutually reliant bank in web needing small change (14)

Down

1 Exploding TNT rocks Terrier: no time to be scared (6-8)
2 Section of church partly collapsed (4)
3 Lock up doctor across the Atlantic (6)
4 Fights less violently about strike (8)
5 Navy supports turnover in rent (4)
7 He flees harsh regime (6)
8 Throngs milled round the RNLI in polar display (8,6)
12 Small kiss makes mark (5)
14 Oz cricketer ignored British copywriter perhaps (5)
16 Position of songster in a difficult duet (8)
18 Bats can't apparently take a quick sleep (6)
21 Fats do nothing to hold middle in! (6)
23 Legal right to sleep late without one (4)
25 Three feet cover dangerous place for sailors (4)

36

Across

6 Stormy 16s yelling for matches (7,7)
9 Heading back, some passed over port (6)
10 Wobbly note during Sunday broadcast (8)
11 Billie's regularly drunk going outside, but helpful (8)
13 Respect German coming in back door first (6)
15 Sally staggered about close to defeat at the end (6)
17 A solicitor received euros, dined in restaurant (3,3)
19 Start getting nervous about English still (2,4)
20 Metalworker with German impressed by subtle hints (8)
22 Incas got displaced, unsure about their gods? (8)
24 This bigotry even makes serviceman furious (6)
26 With pay increasing, maybe I'm able proudly to keep wife (8,6)

Down

1 Awfully dirty big lie in CAP: it separates fact from fiction (11,3)
2 Girl, kind, needs no introduction (4)
3 Boxer supports unnamed ruler in African capital (6)
4 Piece clamping ornate prow's what this could be (8)
5 Nasty eye? This contributes to it (4)
7 Step into oddly grey very casual clothing (6)
8 Bushmen touring US respected politicians (5,9)
12 Children's publication (5)
14 Dark, primarily green weaving machine (5)
16 Trite remark's beginning to leave freedom to move (8)
18 Sturdy Charlie's fine going round in pig-house (6)
21 Slender, originally Navajo weapon (6)
23 Test painter in oil, not writer (4)
25 Old headgear firm provided (4)

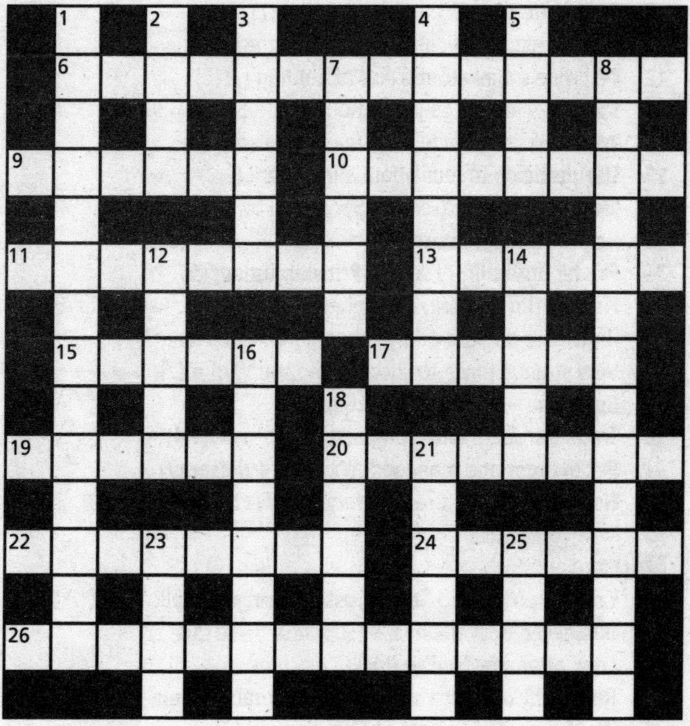

37

Across

1 Some chap with pot disturbed pile of fertiliser (7,4)
9 Contents of pot or tureen put on the rack (7)
10 Poor loser grabs it and hangs about (7)
11 Hairy beast: American's forgotten name (3)
12 Do Wilde's play around end of autumn (7)
13 Spain has tended to invest hurriedly (2,5)
14 What 75% of potage used to cost in Paris? (3)
15 Use pesticide to rectify faults in system (5)
17 Majority of 9 cooked fish (5)
18 Bear British bankruptcy (5)
20 Flower in smallest room in British Museum (5)
22 Fit and trim primarily? Definitely not (3)
24 Birds here do vote oddly, retaining Conservative (7)
25 Very strange place to shop, by the sound of it (7)
26 Ring Arab – punter needs it (3)
27 Trade disrupted with company, 1930s style (3,4)
28 Put in order and managed to get in new gear (7)
29 He went off with a rare variety of pots (11)

Down

1 Courses on playing "Evita" essential in job application (10,5)
2 Influenced Rocker's rival to suppress fierce duel (7)
3 Look after cow (Daisy) (5)
4 Rebuke by monarch surrounded by total mayhem (7,2)
5 Word describing article in English mine (7)
6 Squeeze pair, say, into media gathering (5,10)
7 Street showing no change and no movement (6)
8 Voiced approval for climb (6)
16 It erupts early, involving that yobbo in … (4,5)
18 … plot to strike in scene of uproar (6)
19 Northern university approve this sort of energy? (7)
21 Pole dance? (7)
23 Queen's introduced to new diet, e.g. wedding cake? (6)
25 Cups at home in control centre (5)

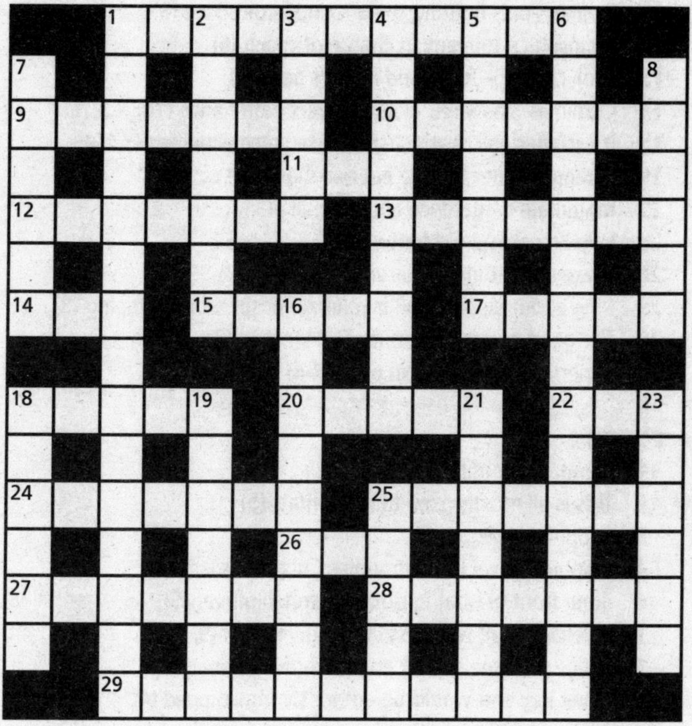
1
2
3
4
5
6
7
8
9
10
11
12
13
14
15
16
17
18
19
20
21
22
23
24
25
26
27
28
29

38

Across

1 Sudden drop in foreign videos in northeast (4,4)
5 Politicos mostly absorb everything around them (6)
9 Be like rebels fighting to surround large space (8)
10 He insults a top lady in charge of coach (6)
12 Look closely – feel-good factor's back (4)
13 Criminals' nasty red wound covers both hands (10)
15 It excluded tab that's suspect, like some expenses (3-10)
19 Arrange dinner time to eat bananas? Not sure (13)
23 Intimidate conference about small plant (3,7)
25 Female collects old footwear (4)
28 Make assault in a tense zigzag pattern (6)
29 Ring about distress call involving phosphorous dumping (8)
30 The good points in strimmer? It strims! (6)
31 Superficial type stuck in ooze (4-4)

Down

1 Slender new missile (6)
2 This is all mostly used to make mats (5)
3 Suppress moisture (4)
4 Disputed naval base straddles Cuba's border (7)
6 Steer front of boat in isolated stretch of river (5)
7 Wretched but, with less clothing, musical (9)
8 Office machine's quiet and more revolutionary? (8)
11 Lover boy and would-be author's wings clipped (4)
14 Leave 11 in Egypt (4)
15 We tried somehow to keep extremely alert in ebb and flow (9)
16 Not very bright and getting less intense briefly (3)
17 Split up in carriage (4)
18 Deny a monkey before Islamic revolution (8)
20 What's left after cutting edges of forestry (4)
21 I climb each peak in central Kenya leading with this? (3-4)
22 Mate married up in cattle fold (6)
24 Fancy coats and hats at this race meeting (5)
26 Detest nabbing son in hurry (5)
27 Yarns are special to one in Paris (4)

39

Across

1   Dreadful xenophobe endlessly used to make calls (5,3)
5   Badger has set about rats, forgetting time (6)
9   Embarrassed and angry, they bring relief (3,5)
10 Composer's longer notes are like two of our letters (6)
12 It's not unlike an early rebec in the middle (4)
13 Fatty stuff old people brought back in handcart (4,6)
15 Seventy filled complex, needing no explanation (4-9)
19 Meddlesome acts very nearly upset aims externally (13)
23 Leeds very excited about date, with justification (10)
25 Man on bench, not George, immortalised by Paul (4)
28 Go OTT in series of balls followed by party (6)
29 Launch new act with Paul anxious and tense (8)
30 Compete against recruit (4,2)
31 Bandit degenerates badly, ignoring setback (8)

Down

1   Wild leopard deprived of last conditional release (6)
2   Command sequence (5)
3   Connoisseur occasionally collects 100 cents (4)
4   Herons flying with duck off the sea (7)
6   What unclothed inamorata exudes when circulating? (5)
7   Joint problem? It is sustaining non-U king (9)
8   Tossed in ship I deviated from right to left, say (8)
11 So far I haven't been proved to exist (4)
14 Slight lack of precision in speech (4)
15 Drunkards inhale oxygen on mountain as it were (2,2,5)
16 Transport service cut up (3)
17 Love flower close to head (4)
18 MEP: "I don't represent area around Turin" (8)
20 Sheep use 15 Down (4)
21 I'll get different one brought in for ploughing (7)
22 It boils dry in leek stew (6)
24 Set commercial in SA port (5)
26 Tissue of reduced value flapping round centre of mouth (5)
27 Friend's final position on board (4)

40

Across

1 Fagin cleverly lured in females for some fiddling (7)
5 Smooth tongue (6)
9 Never-changing English navy (and others circling it) (7)
10 Rice: a bit's cultivated round Massachusetts (7)
11 Last letter amazed? Not half (3)
12 Variety of kitschy vodka disheartened composer (11)
13 Member in row backed authority (5)
14 Cook wet turnip: it's fully described in text (7,2)
16 I hear a young mare swallowed branch (9)
17 Group engaged in coup settled disturbance (5)
19 Stand-in engineers job for student (11)
22 Bream offers no resistance? No, a different fish (3)
23 Last word in cheese with large port for southeast (7)
24 Straddling current, get out soap (7)
26 During which lecturer interrupted card game (6)
27 Julia is editor – partly acted as go-between (7)

Down

1 Cold store releases her, by the sound of it (7)
2 Liberal member tucked into food served up at talk, right? (7,2,6)
3 Austrian river tavern (3)
4 Ravine starts to gradually undermine lovely church (5)
5 Bar is swamped by bloodsuckers? Tell me about it! (9)
6 Girl's old rope (5)
7 Top actors and corrupt priests flag (5,3,7)
8 Put DIY in order? Yes, do just that (4,2)
12 Tenor and alto's broadcast is complete (5)
14 Vessel in which Ahab got entangled with towel? (9)
15 Rely on sudden push to expel hydrogen (5)
16 A father in charge of a continent (6)
18 Tense, I enter hydro for treatment for this gland? (7)
20 Time of year when prince is in trouble (5)
21 Artist's supporter's rent period first to end (5)
25 Motoring organisation covers good range (3)

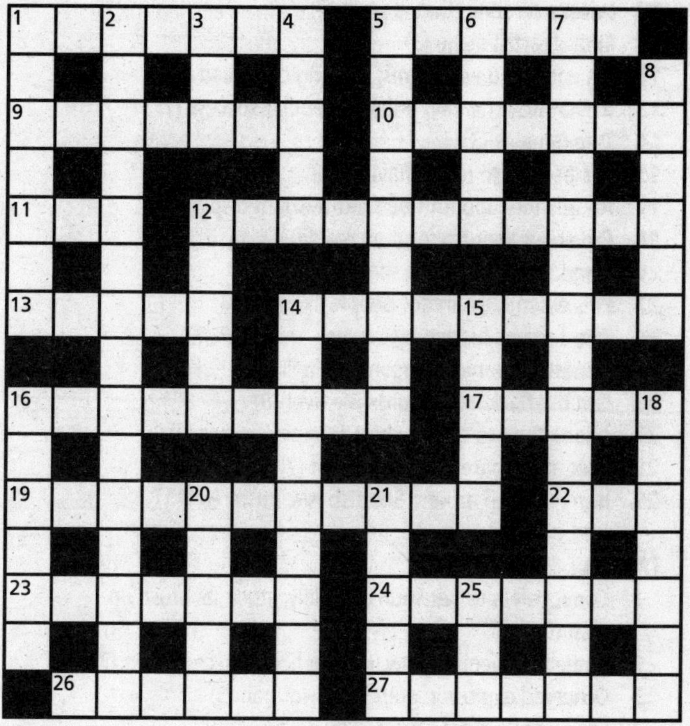
1 2 3 4 5 6 7 8 9 10 11 12 13 14 15 16 17 18 19 20 21 22 23 24 25 26 27

41

Across

1 Arts movement commits Iran to change (11)
9 Frank's at university opening (7)
10 Priest's on song, that is plain (7)
11 English artist's age (3)
12 It's encrusted with gems, say, and contested (7)
13 In that way the king enjoyed popular success (7)
14 Tree remains (3)
15 Pastas tend to retain flavour (5)
17 Recall story about Cuba's extravagant display (5)
18 Old show about rare small mammal (5)
20 Singers appear in "Parsifal" to shriek (5)
22 Pills essentially are for people like this (3)
24 Two squares hidden by flower – this one? (7)
25 Honest puritanical person in dilapidated hut (7)
26 Fish put back in Hertfordshire river (3)
27 A long time to run machine pumping in gas (7)
28 I get all prepared for cultivation (7)
29 Harry messed around Scottish isle, flustered (11)

Down

1 Comic refers to her source crudely; students brush up on it (9,6)
2 Bathed in evening glow, Maureen, drunk, carries on (7)
3 Observed explosion going up? Not half (5)
4 I'm doctor's client, irritated by delays … (9)
5 … suppose I'm a long time getting home (7)
6 Somewhere to burnish shiny Mallard with rag? (11,4)
7 Doctor slices fish in cold belt (6)
8 Wild Crete's hidden away (6)
16 Person with speech problem makes me smarter amazingly (9)
18 Power governs tube at heart, the one in New York (6)
19 It cleans clothes in Wales but has broken down (7)
21 Extra church vestment reported (7)
23 It carried someone once; now it's thrown away (6)
25 Adult rapidly grabbed extremist (5)

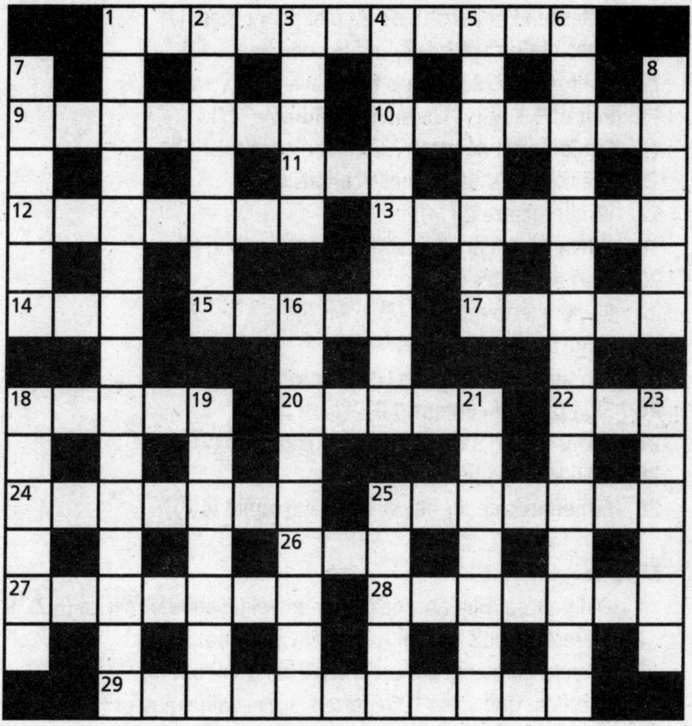

42

Across

1 Lourdes arranged to suppress top amplifier (11)
9 TV police series gets pulled at Christmas (7)
10 Gateshead or perish! 'e's an inhabitant there (7)
11 State of Chicago briefly not in good health (3)
12 Contorted US sequoia is taken away – it's watery (7)
13 Part of 9, say, is "Love in Deep Trouble" (7)
14 Station's got no water? Then don't use this! (3)
15 The old boy's back? That's curious (5)
17 World theatre (5)
18 Dawn French article's superior, outstanding (5)
20 Blag five notes (5)
22 Some ghetto moggy? (3)
24 Huge hit for Kate and 26? (7)
25 Evil male's enrolling in Open University (7)
26 Sign table of contents (3)
27 Victor is in extraordinarily poor condition (7)
28 He'll love to put out play (7)
29 Generous clue for hippo, viper and tapir? (4-7)

Down

1 Old peace group abused as too unfeeling about America (6,2,7)
2 A French king's refusal to accept wife? Strange (7)
3 Eastern garments are cut when sibling's about (5)
4 Excellent golf score I'd reported, not needing glasses (5-4)
5 Wise monarch receives present (7)
6 Model planes are badly coordinated taking turn (5-10)
7 It's hard to interpret start of slight stroke (6)
8 December deteriorated after doctor left retreat (6)
16 Fire clergy to repent in this? (9)
18 Exercises suit various primary school heads (3-3)
19 Pope's point irritated females (7)
21 It describes English article found in mine (7)
23 It's said to bring luck and money at race meeting (6)
25 Who's reported laughter and commotion? (3-2)

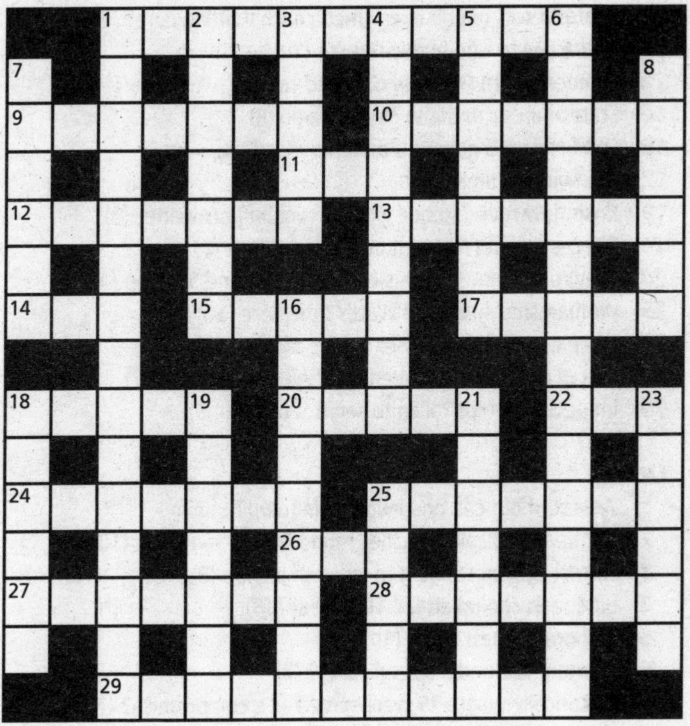

43

Across

1 Doomsday: large complex adjustment about midnight (4,8)
8 A wild dingo guards king, showing deep affection (7)
9 Drunken sots in pub overturned coach waiting here? (3,4)
11 Camaraderie rare in devil's joint (10)
12 Someone from Glasgow disputed cost (4)
14 Statesman's camera in getting fixed (8)
16 Old-fashioned general's a bit nervous (2,4)
17 Tax five at a time (3)
19 Bush flew round Rhode Island, revealing arrogance (6)
21 Dances lacking restraint in Vegas perhaps (8)
24 They're strummed in this country, Spain and Sweden (4)
25 Woman smashed Chris Watt's timepiece (10)
27 More carrot ends in essential preparation (7)
28 Part of agreement entered into? All of it, actually (7)
29 Inadequate steps taken to serve Scotch? (4,8)

Down

1 Typical of big cat, one involved in row (7)
2 Methodical display in cities round France and Cuba (10)
3 Former Balkan resident in jail with big loo (8)
4 European capital addin' 100%, say? (6)
5 Millions request cover (4)
6 Spotted, like undecorated cakes? (7)
7 Historically where 29 were served as a compromise? (7,5)
10 The worst rocks in Peel where vessels are thrown (7,5)
13 Somewhere to cook when in trouble (2,3,5)
15 Some anagrams are constantly annoying (3)
18 Barmen set traps everywhere (8)
20 Insect meets terrible fate in hot drink (4,3)
22 Bats eat nuts for disease (7)
23 Twist worm in odd places – he supports it (6)
26 Child woman abandoned in flat initially (4)

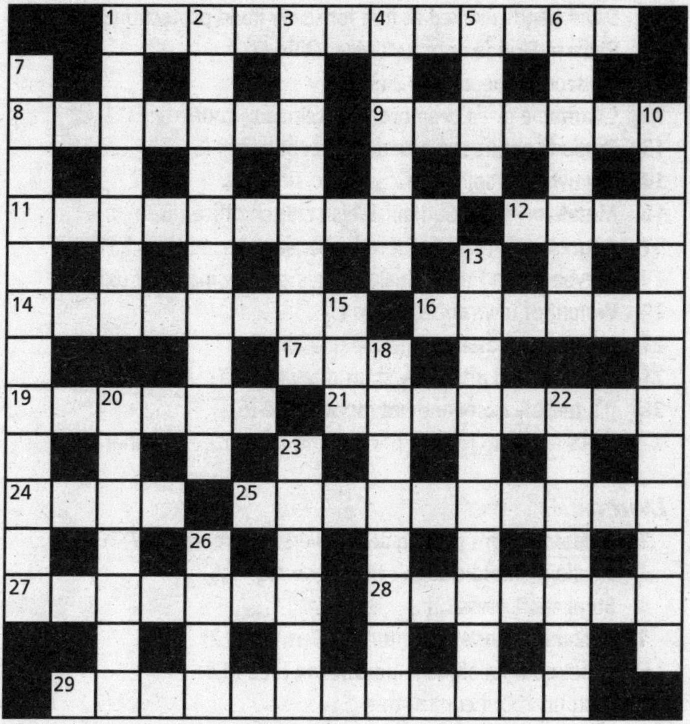

44

Across

1 A Dutch poem's hostile (7)
5 Join special arrangement without America (6)
9 Silver bands worked at first for some flood protection (7)
10 Place in Florida or ground near Ohio (7)
11 No score appearing in 2 (3)
12 Charitable gift's been ordered following court case (11)
13 Property contract pleased all except banks (5)
14 Oxygen user sold plastic with no smell (9)
16 Metalworker's a Catholic Welsh church officer (3,6)
17 Aggressively male Chinese leader suppressed church (5)
19 Maybe get in Tate car-park (edges only) using him? (6,5)
22 Weight of unwrapped stone (3)
23 Not evenly balanced in tune quality (7)
24 I got worried after very short dizzy spell (7)
26 It's terribly misty and hot inside forge (6)
27 Len's about to receive fine, having taken rare breather (7)

Down

1 Football team's playing area covers square, large (7)
2 A villain ruined church's best dessert (7,3,5)
3 Steal short dress (3)
4 Encourage Ronay to entertain German (3,2)
5 Quiet pool for shifts in production area (4,5)
6 Ring up about current tree (5)
7 Eccentric kind of elaborate fraud (10,5)
8 Indicates beer glasses with nothing in (6)
12 Clever boy holds up long note (5)
14 Oscar's libel day collapsed in this court (3,6)
15 Area of responsibility concerning US university (5)
16 Old king's hurt badly in middle of park (6)
18 Lagoon sadly swamps wicket, hence embarrassing score (3,4)
20 Time to clean up and break out (5)
21 First lady's acquired a roof extension (5)
25 Endless street disturbance in SA port (3)

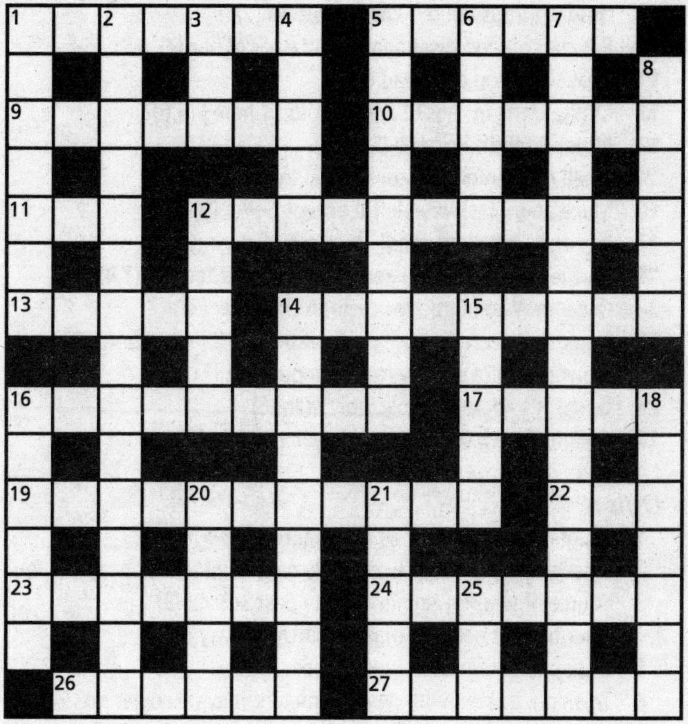

45

Across

1 Royal Highness welcomes family back for revival (7)
5 What Madrid car driver produces if he's stopped? (2,4)
9 Granny wraps injured knee in cotton (7)
10 Put coat on and disappear round back of bar (7)
11 Idiot sliced top off bread (3)
12 Clothe cleric in rags? Surely not to sit here? (5,6)
13 Mole's friend's irritable (5)
14 Smell river among mature exotic trees here (9)
16 Make angry fashionable lot accept Geller (9)
17 You and I have reportedly to produce cloth (5)
19 Brother catches exhausted injured stag "Meteor" (7,4)
22 Oscar in Washington for cartoon character (3)
23 Inspections certain to cover 5 yachts not 8 in Hamburg (7)
24 Stewed apricot's not rare with a pudding (7)
26 Gosh! It's about Catholic holy man (6)
27 Counterattack could be in posterior, or not (7)

Down

1 Bitter hostility sounds as if it's more offensive (7)
2 By engaging gentle officer oddly gain ministers' approval (7,2,6)
3 Source of whiskey somewhere in East Sussex (3)
4 Door fitment helps to make unlatching easy (5)
5 Inseparable princess leaves unseen (9)
6 This dog, trained with new characters, may be cowering (5)
7 Mackintoshes (not old) as well as 6s in bucket (4,4,3,4)
8 Calmness of Prime Minister inspired House of Lords, say (6)
12 Doctor secures 3 – it'll get rid of fluid … (5)
14 … easing pain in a short cut a leg's sadly incurred (9)
15 One of 8 in boat who argues? (5)
16 Soak's employed to entertain foreign leader (6)
18 Leave mobile touring oddly nice isolated area (7)
20 Container transport group's resistant to change (5)
21 Instruct doctor out in Turkey (5)
25 Just beat young Dickens character (3)

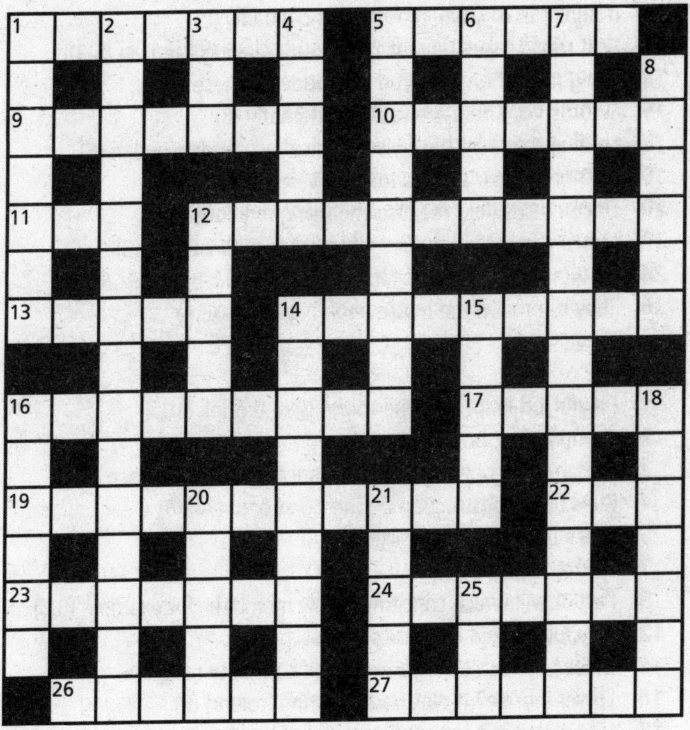
1
2
3
4
5
6
7
8
9
10
11
12
13
14
15
16
17
18
19
20
21
22
23
24
25
26
27

46

Across

6 They're suckers for doing housework (6,8)
9 He receives early deliveries in hope, nervously (6)
10 It ruins top of lawn in home terribly badly (8)
11 Best friend takes time at Tynemouth making fish trap (5,3)
13 Tonight's not on – maybe I've laddered these! (6)
15 Swords from here are tooled differently (6)
17 Sci-fi author sent back visa medical officer dropped in (6)
19 Horrible debtor's notes follow overdraft (6)
20 Doctor's business means rehearsing regularly (8)
22 I must somehow impress republicans with dessert (8)
24 He works very hard training disheartened janitor (6)
26 They run round the house avoiding tables (8,6)

Down

1 Playful kid leapt over ma to get tinned drink (10,4)
2 Examine tins, bottom first (4)
3 French enter one of theirs then another in charity race (3,3)
4 Runs down obstruction during burst of speed (8)
5 Bird's dislodged top a little bit (4)
7 Revive approach (4,2)
8 Part of will which concerns family members, for example (8,6)
12 Silly fool nicked institute's manuscript (5)
14 Miles between Georgia and Utah complete range (5)
16 Lower morale? It dips badly touring Ireland (8)
18 Like mattress or special step on ladder (6)
21 Extract from Rousseau, Thoreau or e.g. 17 (6)
23 Mediterranean port area (4)
25 Shrek makes some progress (4)

47

Across

1 After tough job select boy as striking example (6,6)
8 Following short break many worked for Pope, say (4,3)
9 Revoke misguided doctrines but not Old Testament (7)
11 To accept blame Kate suffered endless therapy (4,3,3)
12 Form sacked head girl (4)
14 Ex-arts centre in county creates piece of music (8)
16 Greek letter has one story set in Paris location (6)
17 Harm one pair of students (3)
19 Broadcast offended (3,3)
21 Roman coin is under a potty (8)
24 Girl finishes programme with a somersault (4)
25 Doctor put a tie on before beginning to treat casualty (10)
27 Condiment put round a salad without notice (3,4)
28 Dish of roasted tortoise (minus tail) (7)
29 What's the *real* reason Dad had engine repaired? (6,6)

Down

1 It keeps fisherman dry but spoils kingfisher a bit (7)
2 Act too soon and gum up the works in June oddly (4,3,3)
3 It often gets scattered after couple's initiation (8)
4 In rotten veal Arab found wriggly creatures (6)
5 Special tree makes window-frame (4)
6 This paperwork ten put in order for emigration (7)
7 Shop price too high for office machines (12)
10 Quid's in it, so I edited long essay (12)
13 One role is limited by ban supported by both sides (10)
15 Former precious metal's not good (3)
18 Golfer dances round a piano? That's child's play (8)
20 Section of orchestra in main pit possibly (7)
22 A tinier novel? That shows laziness (7)
23 Browning brought up name at students' union (6)
26 Poet in pub supported by daughter (4)

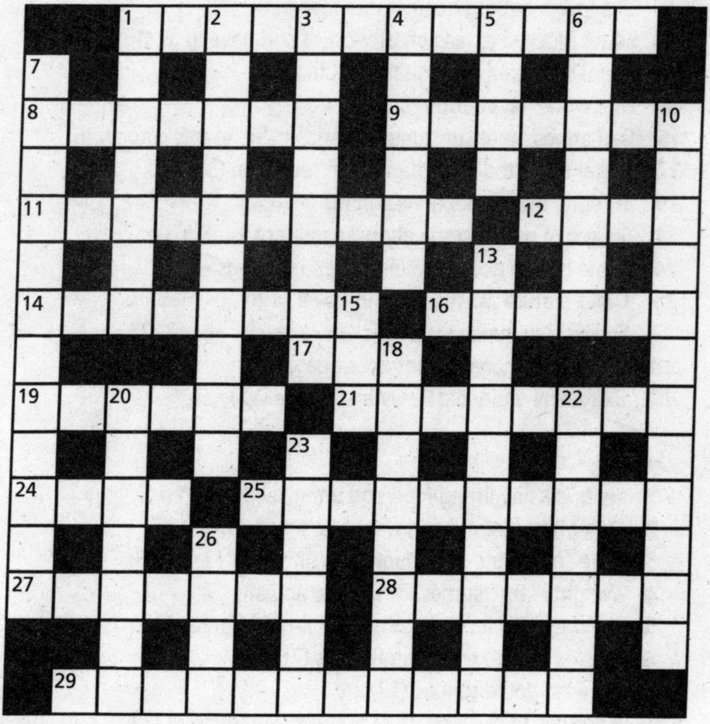

48

Across

1 Gold Cup bills somehow secured with these? (7,5)
8 Returning salesman has seized power maybe (7)
9 Like lovers getting nearly more love in Oz (7)
11 Editor blocked extension of jackpot and gave in (6,4)
12 Metal extracted from quartz in China (4)
14 Fine stone left country (8)
16 Bad atmosphere surrounds American ship in this country (6)
17 Metal extracted from stannite in recession (3)
19 10 enter international design (6)
21 Source of easy income about in military food (5,3)
24 Some French abandon ruin where Paris was (4)
25 Quiet mature artist's exciting novel (4-6)
27 Senior churchman visits markets for tacky items? (7)
28 Enclose fashionable hint about date (7)
29 Extremely angry old Peruvian lineage (12)

Down

1 He breaks in, lifting food and unfinished fat (7)
2 Don't interfere in holiday on one's own (5,5)
3 Take something off in nightclub unit after I leave (8)
4 Weighty large stones? Tiny ones, actually (6)
5 View topless former *Daily Mail* cartoon figure (4)
6 Horses absorb energy in flowers (7)
7 Takes suitable spades (12)
10 She sees to the welfare of 5 aircrews in distress (6,6)
13 He constantly criticises wife and pawnbroker (5,5)
15 Obscure instruction to reduce volume (3)
18 Ulster writer turns up in small group in alley (8)
20 Stood on ghastly rodent round back of shed (7)
22 Behaviour of 100 on tube (7)
23 Produced record that carries a value (6)
26 Water plant in botanical garden (4)

49

Across

1 Non-American girl's pelvis halfway on board? (8)
5 Forces ruined wall-painting (6)
9 It describes faery urn perhaps (8)
10 Governor put blame on weekend (6)
12 Angler uses it in lake and river (4)
13 Tree that's awfully easily cut up I ignored (10)
15 An attractive device, lorgnette came in bits (13)
19 Steering gear's new on car carrying king and prince in India (4-3-6)
23 Production of power in about 35 years (10)
25 Actor fancies having receding hairstyle (4)
28 Rope used by officer cordoning off a deep inlet (6)
29 It's risky walking behind dog's tail (8)
30 Old coins one's found in canals (6)
31 Swinger's nude, swimming in fruit (8)

Down

1 Deaden sound using nearly all of scarf (6)
2 Benefactor makes entrance around noon (5)
3 He accepts Queen's present (4)
4 University in US trip abandoned cycle race (7)
6 Prepare to study at end of May (5)
7 It sends signals in body or rises in tension maybe (9)
8 In work by US writer it's different, utterly different (8)
11 Some say it makes a good pudding (4)
14 Cheese of fine Greek character (4)
15 New civic centre sacked four for behaving oddly (9)
16 Shred letters on grave (3)
17 Help to hide cocaine and another drug (4)
18 Woman, annoyed about kid's horse say, got in a twist (8)
20 Moral obligation assumed by Hindu, typically (4)
21 It's a long time for a region to be in turmoil (4,3)
22 Sidestep male in bumper car (6)
24 Russian ruler got up to eat old popular Sunday lunch (5)
26 Extra lines at end of working week (5)
27 Poet's asleep in Lincoln, beginning to dream (4)

50

Across

6 Being rude about a record? It prevents shock (10,4)
9 Beetle found in Madagascar, Abyssinia and elsewhere (6)
10 A missing girl's pelvis in centre of vessel (8)
11 Crushed thyme in a stone, a gemstone (8)
13 Ray locked up 550 in madhouse (6)
15 Harry Hurst's first to hear singer in garden (6)
17 Far-off meteor exploded (6)
19 One's wobbling, carrying weight? Take a nap (6)
20 It's an honour having old record as base of website (4,4)
22 Remarkable ruling's designed to protect article (8)
24 Countrified Catholic owns new suit (6)
26 Cattle end up here in US in awfully huge ratholes (14)

Down

1 Incidental Tantric music played on a laptop (14)
2 Originally the supreme autocrat and Russian leader (4)
3 Former pupil spilt blood with army finally … (3,3)
4 … one bleeding nearly everywhere, not fit to serve? (8)
5 What engravers do with pocket chisel essentially (4)
7 Salad ingredient also contains meat but no energy (6)
8 Design a New Age pin-up having gold mounting in this country (5,3,6)
12 Sort untidy old trunk (5)
14 Flag day with disappointing turnover (5)
16 Like cat burglar, the last to be foiled by Yard (8)
18 Explosive attack (6)
21 Woman chopped ham, hiding skill (6)
23 Top of Glasgow chimney's down (4)
25 Closed small shack (4)

51

Across

6 Part of UK retains timeless belief in hormone supplier (9,5)
9 Plug opening in pre-Christmas period (6)
10 French Green supporter inspires energy and backbone (8)
11 Like some consonants or private thoughts? (8)
13 Looked for and saw it quickly, so some say (6)
15 No NE lass, Myleene Klass is angry with submission (6)
17 It's pretentious and souped up (6)
19 One of many in multiplex observed to contain chromium (6)
20 Sophistication of a fool in Bury misbehaving (8)
22 Unlikely to be the weapon displayed in IRA flier (3,5)
24 At home with money, say, like remote populations? (6)
26 Strange nodules confused canine experts (6,8)

Down

1 Cigarette seller? Five finish poor Chinamen nearly (7,7)
2 Get this tool or a dozen maybe on leaving (4)
3 Cultivate cacti around Spain containing vinegar (6)
4 Province's received money for mental illness (8)
5 Plant Vera's after for its emollient extract? (4)
7 Vie and, surprisingly, overrun (6)
8 Former PM twice set a fresh direction (5-9)
12 Fat old boy heading 90° clockwise from 8 (5)
14 Limitless future with nuclear reversal of course (1-4)
16 Sailors hope to make it 50, and before autumn (8)
18 Office desk (6)
21 Newly-wed enjoys midnight game (6)
23 Broadcast correct ceremony (4)
25 Volume in reserve (4)

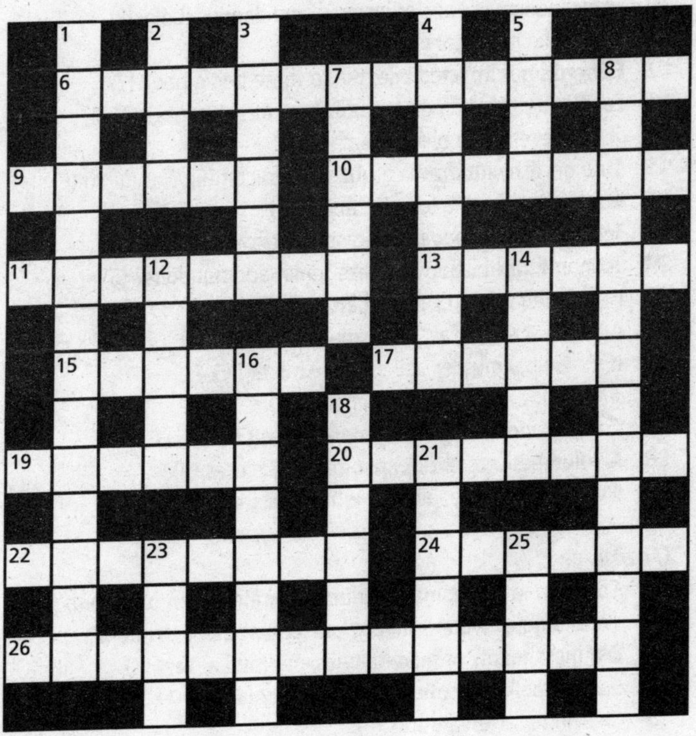

52

Across

1 Power lust in odd game with Romania (left not right) (11)
9 It's just a piano (7)
10 Like windows in Paris museum – and doors initially (7)
11 Samuel kept animal inside (3)
12 Edward's got infected bile due to these being bad? (7)
13 Funny this: odd bits go missing from British tops … (1-6)
14 … and even from bling, great! (3)
15 Strange, like withdrawn pathetic character (5)
17 Writer occupies big seat in capital (5)
18 Telling stories subtly in government circles (5)
20 Touring India, bishop has withdrawn address there (5)
22 Hole in record that's often battered (3)
24 Approve a run in fast cars, small fast cars (2-5)
25 It picks up a murder being reconstructed (3,4)
26 Jolly Jack's abstract art (3)
27 Conductor of energy in a storm perhaps? (7)
28 A volume is brought in, split into tiny pieces (7)
29 It flattens 26, spreading 27 with lines and ruler (11)

Down

1 Congress in Minsk may produce early indication of growth (7,8)
2 What Biggles wore – shabby old leggings, not trendy (7)
3 Old instruments or modern ones, not loud at first (5)
4 Sort of toolkit in both sides of mouth? (4,5)
5 Shotgun scattered ducks (7)
6 A rare RAF critic's sick at rear in naval ship (8,7)
7 Brilliant Rebus worked around Peterhead (6)
8 Foreign port largely passed over heading west (6)
16 High wind wrecks the most sturdy but not the last (4,5)
18 E.g. runner beans, wretched mule ate, say (6)
19 Get rota changed in dispatch (7)
21 Bird blown away across a river (4,3)
23 Less able to understand lighting device (6)
25 She inspired love poems in opera "Tosca" (5)

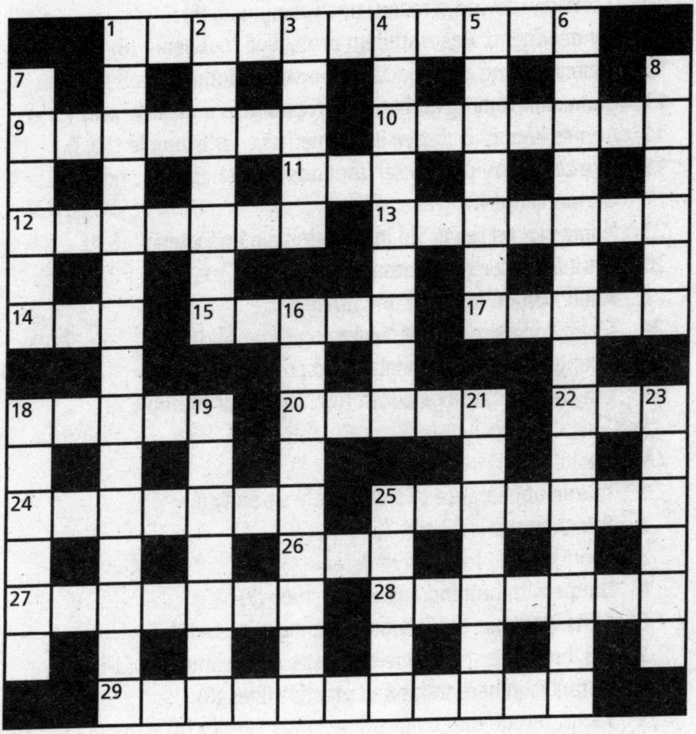

53

Across

1 Paint verbal picture of scatty brides receiving keys (8)
5 Nurse sibling (6)
9 Insect swallowed a rodent nearly very well (8)
10 My goodness! Has a student protective footwear? (6)
12 Source of drug and chocolate powder? Nothing's left (4)
13 Comedian Tommy grabbed microphone at a musical play (5,5)
15 Agrees enough's dispersed as methane for example (10,3)
19 Like cars crazy people sell around French Republic and Germany (4-9)
23 Nasty wound limits Sid in gym doing a handstand? (6,4)
25 Zsa Zsa Gabor's long story (4)
28 Adult portion for each one (6)
29 Claim Yorkshire town's beginning to go off (8)
30 Strongly urge other rebels to accept vote (6)
31 I say insulting things about Hebridean, for example (8)

Down

1 To ruin appearance of French café's barmy (6)
2 French author's 23 tree (5)
3 Short journey to decisive defeat (4)
4 Dance with nothing on? That's swell (7)
6 State response at wedding hugging a husband (5)
7 E.g. birds like small omelette with large contents? (3-6)
8 Listeners in here trained to practise lines (8)
11 Farm storage unit crops up in Polish interior (4)
14 Young dog lacks first aid (4)
15 Poet might perhaps have sold novel (9)
16 Aspire to lose footing in dance (3)
17 Kelvin's recalled occasionally to be QC (4)
18 Kiss formally in foreign consulate, not Norway (8)
20 The chances of Dirty Dancer surpassing leaders? (4)
21 Old frying pans contain recipe direct from factory (2-5)
22 Nurse touring Spain reveals her CV (6)
24 Set designer creates it in wide corridor (5)
26 A 23 tie gets prize (5)
27 Fusses over drink (4)

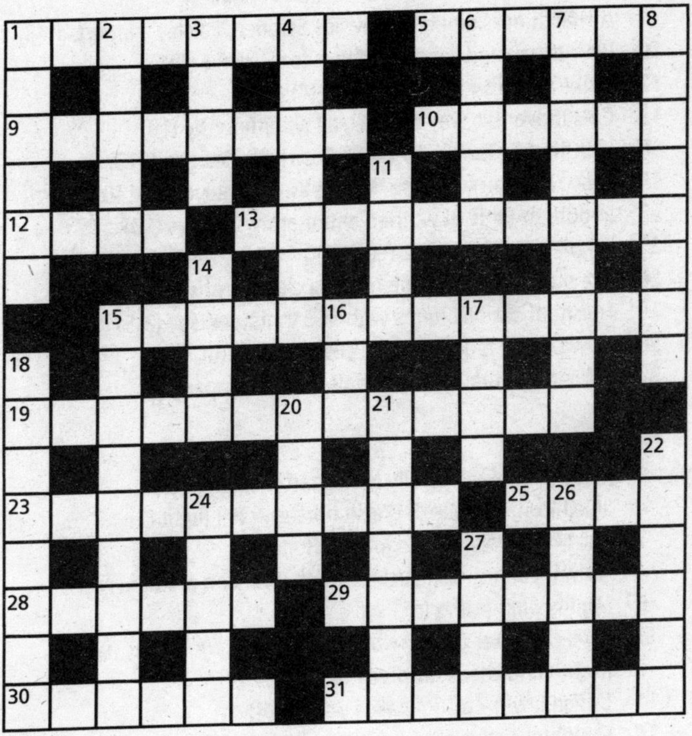
1
2
3
4
5
6
7
8
9
10
11
12
13
14
15
16
17
18
19
20
21
22
23
24
25
26
27
28
29
30
31

54

Across

1 Doctor won't start to help everyone in civic centre (4,4)
5 Call off gamble not having husband on line (6)
9 A French mission abroad avoids Sweden; Paisley supports it (8)
10 I left exhausted captain to have forty winks (6)
12 Strike in the air in upper house (4)
13 Cats move this way but they all sit differently (10)
15 Like power stations he and I'd correctly designed (13)
19 Fancy Elvis on tube line hosting King's anniversary! (6,7)
23 In pub, sit with GI worried about army supplies (10)
25 An area in the Cognac region (4)
28 The one in Delphi made nothing clear surprisingly (6)
29 Finish off various items with 500 tomatoes, say (3-5)
30 How people react to pain? Like cowards (6)
31 Solicitor's work involves deals with a company (8)

Down

1 Make untidy and unruly louts start to explain (6)
2 Smell front runners of Welsh horses in full flight (5)
3 Put 14 on individual following Henry (4)
4 African country in heartless south with lion around (7)
6 Modify plug fitting (5)
7 Paris caretaker could, with time, become egocentric (9)
8 Mouth and cheek drop, say (3-5)
11 British law-breaking makes you cry (4)
14 Daughter enters, say, Spain to get slight advantage (4)
15 Quest for it brings sort of glory in downfall? (4,5)
16 English copper as currency (3)
17 Some pot luck in retreat for its ardent devotees? (4)
18 A nun leaves on Palm Sunday excitedly singing hymns (8)
20 Can German assent to the Italian? (4)
21 British aura surrounds very daring display (7)
22 We'd set about raising flower inside so tidied garden (6)
24 Volley of shots also explodes over bow of Victory (5)
26 Writer's carried in vehicle round African capital (5)
27 David Lean entertained one of the Pythons (4)

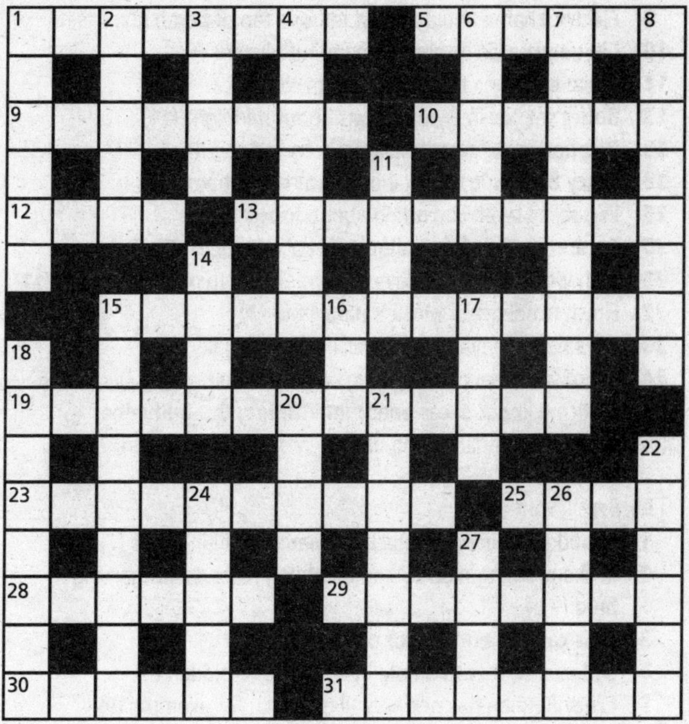

55

Across

1 It's spoken in citadel in different places (7)
5 Native American recalled by old Indonesian islander (6)
9 Electric charge could almost remove top of bomb (7)
10 Clive's irritated by start of erupting blister (7)
11 I hear someone from Haifa's expected (3)
12 Buffet set out in Brad's rooms about midnight (11)
13 Be afraid of engineers invited in by father (5)
14 Make billions in Africa, working at the extremes (9)
16 Top part played by Little or Large finally (5,4)
17 Book consulted by a sailor on return journey? (5)
19 Irish whistler able to have regular duet? No one can deny it (11)
22 Royal Academy of Music's data store (3)
23 It's said in Kenya one follows his law illegally (7)
24 Make wider second-class highway east and north (7)
26 Notice a knock occasionally interrupting this gathering? (6)
27 Maybe surrender, giving up big car for customer (3-4)

Down

1 In middle of action, detectives made up their minds (7)
2 In the morning mad 27 came holding reserves for gaming here (9,6)
3 For example, nothing for one's self? (3)
4 Ordered boat with a hole in it? That's forbidden (5)
5 Crazy Belgian has one very like a canal for example (9)
6 Entry permits superb views after wasting time (5)
7 M. Jackson's autumn deals? He'd tackle anything (4,2,3,6)
8 Interfere with sporting award, say (6)
12 Edge along border around lake (5)
14 Forward troops are French, linked to web, getting tense (5,4)
15 Angry republicans take extreme positions (5)
16 Yen for jazzy T-shirt (6)
18 Study group remains out of control (7)
20 Put on air of being from abroad, or not (5)
21 Book – two books I sent in with French article (5)
25 Strange old churchman (3)

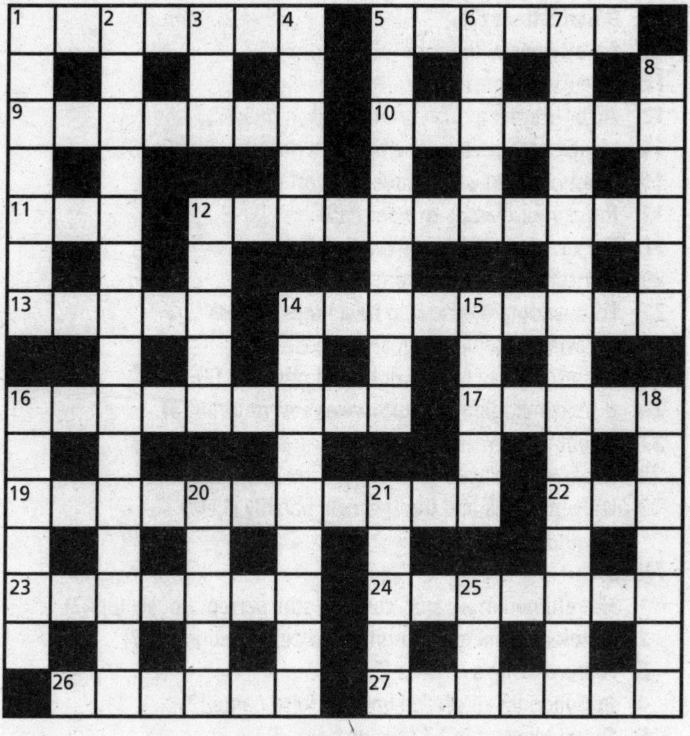
1 2 3 4 5 6 7 8 9 10 11 12 13 14 15 16 17 18 19 20 21 22 23 24 25 26 27

56

Across

1 Airline cuts ordered? That's not practical (11)
9 Heard new variety of buddleia hasn't died (7)
10 9 island trees (7)
11 An attempt in the past (3)
12 Fine yarn's thrashed (7)
13 Actor Hugh imports current English rock (7)
14 Upper-class person, one in youth hostel originally (3)
15 Plants start to complicate first part of play (5)
17 Raise your glasses to a saint (5)
18 Cryptic clue about new relation (5)
20 Our clothes party's distinctive scent (5)
22 I'd abandoned widow to be a huge success (3)
24 Ottawa policeman's second release (7)
25 It's terribly sad to lose right and privilege (7)
26 Bill's companion in court makes soft murmur (3)
27 One has to, when upset, make Japanese pottery (7)
28 Organ solo played staccato without introduction (7)
29 It's venomous and treats an elk harshly (11)

Down

1 He returned in a panic, carrying sum surreptitiously (5,3,7)
2 Automatic change in orbit about zero centigrade (7)
3 A top teacher's in front (5)
4 In Congo it's displayed under a false name (9)
5 Prime Minister in 17 sails up here (7)
6 A RAF crew claim he spread poisonous conflict (8,7)
7 Flautist's county (6)
8 Agreement when dispatched (6)
16 Finish phone conversation near thing (5,4)
18 In Utah Tom's worried in the extreme (6)
19 Give responsibility to nutters? That's crazy (7)
21 Novel about cricket club in airline once (7)
23 Intercept almost always, roughly covering yard (6)
25 Lily's uniform among many (5)

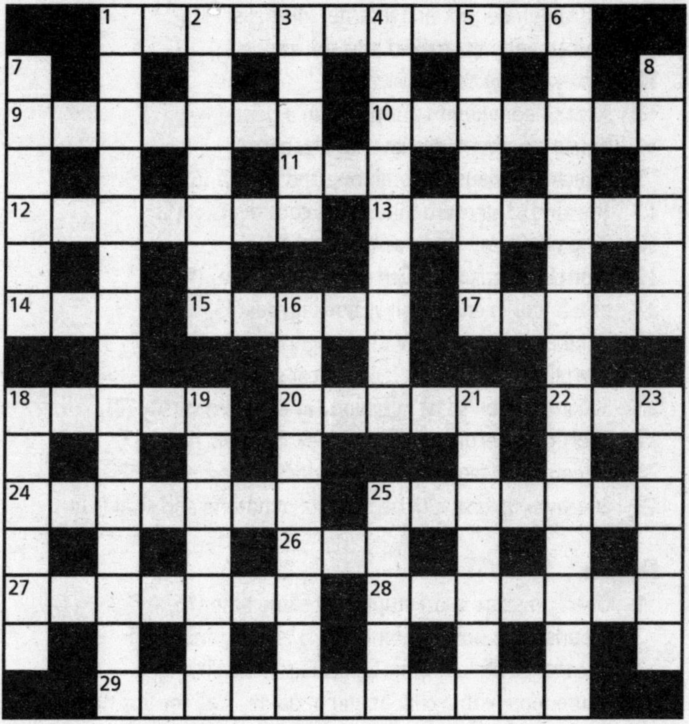

57

Across

1 Child actor got sick following effect of cold wind (5,6)
9 Give title to posh person in middle of Henley (7)
10 British lumberjack and internet journalist (7)
11 African antelope tucked into sphagnum (3)
12 Top executive sacked four (7)
13 A bit's beginning to disappear, in a gentle way (7)
14 House member hides love for cleaner (3)
15 Director managed to grab one and run off (5)
17 The kind of treasure that's a bit controversial (5)
18 Strip club free? That's sensational (5)
20 Worrying signs unsettled some about navy (5)
22 Roe found in endless river flowing west (3)
24 Wine expert cooked TV dinner ignoring daughter (7)
25 Awfully crude male defends Oscar's politeness (7)
26 Second person's last in biology at Open University (3)
27 Short rope secures damaged foot, climbing here? (7)
28 Government regulation covers doctor's complaint (7)
29 Energy source should be this mix of butane and sisal (11)

Down

1 Open on same court stupidly at same time (15)
2 A Parisian in Bondi unfortunately is flying home (7)
3 Tell stories about, for instance, European city (5)
4 Injure man with a club at end of game? Call for this (9)
5 Had an idea, however it doesn't involve writer (7)
6 MP's house title is correct and well intentioned (5,10)
7 Latin hymn? With a different accent it's boring (2,4)
8 Diamond pattern, largely knitted, missing a line (6)
16 A happy comic welcomed old RC raised in scripture (9)
18 Uniform of electrified railway (6)
19 Doctor doesn't possess energy or means (7)
21 Chopped cucumbers without ruler? Give in (7)
23 Marie's annoyed hosts (6)
25 Started eating in entrenched positions (3,2)

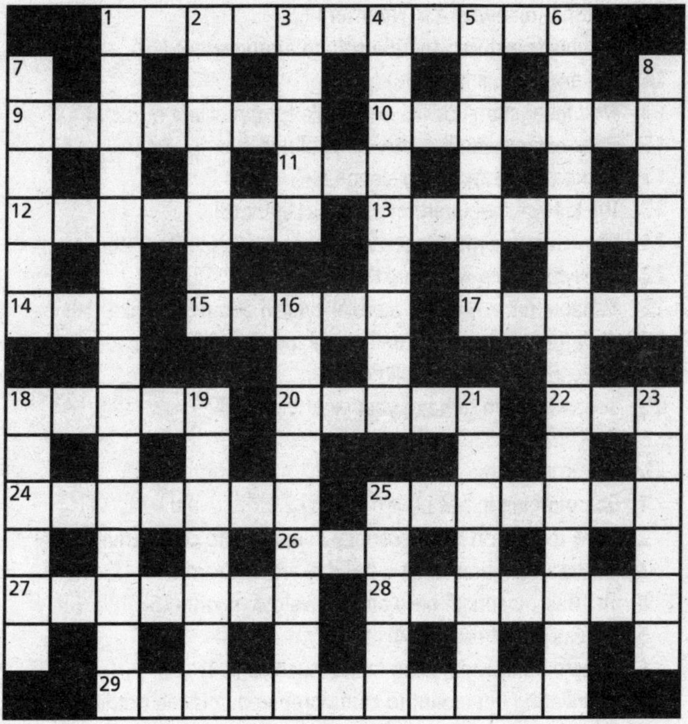
1
2
3
4
5
6
7
8
9
10
11
12
13
14
15
16
17
18
19
20
21
22
23
24
25
26
27
28
29

58

Across

1 I'm sunk in dolefulness maybe, not facing reality (4-8)
8 Purchase too much in past by bringing in unit (7)
9 Animal somewhere in New York (7)
11 Disguise produced to hide square arrangement (10)
12 £25 for a small horse (4)
14 One fated somehow to be unable to appreciate music (4-4)
16 Rock once covered centre of Dublin in a lump (2,4)
17 Avoid taking top off to sleep (3)
19 What I was originally, more by accident (6)
21 Christmas is time to receive volume by this writer? (8)
24 They dangle from a tree, the fools (4)
25 Papal letter in English, awfully cynical about Sri Lanka (10)
27 No attempt to claim small space for road sign (2,5)
28 Hoping endlessly for pill (7)
29 A dandy place to hang your washing (7,5)

Down

1 26s working in hat (7)
2 They're held on May 1 usually in lead-up to confinement (6,4)
3 Dawn's daughter takes a holiday around Yarmouth (8)
4 In "Basic Instinct" hero almost welcomes offer (6)
5 Peter's out of danger (4)
6 Where bumf is enjoying lots of success (2,1,4)
7 In meeting I'm meant to come prepared, missing nothing (12)
10 It's used to cut metal, with eye exactly on cast (12)
13 He sticks his nose into new role in Pinter play (10)
15 It helps stability during surfing (3)
18 He knows lots in metallography oddly but not Elgar (8)
20 Large port? So what? (3,4)
22 Twist vein round copper rod and bend towards centre (7)
23 In a frenzy, medico grabs protein (6)
26 Let it remain in text and in post etc. (4)

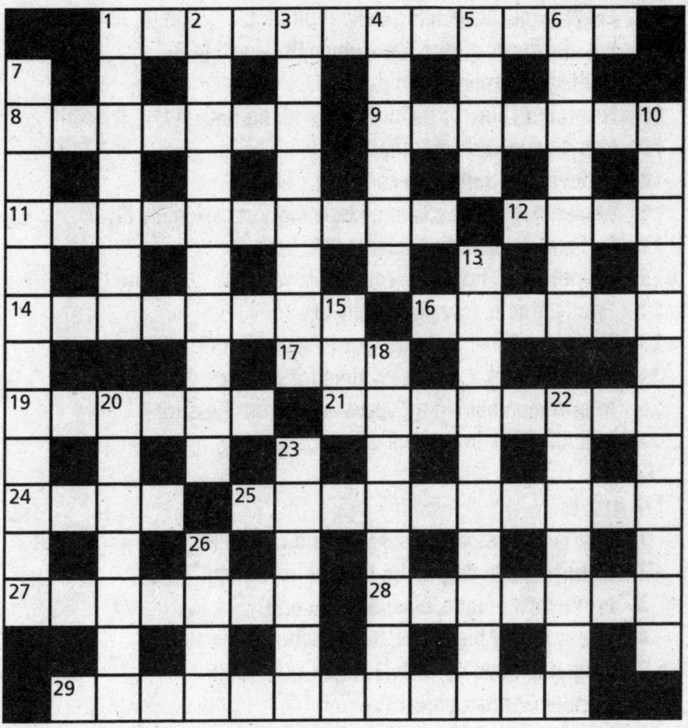

59

Across

1 Oz friend entertains apprentice shoe repairer (7)
5 Give away by introducing revised rate (6)
9 Leaf's large, developing daily round top of pond (4,3)
10 E.g. the stratosphere, into which 6s vanish (4,3)
11 Damage submarine amidships (3)
12 New oil rig sure to include one with no faith (11)
13 Like an egg, old and empty (5)
14 Sudden raid ruins icon controversially (9)
16 Midweek, wife needs to change diary occasionally (9)
17 La Serenissima's first printer (5)
19 It's not clear if pension roughly covers 100 at college (3-8)
22 Erratic little fellow principally (3)
23 Omitting vowel E almost noisily in retreat (7)
24 Person in embassy has no time for exam certificate (7)
26 Information held in a Cyprus service business (6)
27 I double back in gym for accolade (7)

Down

1 Jazz group has endless 3 in island capital (7)
2 British man in dog-collar twirled in "Strictly"? (8,7)
3 Prune tops of lime, olive and plum (3)
4 It may detect high-flyer, acting school radical (5)
5 Slogan devised by cartel? About time (6-3)
6 Slender German object (5)
7 In car-boot sale I'd displayed muscle enhancer (8,7)
8 Nick's son found in 20 (6)
12 Vin Diesel controls unaffiliated film company (5)
14 In first half of December clubs in New York show impropriety (9)
15 Catholic priest brought in memorial of saint (5)
16 Bury whiskey first in season (6)
18 Change direction of erratic centre forward? No wonder (7)
20 Brain particle made of protein (not the margins) (5)
21 Bored US bank's more expensive (3,2)
25 Chopped fruit and vegetable (3)

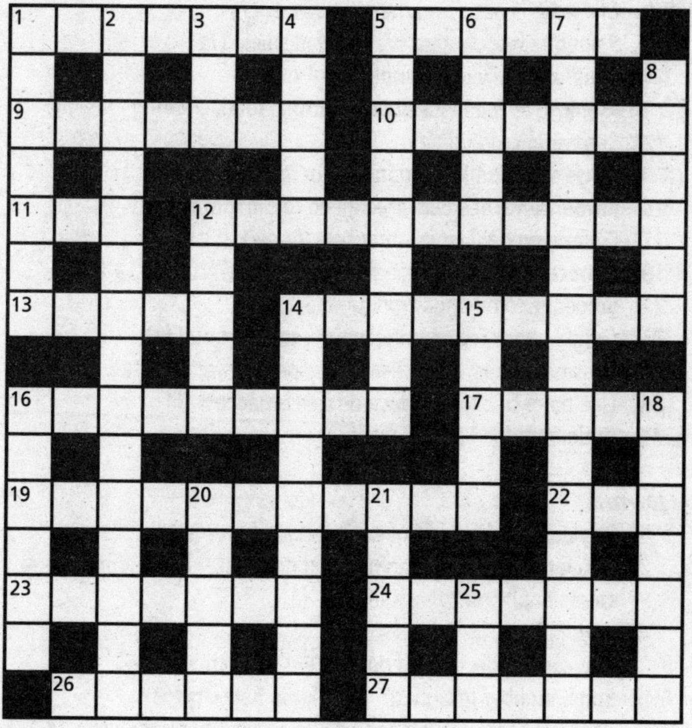

60

Across

1   In street USDAW displayed woodworker's output (7)
5   Mike tucked into fresh stout – the greatest (6)
9   My niche is untidy – it needs a sweep (7)
10 Someone who fastens his belt and shield (7)
11 Beast regularly comes out at night (3)
12 Promote recipe in lukewarm wartime food, creating fear (11)
13 Surrender crop (5)
14 Tense situation feeding injured in half of Kent (5-4)
16 Favourite yacht's damaged: need to dip into this? (5,4)
17 Swimming pool covers rear bottom deck (5)
19 It's a tailor's rule to record act (4,7)
22 Sergeant commands work unit (3)
23 Giggle about receptionist initially in new hotel (7)
24 Missionary and saint hosted by a person from Warsaw (7)
26 Like more publicity to include free broadcast (6)
27 Code found in Parisian vault (7)

Down

1   Doctor is back at end of day, working here? (4,3)
2   Quick trip's spoiled with ruts and potholes – hard going (7-4,4)
3   Occasionally outrun vessel (3)
4   Your old Middle East herb (5)
5   I hit runs, sadly getting bowled – it's not cricket (2-7)
6   Small number left construction kit in holy city (5)
7   Poor Lynn feels guilt having day gratifying her own needs (4-11)
8   Fruit's gone off, artist admitted (6)
12 Twenty went away carrying rum drink (5)
14 Arable ground supports oak ordered for Oz native (5,4)
15 Call up the night before receiving fine (5)
16 Church sustains places in sudden uprising (6)
18 Pork producers beginning to test colour (7)
20 Annual check-up provided dominant theme (5)
21 What's actually said in the States, period (5)
25 Old Roman Catholic character in Tolkien (3)

61

Across

6 Charlotte's behind normal religious organisation (8,6)
9 Food is thrown back over tents (6)
10 Marital custom a pygmy adapted, having heart of gold (8)
11 Brown spots fellow ignored on top of skin, not caring (8)
13 Alluring old flame – it's to do with her ears (6)
15 Make material in big space with son (daughter's involved) (6)
17 Young bird sounds like small seal (6)
19 Knight of the Garter kept a bit crushed in knapsack (6)
20 Young US doctor and alien's source of information (8)
22 Hackman, say, guards most peculiar rock (8)
24 Highly decorated soldiers face a time in north-east (6)
26 Tessa's back revealing all, selling her best properties? (5-9)

Down

1 Exorcism centre rebuilt using these machines? (8,6)
2 One article or a couple? (4)
3 Element that is protecting Norse god (6)
4 Maid works here in front of sink, cruelly treated (8)
5 Stop bribe (4)
7 Stand up to work, then sit (6)
8 Get Act some time perhaps after Bill goes through this (9,5)
12 Kelvin and Ruth turned up for barbecue food (5)
14 Boss needing no introduction to tranquilliser (5)
16 Kennel's a disgrace (8)
18 Long and narrow cruise ship has one (6)
21 Soldiers, tense, pick up animal's track (6)
23 Most employers guard main part of plant (4)
25 Pin number trouble? (4)

62

Across

1 Priest nearby could be a Nonconformist (12)
8 Drink goes off at home – about a litre (4,3)
9 I'm soon battling with union – it's looking grim (7)
11 New machines get approval to light up non-stop (5-5)
12 Old man's son to succeed (4)
14 Boiled rice came as dessert (3,5)
16 Large snake has got in S American capital (6)
17 Young chap's happy but no good at the start (3)
19 Tread warily in game, keeping top spinning (6)
21 Stately, eccentric James I in court upset (8)
24 Animal in central Tibet pursued by ten (4)
25 He tangled with girl in team for trip with Santa? (6,4)
27 Mineral has run in explosive, causing fast flow (7)
28 Czar almost seized Arab port in solo flourish (7)
29 To remain in command over government requires stamina (7,5)

Down

1 Will has to go through it in bare top surprisingly (7)
2 Fussy men ignore having old powerhouse on board (6,4)
3 Good French and English breakfast, say? Put it on bed (4,4)
4 Fancy go-kart no good, I gathered, or 3 h.p. vehicle? (6)
5 Bar bird (4)
6 A party supports leaderless chaos? It's sort of green (7)
7 Head doctor repaired typist's chair (12)
10 Big bird has managed each task in Canadian province (12)
13 Announce in advance who's fared poorly, getting nothing (10)
15 Mother, one among thousands (3)
18 In competition, NI party grabs a viscount? Not half (5,3)
20 Clown: "What caused jetty to collapse?" (7)
22 It's added to paint the short circle round the bull (7)
23 Bread protein's in oversupply, at European limits (6)
26 Money raised by all envoys regularly (4)

63

Across

1 French girl produced German wine – I tucked in (12)
8 Foreign prunes I imported increased in value (7)
9 Sacred river swamps royal country houses (7)
11 Four coats spread over centre of ceiling won't fade (6-4)
12 Spots expert touring end of town (4)
14 In the morning Tories arranged to pay off debt (8)
16 Friend married on the rebound in droopy calfskin (6)
17 Overact in first half of famous play (3)
19 Firm admits a bad mistake somewhere in Las Vegas (6)
21 With this live-in friend he's maybe more at home (4-4)
24 In the outlying parts of Kerry it's very dark (4)
25 Ornate collar that protects communion table (5,5)
27 Lack of sophistication in redesign of navy tie (7)
28 Sorties in south by combined forces (7)
29 Messing about round northern isle causing blushes (12)

Down

1 Romeo's amazed about lines in sour fruit (7)
2 Last of wind is blowing, arousing strong reaction (10)
3 Friar is at harbour catching fine angel sharks … (8)
4 … to eat for fun, by the sound of it (6)
5 Test in middle of Texas on first of May (4)
6 In pub Joe's making sense (7)
7 Sell lots here at knock-down prices? (5,7)
10 The place sees changes for the Grand National, say (12)
13 Scattered liver and lime over cold pasta (10)
15 It helps you pick up things even in Le Havre (3)
18 Girls support Maureen to make treacle (8)
20 Try to obtain, say, man's money for religion (7)
22 Showing love for amateur doing laps right (7)
23 He hands over money to employ large actor (6)
26 British character in Athens creates another one (4)

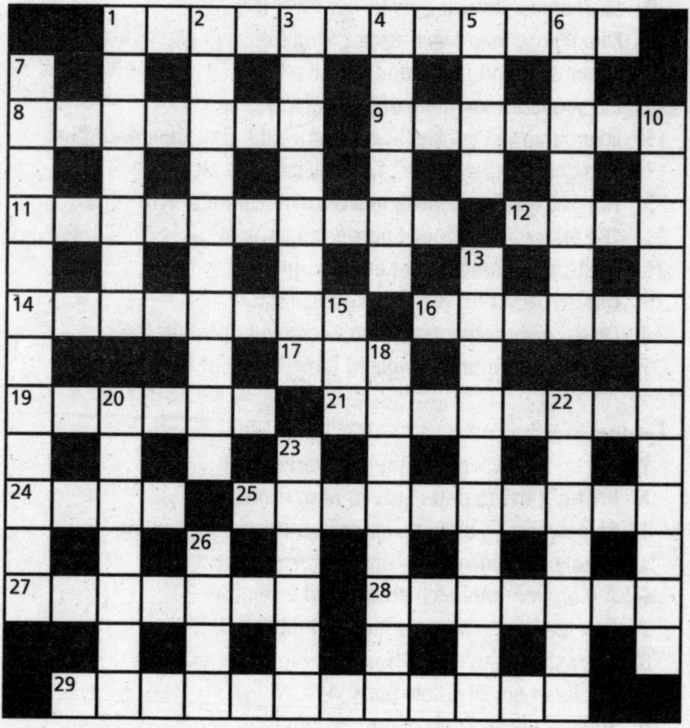

64

Across

1 Craig's after fine iron – it's foolproof (4-4)
5 Pre-match exercise with weapon on horseback (4-2)
9 Sir Thomas has suit altered – it's wet (8)
10 Dread hard men twice seizing king (6)
12 Famous person from Latin America (4)
13 Lie about casual game of soccer (4,6)
15 What gourmet cooked round home? It's very appetising (5-8)
19 Pub game and a bottle of bubbly before dance (5,8)
23 Harsh engineers contributed a smaller amount (10)
25 The States abandoned Spain in this way (4)
28 R. Stein prepared leaflet in magazine (6)
29 Moved over a bit without success (8)
30 Obsequious servants primarily seen in Arab state (3-3)
31 Notice inmate playing inside, jumping about (8)

Down

1 Stir up fellow workers during overtime (6)
2 Writer starts to detect Isle of Man expression (5)
3 Somewhere to build computer systems in Sussex, say (4)
4 Supply vessel to catch fish? On the contrary (7)
6 A man from Morocco proclaimed love affair (5)
7 Volatile, tetchy Maurice circles right then left (9)
8 After short display I'm hosting German for example (8)
11 Cook ran out of edible pods (4)
14 Half of July and half of next month (4)
15 Organises phones to cover island (9)
16 Pay court with old ring (3)
17 Dash in separate lanes (4)
18 It takes ages training tiny tree (8)
20 Go off, search engine, look closely (4)
21 Brown has negotiated best nuclear treaty (4,3)
22 Soar like church over North Dakota (6)
24 Bottle hidden among greener vegetables (5)
26 Lift – innkeeper has one (5)
27 Good stuff doesn't weigh much (4)

65

Across

6 Inspector Moore ransacked lounge etc. (9,5)
9 She accepted Conservative Middle East plan … (6)
10 … time limit in agreement about Germany in Egypt (8)
11 Like Vesuvius, its top's conical after explosion (8)
13 Large snake creates stocking problem (6)
15 Pay, for example, binds leaders of Left and Right (6)
17 Trap company originally backing Internet (6)
19 An alto's confused, not having key (6)
20 Cook quails in midweek to level score (8)
22 E.g. meals provided overflying Norway, insubstantial (2-6)
24 Yank covers wine store in pipework (6)
26 Doctor says NHS policy restricts one to mental remedy (14)

Down

1 Old American rock group support special price for gems (8,6)
2 Spots a name in church (4)
3 Organ noticed outside public library (6)
4 Oil giant interfered with relief work (8)
5 Also left hammer for instance (4)
7 Cause continued to be broadcast, not abandoned (6)
8 King probes finance company for funny goings-on (6,8)
12 Army officer stops short of the Spanish mark (5)
14 Peg making joint prosper almost (5)
16 Mostly rely on recruiting one US soldier in church (8)
18 Agent in a jam expecting to be stripped (6)
21 Incredibly large union don't sadly impress Liberal (6)
23 Secure part of canal (4)
25 Lie in the sun in tight-fitting bodice, say (4)

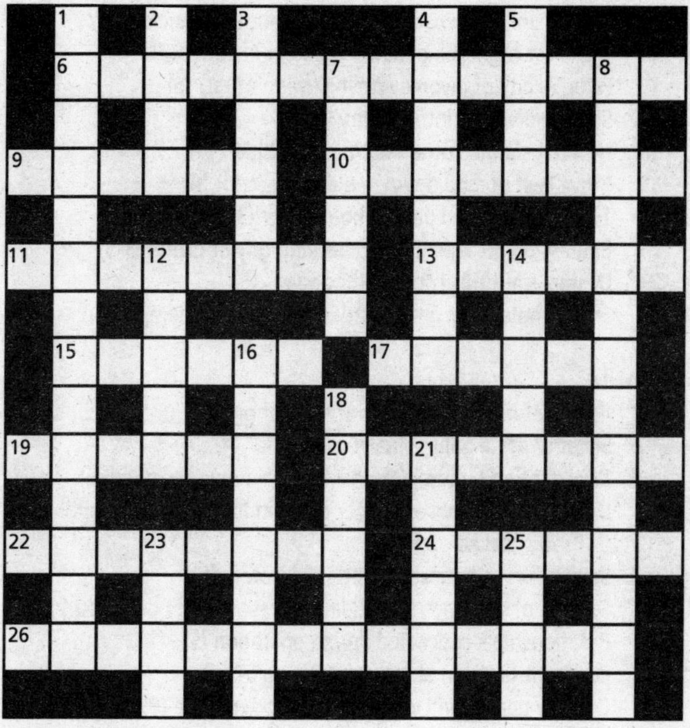

66

Across

6 "Only the fittest survive" may be the Lions' rule? (3,2,3,6)
9 Practical American sailor meets the French (6)
10 Sort of sink, brown, on desktop author used once (8)
11 The most frightening dental problem in street (8)
13 Fame in city of divorce (West Nevada's first) (6)
15 Sodium diverted into country (6)
17 He serves a magistrate during prohibition (6)
19 Move text up and down in old manuscript (6)
20 Top executive and paddle-boat driver (3,5)
22 Endless revolt against hero backing guy at Crufts (3-5)
24 Design a no-frills convent for prayers (6)
26 Spy Nicholas, say, getting treated in mental therapy (14)

Down

1 Aware of his status, it's what teacher prefers! (5-9)
2 Sister wipes a baby initially using this? (4)
3 Decadent and effeminate, having main novel banned (6)
4 Deejay also known as keeper of art in former Asian capital (8)
5 G. Brown picked up fly (4)
7 So this has to be transported in elevators (6)
8 Feature of speeches in wedding no less; sadly, I departed (4-10)
12 Relationship's concealed during operation (5)
14 Orchestrate hymn about quiet young 5? (5)
16 Old boy nearly livid working in forgotten state (8)
18 Queen replaced 51 and 6 in 16, creating fairy king (6)
21 Delicate information's let out (6)
23 Speed? 22 often receives it (4)
25 Some love stealing underwear (4)

67

Across

1 From this angle, option five bewildered women (5,2,4)
9 Palaver and 'assle in fraud (5-2)
10 Supervise six deliveries to bishop's place (7)
11 How to exist and thrive principally (3)
12 Milton's excited about love "bathed in lunar glow" (7)
13 Be smart when describing Rhode Island in few words (7)
14 Japanese anemones absorb lots of water (3)
15 Copper fragment used as old measure of length (5)
17 Material that's only broadcast after noon (5)
18 This animal's ferocious horn impresses one (5)
20 Stormy 14 separates opposing sides in strong light (5)
22 Tricked school boss out of euros (3)
24 City PC's trained to keep royal secret (7)
25 Poison – bad omen grips odd characters in Vienna (7)
26 There's some trouble ahead in meadow (3)
27 Old state put pressure on much bigger one … (7)
28 … getting bigger, government quarrelling, … (7)
29 … endangering reformation of a tenth reign (11)

Down

1 It builds up round star or mad plutocrats in Ely (11,4)
2 It's blissful playing idly with chopped fruit (7)
3 Belief, whichever way you look at it (5)
4 Places to soak corn and fine oats, both milled (9)
5 Someone from Spain, i.e. Brian possibly? (7)
6 False optimism – WI flush out meagre monarch (7,8)
7 Rascals hide money in school headgear (6)
8 African, unknown man, topless, followed Livingstone (6)
16 Hood's disguise in Crimean battle (9)
18 Cook precise but not satisfactory list of ingredients (6)
19 It's less pointed but sore otherwise (7)
21 Artist on the fiddle not finishing dish (7)
23 Injure father, an old sorcerer (6)
25 Excellent score in Gleneagles (5)

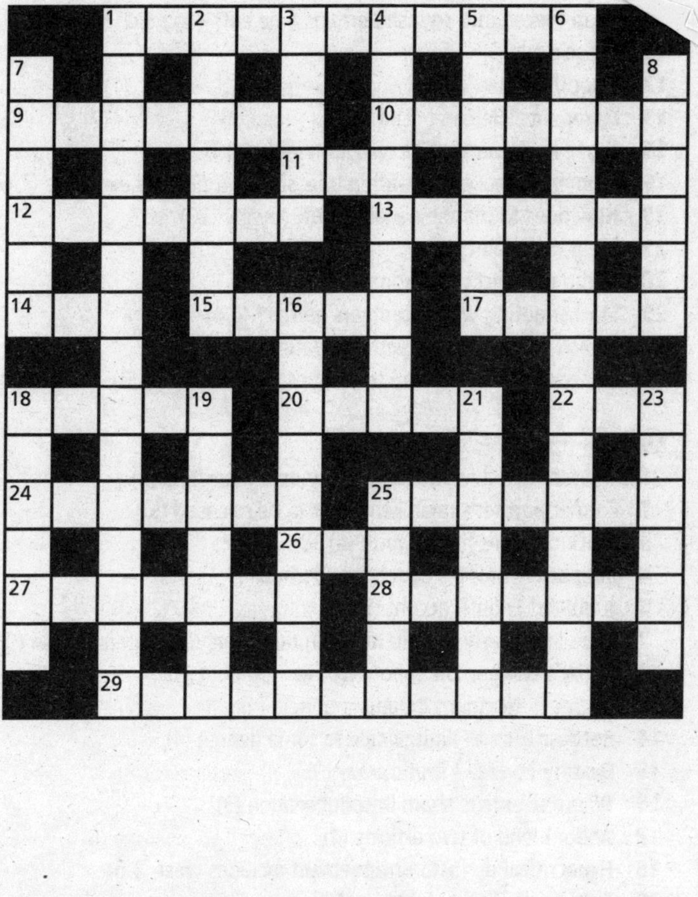
1 2 3 4 5 6
7 8
9 10
11
12 13
14 15 16 17
18 19 20 21 22 23
24 25
26
27 28
29

68

Across

1 Amazing study about English females' colouring (8)
5 Delete start of hymn leaving end of nave (6)
9 Chap tucked into squash perhaps – he eats too much (8)
10 Office desk (6)
12 Smooth 7 head off (4)
13 I'll repeat: "He can't read" (10)
15 Those in power change NHS timetables (13)
19 Woman collapsed beneath a tree, showing signs of exposure (7-6)
23 How does Marianne behave? With loyalty (10)
25 Meat complaint (4)
28 Damp and sticky, like some shellfish? (6)
29 Start shooting where campers gather? (4,4)
30 Stylish European ship with no water around (6)
31 Abandoned rotten dead trees after one's removed (8)

Down

1 Old-fashioned Australian earth-moving machine (6)
2 Former partner's mistakenly due to be released (5)
3 Black cat goes first in vault (4)
4 Supporters group's cool driver perhaps (3,4)
6 A diluted English accent (5)
7 Top of Cromarty and tip of Malin take in new sea area section (9)
8 Hardy's companion almost worried top poet (8)
11 Decree in Northern Ireland is upheld (4)
14 Restless urge to limit choice to some degree (4)
15 Destroy 26 area? That's crazy (9)
16 Where scientists share in collaboration (3)
17 Abhor blend of two articles (4)
18 Hypocritical de facto arrangement includes west (3-5)
20 Rake circle in French street (4)
21 Obscure bits of film found in middle of Greece (7)
22 Old fellows' death hurt (6)
24 Compost smells when you get in it (5)
26 Formal proclamation's essentially unpredictable (5)
27 Ken vandalised European joint (4)

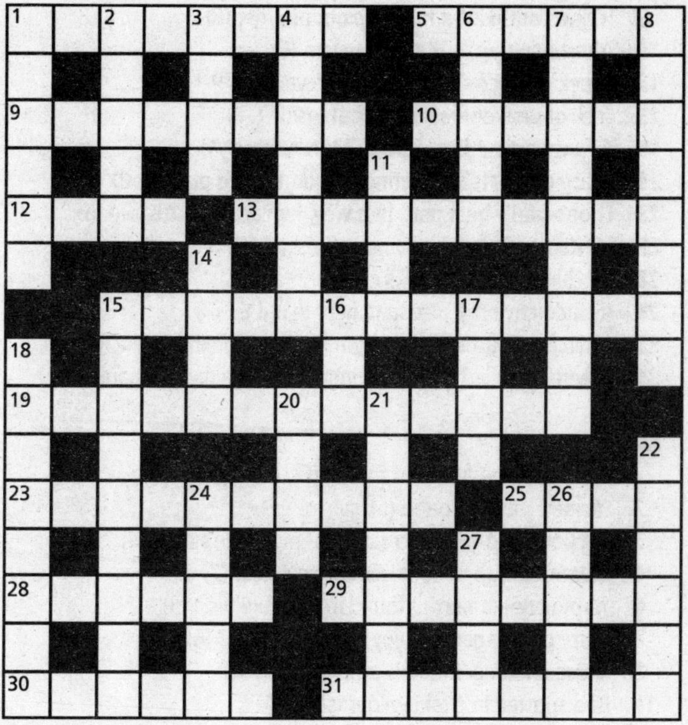

69

Across

1 Optimistic, I'm in job at a quarter past four (8)
5 A good queen held book for dominant sister (6)
9 It gives out light if mantle's out of order (8)
10 Afternoon nap in Maisie's tavern (6)
12 Greek character's back in conservatoire (4)
13 Task of worker messing about inside (10)
15 A fancy airline flies April to March, say (9,4)
19 Crazy magnate's maturing and organizing plays (5-8)
23 Looe's oddly best port, in a way, for catching crustaceans … (7,3)
25 … Kent port lost lead and is finished (4)
28 EU dumps housing links (3-3)
29 It's addictive but pleasant, kept in old tin (8)
30 Churchman accepts new rota – he's becoming senile (6)
31 Where qualified chap may introduce remedies primarily (8)

Down

1 Sea bird's nearly out of breath (6)
2 Divided city in Croatia (5)
3 Big book and where to send it if my name's on it (4)
4 Meat from top of 19 is expensive, I hear (7)
6 Young one up north I found in farm building (5)
7 Harry gets eager to enjoy this next week? (6,3)
8 Nurse drinking coffee is an untidy girl (8)
11 Bird spotted in Otaki wilderness? (4)
14 Queen's standard has edges removed (4)
15 Lift 5 Across, short, awkward and extremely fat (9)
16 Chain occasionally in prison (3)
17 Where to hide revolutionary Iranian money (4)
18 I'd steal away, carrying nothing, to be on my own (8)
20 Area in which a church houses rector (4)
21 Get rid of remains containing black crude oil (7)
22 Cook fish brought in without constraint (6)
24 Someone who records spill (5)
26 Hey presto! Ravioli's unwrapped and boiled (5)
27 This time son worked to get honours (4)

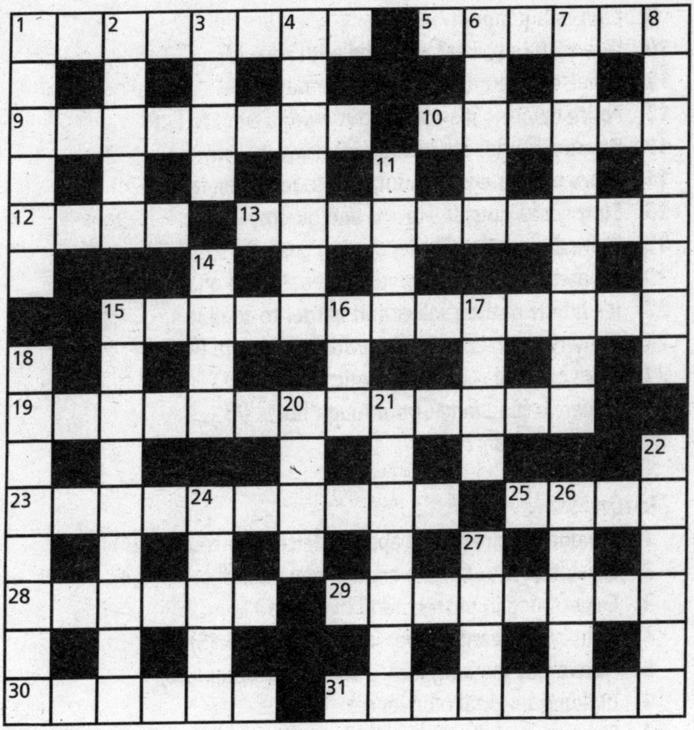
1
2
3
4
5
6
7
8
9
10
11
12
13
14
15
16
17
18
19
20
21
22
23
24
25
26
27
28
29
30
31

70

Across

1 Flower in border of Hereford? (7)
5 What smokers do in Hungary with beer (6)
9 Captain's jumper (7)
10 Less mature solver's no good with ruler (7)
11 Dismissed for a duck just occasionally (3)
12 Police device – it's constructed with electrode (3,8)
13 King's oddly let off, having got down to pray (5)
14 It takes tuber ages to mutate into root vegetable (5,4)
16 Stormy sea outside – go to bed gloomy (9)
17 More daring after leader's gone, contrary to 10 (5)
19 Amazing pirouettes I produced again and again (11)
22 It's briefly getting softer and harder to see (3)
23 Dessert of superior quality with cold centre (4,3)
24 From one cell is born romantic Irish lass (7)
26 Underclothing made from rough fibres (6)
27 Sharp rejoinder? (7)

Down

1 Russian cavalryman swaps two letters for soutane (7)
2 Quick trip with time to engage new test pilots (7-4,4)
3 Cut nothing in old record (3)
4 Hunt non-U handbag for lady in New York (5)
5 I leave guy working for US university group (3,6)
6 Building hospital on river (5)
7 She ingested dhal by mistake, getting giddy feeling (5-10)
8 Fungal problem the right way up? (3,3)
12 Sick earl had temperature after a while (5)
14 Remove a smaller amount, lacking ambition (9)
15 Origins of 14 Across, for instance (5)
16 Hit lorries back to front (6)
18 Cameron spread heroic story (7)
20 What's used to secure the claret after tea, say? (5)
21 Only five-eighths of Acrosses solved to win prize (5)
25 Mate turned up for part of journey (3)

71

Across

1 Cold stall in Billingsgate? (11)
9 Drama writer in children's area (7)
10 Clothes engineers wear to shock (7)
11 Salad vegetable's price reduced (3)
12 Record poem about one's part in serial (7)
13 In lobby fellow replaces student at the centre (7)
14 Note leaders in Department of Health (3)
15 Farewell to a daughter that is going to university (5)
17 Terrorist's mistake (5)
18 Allow in a director with German (5)
20 Clever machine, British in origin (5)
22 Man kept old garden implement (3)
24 Paul and Reg break sound barrier? (7)
25 Part-time 8 perhaps shows promise afte training (4-3)
26 Girl's somewhat fortunate (3)
27 Rude non-stop Vilnius comic entertains clubs (7)
28 Renting a single mobile (7)
29 Interminable evening out touring about N Dakota (5-6)

Down

1 Clever Inca seamanship inspired right man from Mexico, say (7-8)
2 Weird aroma masked sign of acidity in old wine jar (7)
3 Person from Copenhagen has caught ball (5)
4 Briefly expose corm to source of bright light (9)
5 Sudden urge that's sort of simple – it grabs you (7)
6 Adoring poor Gershwin dancing around joint (4-11)
7 Add a very quiet finale (6)
8 Golfer wasted year sustaining place (6)
16 Soldier: sort of guerrilla deserting left for right (9)
18 Drive a goddess almost to Egypt (6)
19 Manservant raised four in ME capital (3,4)
21 Drums played in a pit with Mike (7)
23 The Queen ought to receive an adequate amount (6)
25 Boy keeps nearly everything in drawing room (5)

72

Across

1 He discovers new stars – latest count's disputed (6,5)
9 Deliveryman covers kilometres in Italian city (7)
10 Awful mess in Greece? No, Middle East (4,3)
11 Hack found in Fermanagh (3)
12 Garden sculpture pair displayed in miniature (7)
13 Is it raised when questioning posh Cockney, say? (7)
14 What pigeons do in unfinished henhouse (3)
15 Start where filming takes place (5)
17 Having misused rifle, he's sent down for good (5)
18 Signal heard often during unsuitable episodes … (5)
20 … or produced by this detection system, either way (5)
22 Sailor volunteers to run (3)
24 Particle changes route between same poles (7)
25 Lady of rank, she's sadly caught by missile going back (7)
26 I'm surprised, for example, about including Spain (3)
27 Take in Aussie birds on coach heading west (7)
28 Diver's tool for dislodging gunge (7)
29 Rich bathtub transformed into pet accommodation (6,5)

Down

1 Very large figure's often unobtainable (9,6)
2 Gambol madly around university, getting backache (7)
3 Kid's mother Ann resides in New York (5)
4 Proposed cooking eggs with suet at start of dinner (9)
5 How to remove friction, one of the causes of 10? (3,4)
6 E.g. northwest fort may offer source of support (5,2,8)
7 Nurse meticulously hides what makes you sick (6)
8 Good oarsman and gardener (6)
16 East African park, amazingly green site (9)
18 Send away party touring Ulster (6)
19 Shake and spin dry cloth (7)
21 This new member once managed to be Eurocentric (7)
23 Spend holiday here up in Montrose, relaxing (6)
25 He'd managed to secure part with some penetration (5)

73

Across

1 Senior officer works off-site amid banter (5,2,5)
8 Copper has cares unexpectedly about prosecutor (7)
9 Big dog – it's over in old agriculture ministry (7)
11 Model, actress and catholic girl in cheap seats (5,5)
12 Some unfortunately get fish (4)
14 Sporting event that's punishing? (4,4)
16 Not much change in Moscow? That's a blow to Gregory (6)
17 Bill returns club (3)
19 Obama managed to conserve energy in tiny organism (6)
21 Chap has a rare vigour – it's the icing on the cake (8)
24 Terrible guy navigates back without Bill (4)
25 Gin grew fitfully in East; this drink is weaker (6,4)
27 Drop version of EU blog containing Latin (7)
28 After Belgium Whicker's toured Cambodia and European area (7)
29 Spa treatment refreshed hardy type and other oddly (12)

Down

1 Stick round yacht club and activity in velodrome (7)
2 5 in home teams commit these crimes? (6,4)
3 Crashing film bore gets leg in front (8)
4 Female Mennonites go hungry (6)
5 Time to request some work (4)
6 Loss of current in one river then another (7)
7 I.e. half a night spent in treatment by minister (5,7)
10 Fragrant resin makes Bruno almost furious (12)
13 Last 60% of pizza in Rome all rotten – was this off? (10)
15 Ms. Ayres in chart upset (3)
18 Bing's involved in story – it's not imaginary (8)
20 Where either a Liberal can pray – – – possibly? (7)
22 Catch a cold in outside loo? Hermit prefers it (7)
23 One's rising fast still (6)
26 Contented sound picked up during interruption (4)

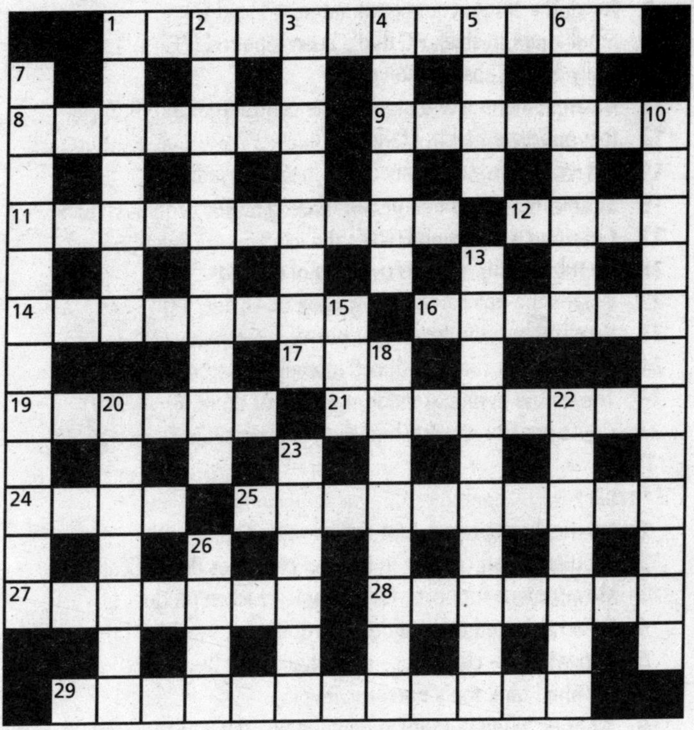

74

Across

1 Very old soldier owns nice ground (7)
5 Dutch scoundrel's small parachute (6)
9 Jones the singer commands stage, it's said (7)
10 Small mark in sleek PC that's been repaired (7)
11 Daily outing absorbs solver (3)
12 Molar somehow withstood some central packing (6,5)
13 It supports leg a bit, I fancy (5)
14 Power of disease curtailed rule in Venice sadly (9)
16 Strengthen control on behalf of church (9)
17 Get drenched in small river (5)
19 He rubbed oily mixture over top of deltoids? (11)
22 What's the point of penning book on Ulster? (3)
23 He casts his vote for former prince in Germany (7)
24 S American country reduced monarch's barbecue (7)
26 They show in ambassador in turbulent USSR (6)
27 Cry to control all Yorkshire Hunt's leaders? (5-2)

Down

1 He breaks down any last components (7)
2 Problem of perception in London club rises dramatically (6,9)
3 Government supports, for example, chicken product (3)
4 Is Ted annoyed by comings and goings at seaside? (5)
5 Formal talk – clever ruse to sustain party (9)
6 Finished tank top's open to view (5)
7 Note fashionista Mary in new wonky unit x, y or z (7,8)
8 These thieves occasionally giggle (3-3)
12 Quay where harbourmaster admits raw food first (5)
14 Greek is after Italian composer's film on copper (9)
15 Cryptic solver forfeits victory – he doesn't win (5)
16 Disease in Siberia spread after I departed (6)
18 Arrest writer upset over old trade ban (7)
20 Wash black articles (5)
21 First performance by bass in complicated duet (5)
25 Tool for making holes at will in odd places (3)

75

Across

1 Biker put 150 yen first in old box (7)
5 Notice present and past playground item (6)
9 It opposes prosecution of French dealer in stolen goods (7)
10 This disaster with trip is potentially predictable (7)
11 It's in the Arctic everywhere (3)
12 US novel cast light on two chaps tackling the French (6,5)
13 New York opera's about to back choral music (5)
14 Wearing warm coat, mad lunatic lost it finally in 15 railway (9)
16 High level area shocks ballet dancer? Not half (9)
17 Society's locked in boom and bust (5)
19 Nearly 27 admitted new price is too meticulous (11)
22 It's found in odd places in mound (3)
23 Quiz champion collapsed on walk to Leatherhead (4-3)
24 News articles I'd sent in instead of Henry (7)
26 Make last effort primarily with UK to maybe conserve energy (3,3)
27 Supervise poem in Old English (7)

Down

1 Ill-mannered man's silent about current element (7)
2 Cook able to cook beef, having fine glossy tome (6-5,4)
3 Hostelry's trendy name (3)
4 Send short messages in tiny non-alcoholic bottles (5)
5 Denis's up ringing food shop, like a poor player … (9)
6 … having been given this joint? (5)
7 A cold remark's got Phil ruffled about son's talents (15)
8 Note dairy product's on the rise (6)
12 Machine used by woodworker in agitated state nearly (5)
14 Somehow tell age of small wind instrument (9)
15 Liberal minister about to have the necessary power (5)
16 3 h.p. Russian vehicle or a kit to be assembled (6)
18 Jellyfish in Mediterranean, America and Spain (7)
20 It could be grand playing it in Olympia non-stop (5)
21 Some begin trouble in leading bars (5)
25 Deer seen occasionally in back of beyond (3)

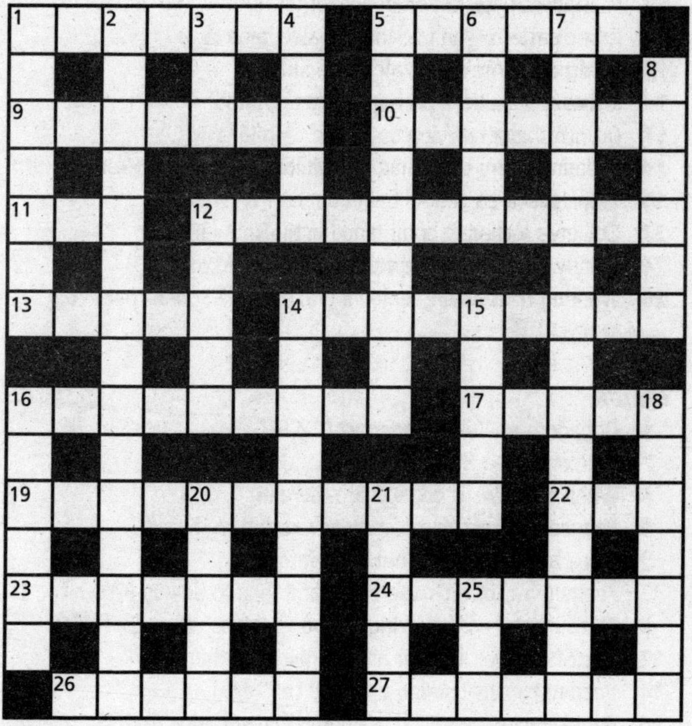

76

Across

6 They identify birds sadly shot on oil rigs around Tynemouth (14)
9 Notice bad habit in counsel (6)
10 Paint verbal portrait of French writer (8)
11 Fabric pattern seen in dance at party time (5,3)
13 In response, Arab wins all four points (6)
15 It makes 6 twitch – perhaps 'arry's got it (6)
17 Outbid doctor carrying unlimited cash (6)
19 Balkan country shows no bias after reconstruction (6)
20 Crank split kitty (8)
22 Coe tries elaborating for those in the know (8)
24 Soft seat US writer had stuffed in the middle (6)
26 Working class able to enjoy a real display? Sounds perfect (2,5,2,1,4)

Down

1 Ooh, do hurry less somehow? (4,4,6)
2 Vote against a National Trust island (4)
3 When the news is on, 500 are there (6)
4 Reduced dessert also known as Greek dish (8)
5 Place to fish quietly? That is right (4)
7 Funny thing, but it's good now and then to tidy up (6)
8 Measures taken if cooking up lots of beans, about 50 (14)
12 Sacred book or another one contained within it (5)
14 Puzzled by cuts coming up at ski centre (5)
16 Poor Kate ate nearly all the bread in rest period (3,5)
18 Bush accountant met his spies (6)
21 A former PM announced request for donations (6)
23 Drier installed in oriental company (4)
25 Exploits American art in France (4)

77

Across

1 VIPs were upset with "Kane" in early screening (5,7)
8 Moneylender seizes power? That's just what he does (7)
9 Give orders to detectives to return to gallery (7)
11 Ladies of like mind waste Tories' dosh (10)
12 What's regularly consumed in Geordie town (4)
14 Metal from guns melted down in fancy tent (8)
16 Chap, say, gets introduction to equestrianism here (6)
17 Almost discover swimming aid (3)
19 Male, old, well developed and well matured (6)
21 Flower in odd places in Louvre, around parks otherwise (8)
24 Insipid meat in stew (4)
25 Capture unstable charged particle as safety measure (10)
27 What good sailors have, say, with marine mammals about (3,4)
28 Dramatic scene thanks to a blue comic (7)
29 Flimsy structure has of course collapsed around duke (5,2,5)

Down

1 Confines in shacks when 5's about (5,2)
2 Strange noises following former priest's term (10)
3 Raucous cheer if king's put on head covering (8)
4 Very exciting, like pokers in bed (3-3)
5 Struggle to control constant bad habit (4)
6 Inspect and chop up bomb (7)
7 Vague assessments assume it gets tricky (12)
10 Businessman displays tree pruner, having little space (12)
13 Old periodical's investor gets shock (4,6)
15 Long river's reduced to nothing (3)
18 Injured actor in Nice almost produces drug (8)
20 Gambol madly round university, getting back pain (7)
22 Proper queen's schoolbooks (7)
23 French firm owns French art now – wall painting (6)
26 Professional charges in coffee shop (4)

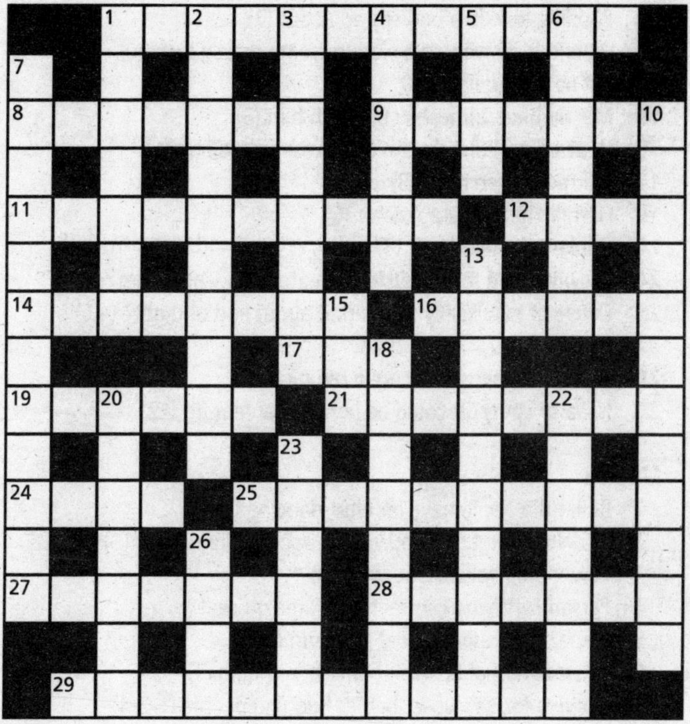
1
2
3
4
5
6
7
8
9
10
11
12
13
14
15
16
17
18
19
20
21
22
23
24
25
26
27
28
29

Across

1 Fellow crime writer's scene involved aromatic resin (12)
8 Embarrassing score in Portadown? Go along to see it (3,4)
9 Pudding, one in a pot, stirred about (7)
11 Wenger's reinvented a way to create grassy turf (10)
12 Eat nothing quickly (4)
14 Metalworker arranges stint with him (8)
16 Heat's dreadful in centre of Dallas – it's killing (6)
17 Hill recaptured in 21 (3)
19 German in E9 makes motor (6)
21 Choke or accelerator? (8)
24 Crewmen are tops in Oxford Amateur Rowing Society (4)
25 Cause of mawkishly staggering about end of night? (4,6)
27 Pinch a bit (7)
28 It protects lungs bursting in big race (7)
29 Is Daisy corny? It could be her special feature (12)

Down

1 Ballet dancer, female, on Tyne, dancing (7)
2 Ritual consecration and what's applied during it? (10)
3 Power unit trained it to walk (8)
4 Person certifying contract put name on seal (6)
5 Trade show appearance? Not sure (4)
6 Tolerate half of Scottish ham after boiling (7)
7 Flowers for, say, upset babies hugging people (6-2-4)
10 I'll enter army in order to form tank crews, say (12)
13 Hanoi 5 worried about British fear of them? (10)
15 Burning each other's clothing (3)
18 Nouveau riche tours 17, making study of speech (8)
20 Wreath for Judy (7)
22 In Italy you can stay within limits of Sicily or other region (7)
23 In recent times Greek character left stamp-collecting (6)
26 Hairstyle for a crinkly? (4)

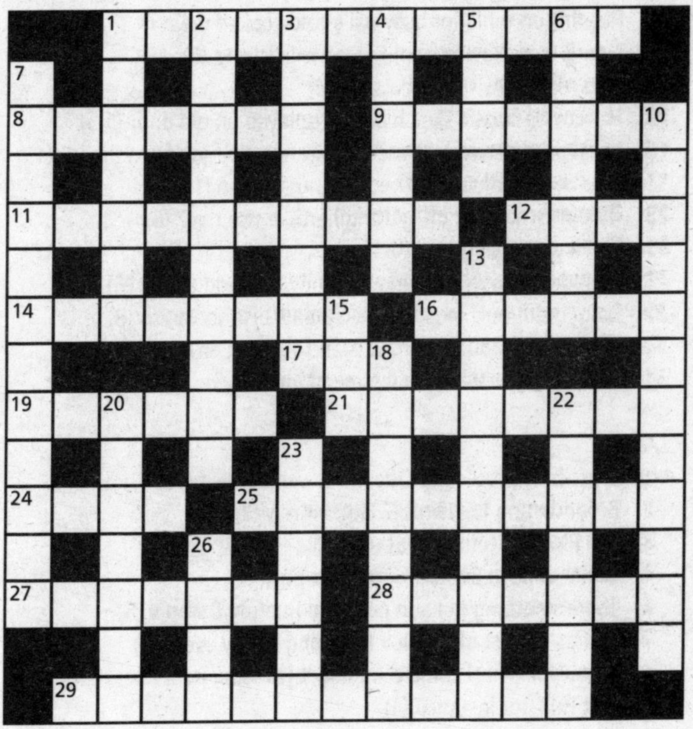

79

Across

1 Clive wrestled with one, getting harsh treatment (8)
5 English immigrants' fluffy ball (6)
9 Put this on table for busy pal's cold cooked meat (5,3)
10 Nearly seek advice from Roman magistrate (6)
12 Two regiments not often seen (4)
13 Hancock's classic sketch book displayed on old door (5,5)
15 Local area network attracts in strange clothing from the US (13)
19 Ronnie stupidly swallowed five nuts, green (13)
23 Risk prawn going off, getting hard, or use this? (6,4)
25 Wake up in jail (4)
28 Prejudice annual meeting about evils in odd places (6)
29 Balm or lotion's meant to be spread, also to vanish (8)
30 Shortly see around a small island without any trouble (6)
31 30 ruin hay maybe, having raked top (2,1,5)

Down

1 Brass hats protecting Queen are venomous types (6)
2 Broadcasting to Nairobi? Not entirely (2,3)
3 Old PM's eastern retreat (4)
4 White wine in Switzerland upset Basil (7)
6 There's nothing in Latin poet like Humpty Dumpty (5)
7 Letters to part of S Africa following happy event (9)
8 Water for wheel came tumbling, bypassing poor river (4,4)
11 Left Hull, for instance (4)
14 Writer separated average couple (4)
15 Old publicans and sailors entertained Jules (9)
16 Weapon used in Wagram intermittently (3)
17 Stravinsky's initially revolutionary skills (4)
18 Rising salesman used a mobile to be convincing (8)
20 It's usually on at 10 in all quarters (4)
21 Delight when uncle, for example, loses his head (7)
22 It's awful not drinking in wild orgy (6)
24 Alan's had surgery around nose (5)
26 The Irish or belonging to them (5)
27 What to do with some pocket chisels? (4)

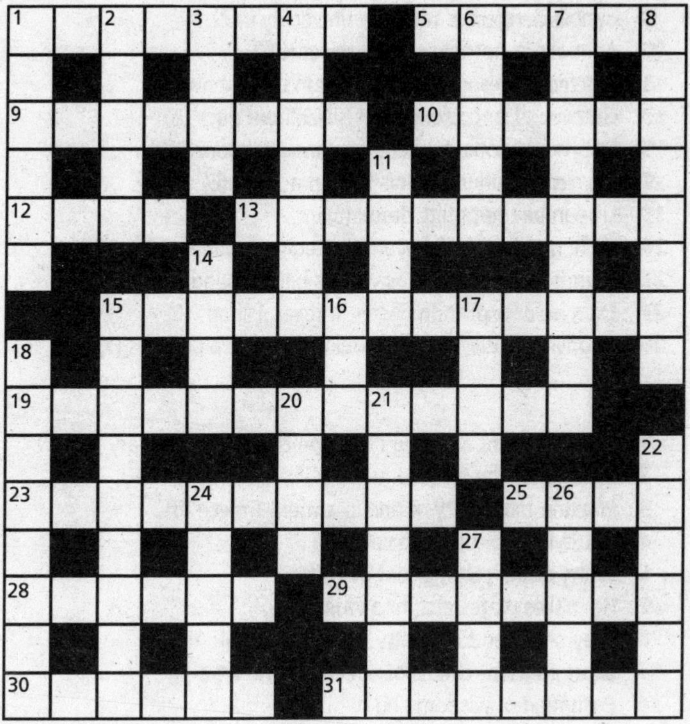

80

Across

6 The very best cold remedy? Mostly mixed cereal, more or less (5,2,2,5)

9 Bungle dangerous tackle at university (4,2)

10 Animal's in horrible crate on river (8)

11 It delivers poisoned dart in spot in sore elbow (8)

13 Guffaws after cooking goulash without duck (6)

15 Unorthodox opinion here, say, one abandoned (6)

17 I'm a don working in this field of activity (6)

19 Litre in bed not quite drunk (6)

20 He hogged ground, becoming frequent road casualty (8)

22 Mum's father's Greek as well as her husband (8)

24 Exercise care putting poster in several shops (6)

26 Anonymous warrior, kind soul with renown perhaps (7,7)

Down

1 They're taught amazing old chronicles about Hungary (14)

2 Inventor of the telephone call (4)

3 Priest in Indian city or one in ancient Greece (6)

4 Battle later disputed in court (8)

5 Worry about putting foot out (4)

7 He makes plates etc. for a woman (6)

8 They're issued to infantry in the sack (8,6)

12 Least pleasant choice of directions and time (5)

14 Posh man of wisdom and habit (5)

16 Reduce speed in small depressed county (4,4)

18 She's hired a director for summer spectacles (6)

21 Fatal delay rectified when duke takes the lead (6)

23 It's not available on two occasions for 22's wife (4)

25 Money invested in amniocentesis on the rise (4)

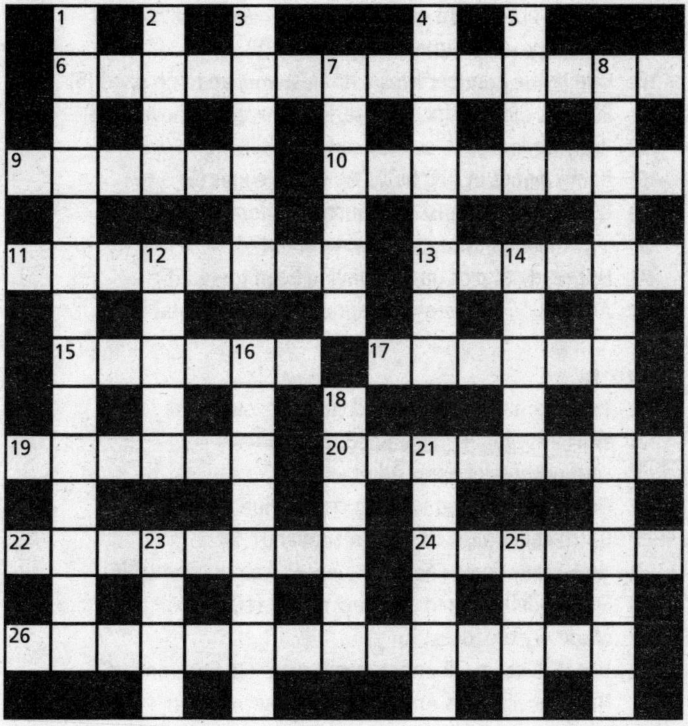
1
2
3
4
5
6
7
8
9
10
11
12
13
14
15
16
17
18
19
20
21
22
23
24
25
26

81

Across

6 Scots abhorred a novel that affects everyone (6,3,5)
9 Wasted weeks on recipe for kebab item (6)
10 Dietary fibre ought mostly to stop violent behaviour (8)
11 Main's nearly all intact, surprisingly (8)
13 One house member lives with husband, up to no good (6)
15 Perhaps they are incomplete, like Lawrence's novels? (6)
17 Put your foot in it, as they say in Dublin? (6)
19 Rock cavities in ring between rough edges (6)
20 US doctor and Parisian's source of information (8)
22 Short rest for swimmer circling about (8)
24 Not ready to pick up rein having been tossed (6)
26 Absorption of energy by various hot shiny spots? (14)

Down

1 Three car-makers organised customer survey, say (6,8)
2 Wartime captive maintained rare front (4)
3 Lively character annoyed priest (6)
4 Odd pair struggled tackling cryptic clue (8)
5 Catch cold up round here in Scotland? (4)
7 How many times energy's released from the cereal (6)
8 Special delivery had an effect on job (10,4)
12 Made dry broadcast (5)
14 Use it to call a GP after surgery to emergency room (5)
16 His Holiness tours America twice in secret (4-4)
18 Medium club covers constant very short distance (6)
21 Sensitive youth meanders round college … (6)
23 … where these may be fine roles starting out (4)
25 Knock over small file (4)

82

Across

1 Where Mariner alit after flight? (3,8)
9 Replace a carpet to limit property charge (4-3)
10 Top bowler (7)
11 Fool while at school (3)
12 Day of rest organised to thaw out (7)
13 Hormone transformed bird (7)
14 Odd bits of starch in small pouch (3)
15 Young dragonfly frightened Diana (5)
17 When margins disappear, developers run away (5)
18 In Japanese city large area houses a king (5)
20 Instrument used in Fallopian operation (5)
22 Old soldier's base in outlying parts of Vermont (3)
24 S. Carolina girl's backing Australia in brisk piece (7)
25 Drives a goddess across Spain (7)
26 Nuts produced without using energy (3)
27 Violent outburst indicating emergency at sea? (5-2)
28 Swimmer Phil angrily interrupts professor (7)
29 What people with colds should use, I'd say (6,5)

Down

1 Machine on bypass hit trailer – facia damaged (10,5)
2 US animal dashed round county in Colorado (7)
3 Sussex pathologist entertains resident abroad (5)
4 Service aimed specially for press, TV etc. (4,5)
5 Number One's a bit repellent (7)
6 Working on clever hunch, OU introduced meal ticket (8,7)
7 Edgar's dancing classes (6)
8 E.g. mandarin in William's house (6)
16 I'm on time at university for short piece of music (9)
18 Kept in by the boss if you become inflexible (6)
19 Stuffy, like a bald man in London? (7)
21 Partly cover old volume with paler plastic (7)
23 To some extent artisan enjoys herbal tea (6)
25 500 in a NI political party make sense (3,2)

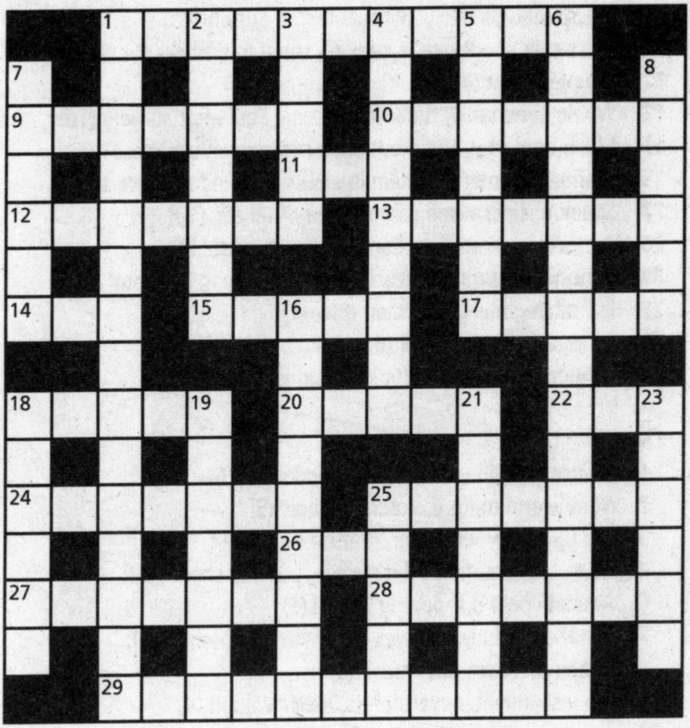

83

Across

1 Wave cereal bowl (8)
5 Hundreds take lithium around popular health centre (6)
9 Precipitation's really awful at first in autumn (8)
10 Firms that cooperate in backing some title tracks (6)
12 Couple object (4)
13 Whole community drink to welcome Paul after surgery (10)
15 Much fine art is awful but more profitable than these? (5,8)
19 Morris men perform them in elaborate Sunday concert (7,6)
23 Speak distinctly in a complicated ritual etc. (10)
25 A much admired contributor to the royalists (4)
28 Republican group regularly equips people in Baghdad (6)
29 Evil sibling has got elected (8)
30 Syringe found in sewer (6)
31 Former lover's fine in topless gold lamé (3,5)

Down

1 Frustrated bride secures one good score (6)
2 Nimble and mature crossing Illinois (5)
3 Fed up with your leader? Refuse to obey (4)
4 Harry tells you first off it's a very popular show (4-3)
6 Animal upset a shopping centre (5)
7 Bananas include complex inert vitamins perhaps (9)
8 Settler lost coin after crash (8)
11 Big instrument, nevertheless lifted by adult (4)
14 Arrest coach and team leader (4)
15 Prevent ruin after corrosion set in (9)
16 Put money on commercial? That's crazy (3)
17 Pawn wine (4)
18 Suitable time for special event (8)
20 The old disc causes cry of pain (4)
21 Where lots of 8s live, all drinking thin liquid (7)
22 Old Irish enter bishop's place for evening 18 (6)
24 Cold? I'll put central heating on (5)
26 Former painter has time for more (5)
27 Vassal's property that is seized by females (4)

84

Across

1 It's used in laboratory trial underground (4,4)
5 Tablet for dental problem (6)
9 Uproar when family go to ancient city (8)
10 It's primarily made of squares, all in colour (6)
12 One article or a couple (4)
13 I reset alarm time but it's not significant (10)
15 Cinema worker's scheme is to perhaps tour Ulster (13)
19 Bitterly disappointed, Robert had knee dislocated (6-7)
23 I study diplomacy, say, achieved in tête-à-têtes? (3-7)
25 Stone ring given to friend (4)
28 At home keeping reserves within reach (6)
29 Rhodes statue stirred souls in another Greek island (8)
30 Apprentice doesn't start job (6)
31 My pony's trained with Beethoven's Fifth? Could be (8)

Down

1 Alarm bell in Ulster-Scot uprising (6)
2 Digger's residence in Kent, for instance (5)
3 Classic wear in Pacific islands (not north) (4)
4 British spirit I imported into Middle East from Birmingham (7)
6 Free society in Cornish port (5)
7 I failed miserably to follow question but passed (9)
8 'E's recently baffled about increase (8)
11 Fruit of the forest appears during Christmastide (4)
14 Extremely old injury (4)
15 Cromwell College enforcer restricts half term (9)
16 Scouser regularly produces signal to act (3)
17 Man left seat for Bismarck, say (4)
18 Deny ignoring four in rare blood group (8)
20 Don't like mixing up two English articles (4)
21 Swimmer gets axe nearly in navy reorganisation (7)
22 Elegant ship stuck in mud (6)
24 Where to keep wines cool maybe – slow going (2,3)
26 A portion of grape stones in this sauce? (5)
27 Local supermarket usually has several layers (4)

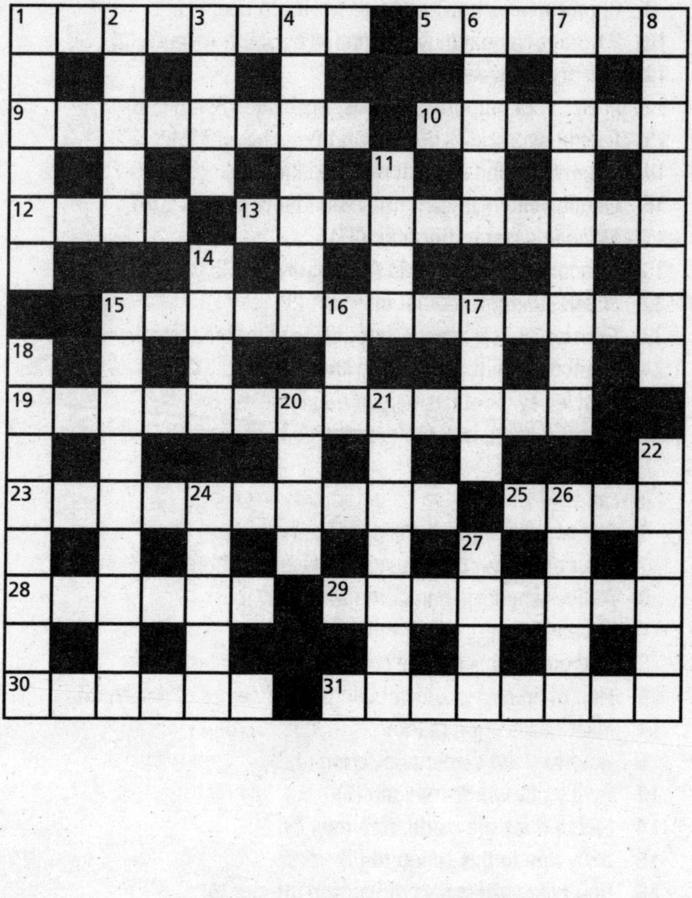

85

Across

1 Vanish here in Thailand, China, Ireland, not Cuba (4,3)
5 Put them up to show approval? It's what hitchhiker does (6)
9 Chop supplier, however dear to French people (7)
10 Vigorous campaign for oil drilled by South America (7)
11 Attention! Queen has answer (3)
12 In which to put dirty blankets, clothing in Spain (5,6)
13 Person who shows you around Poe's house? (5)
14 Lickspittle's fed up with relative, I hear (9)
16 German city restricted one friend belonging to it (9)
17 Milligan's first to finish fish (5)
19 Shortage of water round Aden sadly for old warship (11)
22 Union strikes at regular intervals (3)
23 Corrupt TV user abroad inspired head of broadcasting (7)
24 Cram damaged 11 blocking Ovett endlessly (7)
26 People say it detects person making cuts (6)
27 Sweet wine may contain various bits of elms (7)

Down

1 Bill's on the water in Paris in dramatic scene (7)
2 Their angle can be adjusted and can be alternated (15)
3 Airline schedules hampered at first by it (3)
4 Repeat timeless Turner broadcast (5)
5 With goals, this college could be teaching locals (9)
6 Flap of limited value wobbling round centre of mouth (5)
7 Illicit dealers flog mackerels at kerb (5,10)
8 How to clean carpet and scram (4,2)
12 Cyril's silly words for song (5)
14 Fan to drink ale made from malt (9)
15 8's a clue to this songbird (5)
16 Reserved largest part of Parisian interior (6)
18 Time in Lewes spent at end of holiday in harmony (7)
20 Trim costume (5)
21 Dumps German weaving machine (5)
25 It may be electric to some extent (3)

86

Across

1 Promise non-English introduction exactly as written (4,3,4)
9 Prize for rider or, on the contrary, me nearly (7)
10 Glad top of property's let (7)
11 Her Majesty's eating a little bit of cereal (3)
12 School pupils rejected mistakes (4-3)
13 Little effort to twist pole and rod together (3,4)
14 Pester unlikely winner of 9 (3)
15 Photography enabled this animal to be captured (5)
17 Cathy rebuilt boat (5)
18 Dominant male appeared during critical phase (5)
20 Conservative and radicals split (5)
22 Unfinished stone bird in "Arabian Nights" (3)
24 Rider puts foot in it, trips badly over endless rut (7)
25 It's for people to enjoy and exploit any time (7)
26 A little strand with no odd characters (3)
27 Chap returned in funny suit giving big wave (7)
28 Understanding one thing's difficult (7)
29 Minor crime: Quinn and Clyde stupidly nick euros (11)

Down

1 Wife's dishing up quail, stewed? This'll be needed later (7-2,6)
2 Make minor repairs to rocky route to church (7)
3 Releases in very cold weather, say (5)
4 Professional blocks discount? He's unprincipled (9)
5 Any dope could create occasion for public to visit (4,3)
6 Worryingly, princess alone defends musical event (15)
7 Nick is working to sustain spin (6)
8 Plug opening in period before Christmas (6)
16 Bar at home contains nothing; it's not like others (9)
18 Hounds head off in property (6)
19 How to distribute Maria's letters to the Italian? (7)
21 The original justification for Guy Fawkes' crime (7)
23 Seb carries up miniature dog (6)
25 A department that's posh, possibly the last word (5)

87

Across

1 Face wily owl flapping in tree (5,6)
9 E.g. scallop or mussel maybe, so pearl's extracted (7)
10 Look after child: adjust bib, say, and temperature (7)
11 He's primarily chief Olympics expert (3)
12 Retained this in nasty accident with earhole? (7)
13 Endless ruse to trap a pair of fellows in illicit trade (7)
14 Small bag is oddly scarce (3)
15 Divine woman does broadcast about … (5)
17 … girl's excursion (5)
18 Stainer's numbers tackled by male alto (5)
20 They say it takes two to beat attempt (5)
22 Limited aspiration to make trip in plane (3)
24 Partial brunette, say? (3,4)
25 Class study Catholic writer in difficult scene (7)
26 *Epidemic*: odd film everyone can see (3)
27 U-boat's fuel lying beneath the surface (7)
28 People in government accept American import (7)
29 Remarkable new Hygiene Act impressed Conservative (3-8)

Down

1 Cop notices label's been falsified – this cop? (6,9)
2 Nearly everyone tucked into calamari? It's dirty (7)
3 Accuracy comes back after scrubbing car plant (5)
4 Bee went in dancing but not at the edges (2-7)
5 Liberals contain any mix-up for north Africans (7)
6 Women's Institute flush out item about family? Some hope! (7,8)
7 Beats fishing boats (6)
8 Handy note saying "WET PAINT"? (6)
16 Small swimmer's left ear burst in W. Australia (5,4)
18 I swear he's not drunk (6)
19 A bishop sits on his own for 9 (7)
21 Baltic city opens centre in booming oriental art (7)
23 Promise to start painting windowsill perhaps (6)
25 French author climbs tree (5)

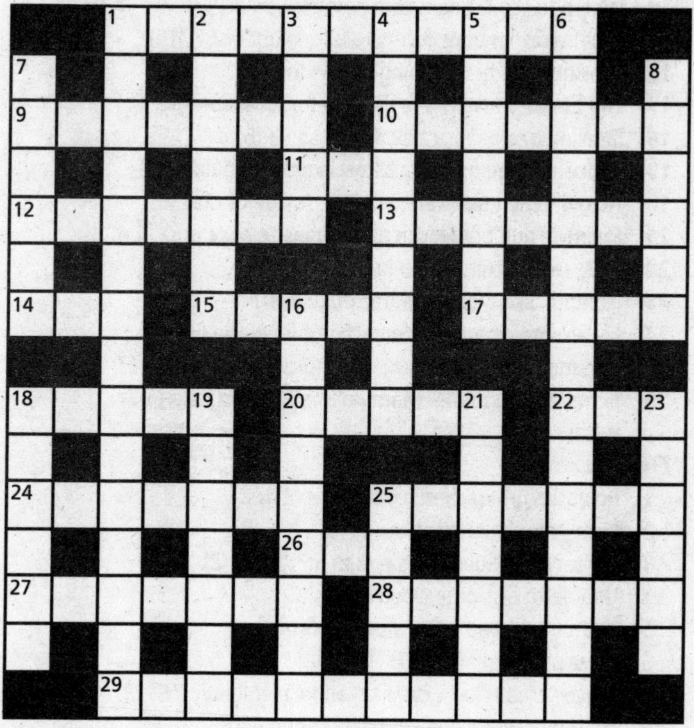

88

Across

1 Clue for "polo" maybe and somewhere to play it (8,4)
8 Bouts of sickness at movements by yacht (7)
9 Where to scrub books that perhaps you kept inside (4,3)
11 What wrestler aims for – protection against 8 (10)
12 The sound of bells ringing in IoM town (4)
14 The Conservatives have no time for ideas (8)
16 Stunted tree needs carbon, said some (6)
17 Cry of outrage formerly heard in office regularly (3)
19 Actors' union quite annoyed by closure of play (6)
21 Rumour: quiet hotel's in for millions at busy time (4,4)
24 Eject Diana from studio in disorder (4)
25 Isolated, like a cat up a tree? (3,2,1,4)
27 Fly around on empty stomach not long ago (7)
28 Commotion when impure rum's brought into work (7)
29 Bears, bulls and other farm animals traded here (5,7)

Down

1 Released group charge over river (3,4)
2 Burn entire Inca compound (10)
3 Military intelligence's top man in trouble (8)
4 Unable to dissipate cloud of gas (6)
5 Part of Spithead – the most important part (4)
6 Issue points in shops (7)
7 Maybe create loft extension and cheer loudly (5,3,4)
10 It's red or white and very bald in comparison (8,4)
13 Type of yucca a horse masticated with jute (6,4)
15 Father doesn't finish formal address (3)
18 Different routes are cut in cross-channel transport (8)
20 Like some hair on wet pups in a mess? (7)
22 Ring in sumo wrestling looks threatening (7)
23 Mikado maid of good taste (3-3)
26 Stylish and partial to French ice-cream (4)

89

Across

1 Officer not fully in command of grand place in Germany (7)
5 US president hasn't finished getting over a shock (6)
9 Emma Peel, say, introduced English into state (7)
10 Character from Athens may make one slip (7)
11 Leaves in the afternoon? (3)
12 Egoistic Gene likes cast to impress film stars first (4-7)
13 Elvis strangely defies death (5)
14 Illumination for sailors easily carried? (4,5)
16 Knowing generous client, he dumps litter anywhere (3-6)
17 See 15 Across
19 Bad manners displayed by dirty Scouse (11)
22 Mercury entrances a witch (3)
23 They emphasise changes in CIA list (7)
24 Plant a big one in different places (7)
26 Like bad eggs, showing signs of age when unopened (6)
27 Seedsmen ignore small nuts in country estate (7)

Down

1 The cat's in distress, left in property (7)
2 Shock as we heard volley from him in Dallas (3,6,6)
3 Regularly going to see live music session (3)
4 Upcoming tailor needs to keep register (5)
5 Value highly radical fund-manager (9)
6 Passageway is swamped in drink (5)
7 Mike likes Ming china displayed as dairy equipment (7,8)
8 Think about German overturning man on board (6)
12 American divided his various fish in Tokyo (5)
14 VIP soared away and suddenly disappeared (9)
15/17 Lucy and Mark split up over chain for talisman (5,5)
16 Slow increase in volume disorients deaf at home (4-2)
18 Motorway's especially great for what some birds do (7)
20 Window broken in Loire (5)
21 Bass in European sea sink (5)
25 Eucalyptus originally gave us medicine (3)

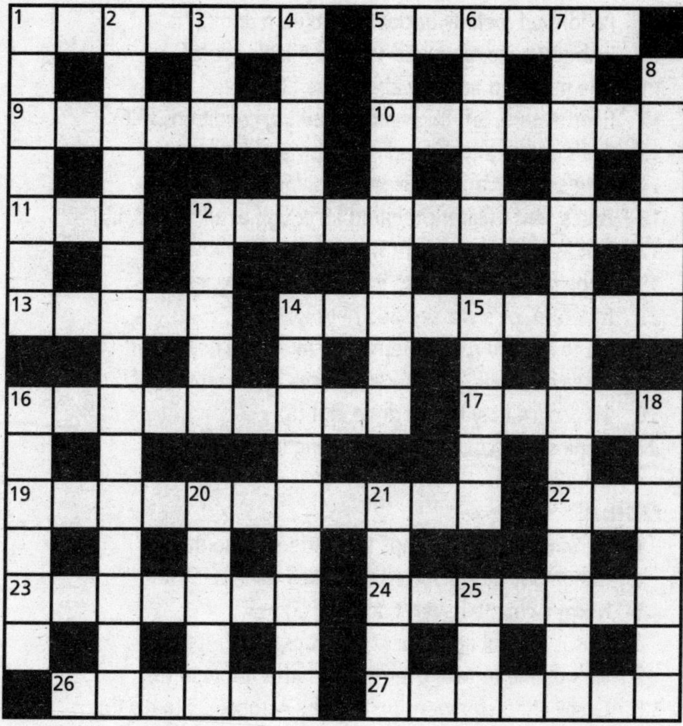
1
2
3
4
5
6
7
8
9
10
11
12
13
14
15
16
17
18
19
20
21
22
23
24
25
26
27

90

Across

1 Get ready to shoot mine in front of plane (7)
5 Calm, seated after refreshment (6)
9 Performed melody backwards to earn drink (7)
10 Irish girl once managed to steal Allen's heart (7)
11 One man in a boat, or about one (3)
12 Rescue party left in dreadful working conditions (5,6)
13 She's one in a thousand at a marriage (5)
14 Joke spoiled races in Scottish town (9)
16 Peer's sent in later prepared for tough assignment (4,5)
17 Not as high as a cow? (5)
19 Hope carotid's working in this sort of surgery (11)
22 In return, he's worshipped pet (3)
23 Go to and fro round Germany, say – how delightful! (4,3)
24 He says "I will" in different places in the morning (7)
26 13 and 24 may live or drive in it (6)
27 Drink single cocktail with nothing in it (4,3)

Down

1 Ukrainian warrior swaps two letters for soutane (7)
2 Canon got rituals sorted out? Well done! (15)
3 Normal couple haven't got one (3)
4 This is a regal adornment, the tops! (5)
5 He's in line to take over soldiers after triumph (9)
6 Greek character went first up the Acropolis initially (5)
7 13 and 24's big day, with legendary do arranged (3,5,7)
8 Outdoor garment for woman in a thousand (6)
12 US typist? About time one's turned up (5)
14 We hold leading ground offering panoramic views (4-5)
15 Cooking oil in small volume causes pain (5)
16 Hard to control onset of real depression (6)
18 Soldiers don't finish medical course (7)
20 It's the last thing in home gadgets (5)
21 Hills in Sussex, NI county and Sweden (5)
25 Stripped floor in smallest room (3)

91

Across

6 Bush says guy is revered old politician (5,9)
9 Gems and stones lyrebirds hoarded in recess (6)
10 Girl nurses Bert's damaged bone in back (8)
11 Child argued playfully about her toy at first (8)
13 I'm a female in Paris holding money that's exempt (6)
15 Collision: it involves politician (a Conservative) (6)
17 Needing glasses to see writer's old photograph (6)
19 Churchman crosses unknown ravine (6)
20 Scorn MP taking over from son in competition (8)
22 Computers etc. in retail organisation for book fans (8)
24 Drink some, ignoring recipe (6)
26 Ms. Stubbs forced comic to ring nobleman, lost (11,3)

Down

1 Vague words by foreign legionnaires guarding heart of Bath (14)
2 Mary Baker's current movement (4)
3 Gift (name withheld) programmed to start by itself (6)
4 Gnarled tree in borders of Turkey – it's timeless (8)
5 Man perhaps turns back in Elsinore (4)
7 Bird consumes a small volume in hostelry (6)
8 Dry place at home for curing rabid OAP, poorly (6,8)
12 Chap catches very quiet fish (5)
14 A small place in Maine for tree (5)
16 Curiously, Monica has two names for spice (8)
18 Director's order to start filming court case (6)
21 Child pinching bit of lobster (6)
23 Every ache hurt (4)
25 No introduction in formal dispute (4)

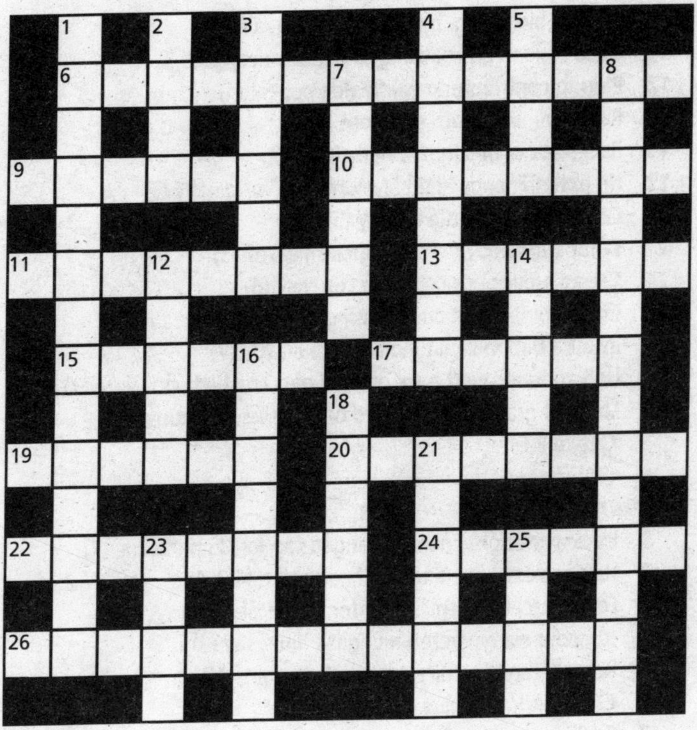
1
2
3
4
5
6
7
8
9
10
11
12
13
14
15
16
17
18
19
20
21
22
23
24
25
26

92

Across

1 Generous woman's been trained by fine woman in play (12)
8 Dish gold in flat area (7)
9 Endless bleaching, by the sound of it? (7)
11 Child stars need coaching to a lesser degree (5,5)
12 Plan to contribute to worldwide appeal (4)
14 Reject far worse arrangement (8)
16 Races about in county briefly (6)
17 He liked "Friends" and "Neighbours" originally (3)
19 Large hint with little energy (6)
21 What stable boy uses to expose sleaze? (8)
24 Connoisseur once collected currency (4)
25 Chain came apart on line using non-human means (10)
27 Insult a nabob including his wife maybe (7)
28 Ugly rodent round back of shed gets crushed underfoot (7)
29 Show of gratitude displayed on the TV sofa impresses King (4,2,6)

Down

1 Ex-heavyweight champ changed top for US barbecue (7)
2 He's useless – we enrolled by mistake (4-2-4)
3 Fellows scour our meadow for a type of clover … (4-4)
4 … scour everywhere on English links, say (6)
5 Regret recruiting director who's impolite (4)
6 Cheat pork suppliers, about 550 (7)
7 Fuel's spread between two headlands in show of malice (12)
10 Selling cigs a surprising barrier to promotion? (5,7)
13 Sorted into groups, like old bangers (6,4)
15 Farm animal appears in odd parts of realm (3)
18 Hunt chat abroad, or other bird (8)
20 Extra lines on old cherry (7)
22 Agrees record company rises by two points (7)
23 British Expeditionary Force captured Henry's part (6)
26 First of two vegetables in cock-a-leekie (4)

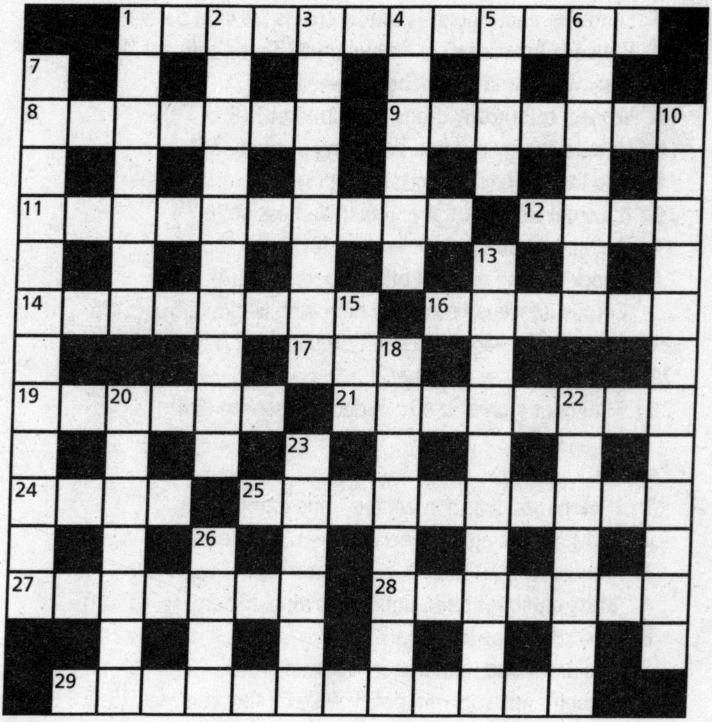

93

Across

1 Second tie contains Latin translation for "big cat" (8,4)
8 Stop chorus (7)
9 Edit a file about good fellow; it covers his vital parts (3,4)
11 House in America with nothing in it? That's criminal (10)
12 Just swings and roundabouts here (4)
14 What a colt mostly drags, if mistreated? (8)
16 Unique energy put into switching positions? (3-3)
17 Like the sea back in Portstewart (3)
19 It's cruel to be partially sunk in depression (6)
21 Tramp with flashy jewellery, 25 (8)
24 Knock a small amount off computer part (4)
25 Confusing trendy company here with National Trust (10)
27 Recently deceased artist left on the side (7)
28 Whole unit, say, in Bury (7)
29 Minimum workable size in decisive service (8,4)

Down

1 It keeps you warm in winter – and damper (7)
2 Sadly, Vilnius again is excluded – it's useless (10)
3 One wasn't designed for carpenter? Yes it was (5,3)
4 Mass immigration in times following epidemic (6)
5 Record disc as trademark (4)
6 Old ass brought up pungent leaves (7)
7 Queen's advisors ruin policy with CV unfortunately (5,7)
10 Get fish frier? If it goes up you'll need these (12)
13 I pinch a stein, specially when away (2,8)
15 She used to come out to turn over plot (3)
18 University class worked out experiment outside (8)
20 Someone who makes 1 Down perhaps out of trinket (7)
22 Writer and wise men, say, in freezing conditions (3,4)
23 Once wandered round centre of Dublin together (2,4)
26 Legal breach upset extreme radical (4)

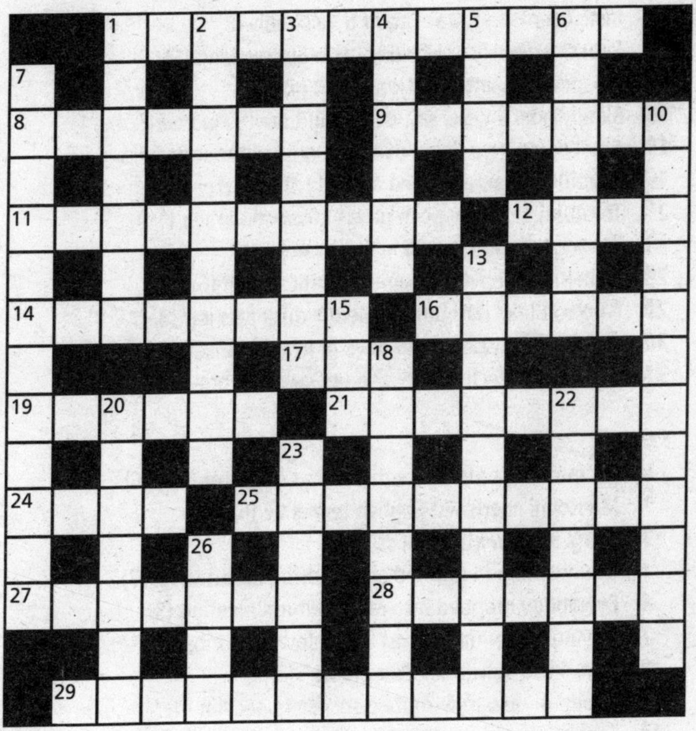

94

Across

1 Unionist grandee's surprisingly not old enough (8)
5 Skilfully makes 100 floating platforms (6)
9 Instruments in Britain and EU sell badly (8)
10 React nervously in Florida and in Switzerland (6)
12 7 needing no introduction in flat (4)
13 Sleepy poet's wise, say, conserving energy in bed (6-4)
15 Ron couldn't go flying over Romania without its help (6,7)
19 Reveal tableau designed as basis of property charge (8,5)
23 To brutalise Henry posh guy is dropped in river (10)
25 Darling's back in position in hierarchy (4)
28 Catholic church has managed critical time (6)
29 Partition leak had burst violently after rats left (8)
30 Burglar he suspected to have pinched monkey (6)
31 Figure of speech Homer used to describe brief strike (8)

Down

1 His interest is high in addict round centre of Bury (6)
2 Mussolini cherished English tennis tie (5)
3 Grass on newspaper boss (4)
4 Naughty imp in gnarled elm wearing broad smile (7)
6 Everybody dropped into railway mass meeting (5)
7 Having no commitments, like fellow on 3 mostly (5-4)
8 Clue she'd solved for "timetable" (8)
11 Group of upwardly-mobile socialists, secular (4)
14 Star in river, ascending (4)
15 Housing estate isn't built with this entrance lodge (9)
16 Occasionally drives lose strength (3)
17 Egyptian banker's line gets tangled (4)
18 He makes films on behalf of crude comic (8)
20 Small road in Los Angeles needs extending initially (4)
21 Old garment seen in new revues across West End (7)
22 Arachnid spotted her, some say (6)
24 Gold sustains Scotsman in former Portuguese colony (5)
26 Committee thought about power (5)
27 Old vessel raised by lady's fingers (4)

1
2
3
4
5
6
7
8
9
10
11
12
13
14
15
16
17
18
19
20
21
22
23
24
25
26
27
28
29
30
31

95

Across

6 Sport in which I'll win with strangle possibly (3-2,9)
9 Ditch or river with fish around (6)
10 Grievously err with 14 in opening (8)
11 Time constraint: reverse one mile in a sports car (3,5)
13 Irritable, tense etc. then extremely happy (6)
15 Soup made from crab is questionable … (6)
17 … souped up and not genuine (6)
19 Tool suppliers throw out drink (6)
20 Petition to dine in passage (8)
22 Endless purée, alias meat dish in Athens (8)
24 Bereaved women remove name from 10s perhaps (6)
26 Societies, for instance, or guttersnipes on the loose (8,6)

Down

1 Barbara and Noel go wild about large wartime cover (7,7)
2 Incomplete aircraft drawing (4)
3 A bunch of chrysanthemums for work by choir (6)
4 A call for help drew in top firefighter (8)
5 Conspire in bed (4)
7 Irish turned up singer in Venetian area (6)
8 Direction of bygone Hitchcock film? (5-9)
12 Fabric left on Capri, say (5)
14 Grey-brown colour everyone can see in record (5)
16 Nuns have ground covered in stubble (8)
18 Fussy old teacher's favourite to retain black belt (6)
21 Frustrate what spoiled arts centre (6)
23 Observe pressure leak (4)
25 Diameter's odd in cylinder (4)

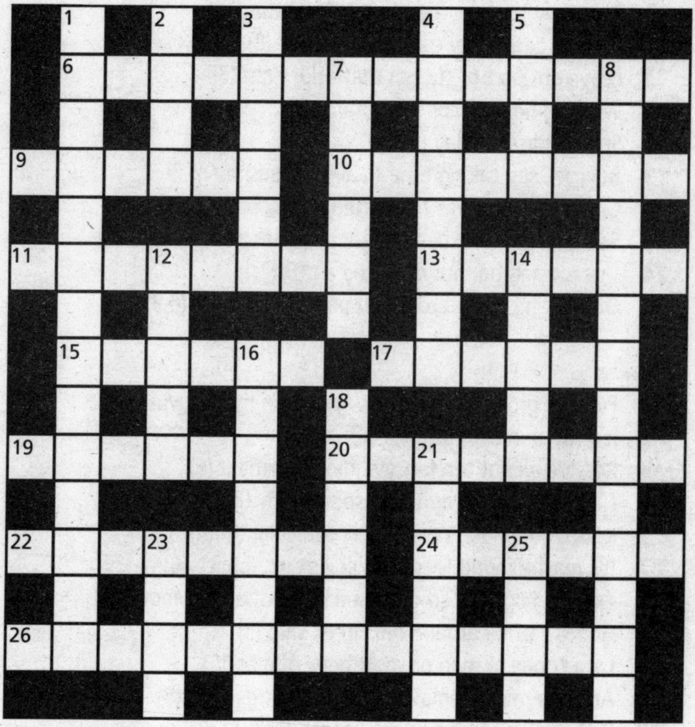
1
2
3
4
5
6
7
8
9
10
11
12
13
14
15
16
17
18
19
20
21
22
23
24
25
26

96

Across

6 Sort of parade? Not if I indicate otherwise (14)

9 Charlie may be confusing this cake with heroin (6)

10 Romantic tune for a duke in calm setting (8)

11 Brother gets nasty colic, eating this? (8)

13 Leave out part of speech that's not right (6)

15 Working hours incur new charge (6)

17 Spoil bride's display (6)

19 Boycott, say, taking time to avoid punishment (3,3)

20 Cut in foreign coins I imported (8)

22 Series about a taxi passenger or yachtsman perhaps (8)

24 Unexpected bar put up in the air (6)

26 Outré gang slang broadcast post-watershed? (6,8)

Down

1 Political group supports new prince in manoeuvre (6,8)

2 It's eaten in café/taverna (4)

3 Restore all but top fancy audio equipment (6)

4 Film director, not quite 20, sees poorly (8)

5 Knock out endless piece of spectacular PR (4)

7 It's maybe found following soil's disturbance (6)

8 Exclude Pop? I'm so confused in devotion to Mom (7,7)

12 Goods carried around old Greek ship (5)

14 Large body of men or short body of man (5)

16 America raised females' fury for voting rights (8)

18 Perhaps it's among the easier ranges (6)

21 Church has to suspend coins mostly (6)

23 It can hop for long at regular intervals (4)

25 Raise behind (4)

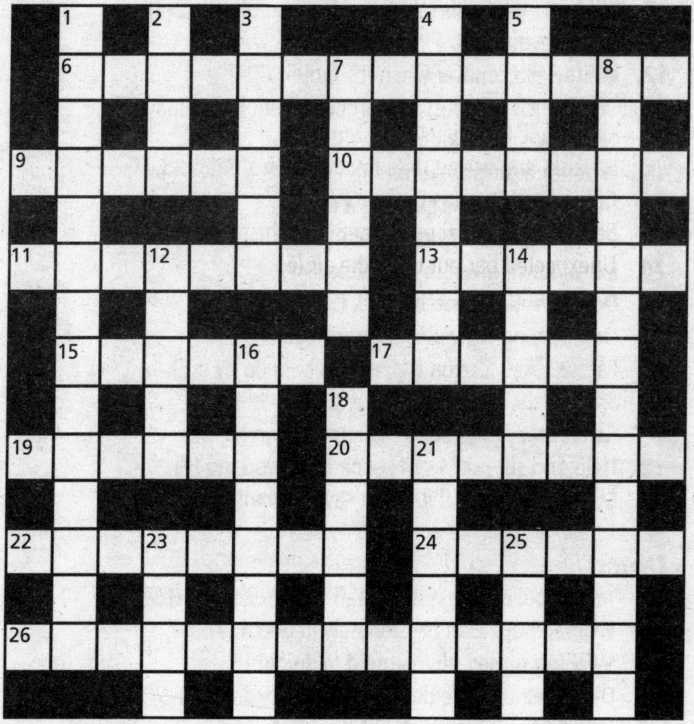

97

Across

1 War planes I observed flying over Manitoba (4,7)
9 Clothes appear slightly altered on lecturer (7)
10 Someone who's sure to lose plastic or phone (2-5)
11 Oddly revolutionary young chap (3)
12 Whitewash counter when it's rebuilt (7)
13 One French poet last to start complaint on holiday (7)
14 Grope around, taking pulse (3)
15 Prize for a hospital room (5)
17 Hunting dog drops black bird (5)
18 Go up and start chopping branch (5)
20 Extra notice given to professor (3-2)
22 Doze in vessel heading back (3)
24 Outstanding deliveries support record (7)
25 Father takes foreign trip; mine's held up by it (3,4)
26 Spain – the old hurricane centre (3)
27 Sends crazy amateur to spike relaid greens (7)
28 Help and support were keeping Alf working (7)
29 Sort of talc I found in US in cave formations (11)

Down

1 Tactful police arrest right staff in embassies (10,5)
2 Woman hugs Dan passionately in porch (7)
3 Swelling turned blue around midnight (5)
4 D-Day mines were designed as polyhedrons (4-5)
5 He and Ann ordered church to improve (7)
6 Elderly people, I argue en passant, need training (15)
7 Access to fuel, like reserves held by doctor (3,3)
8 Government limit farmstead (6)
16 Relief for wounded Asian nursing a sore leg (9)
18 Trap firm initially backing Internet (6)
19 An uprising after web diary about old city in Italy (7)
21 Memo, not article in Spanish and French (7)
23 Judy, say, set to entertain very quiet earl (6)
25 Phalarope withdraws; another bird flies in (5)

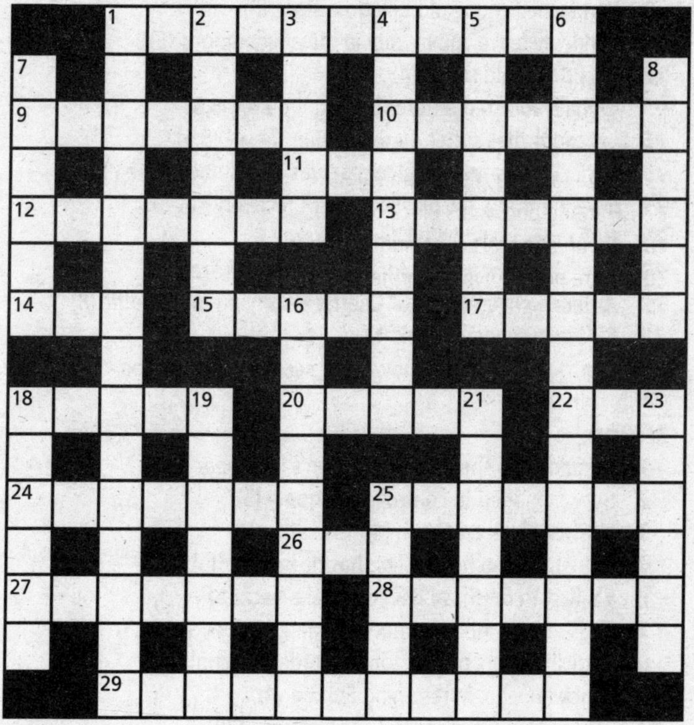
1 2 3 4 5 6 7 8 9 10 11 12 13 14 15 16 17 18 19 20 21 22 23 24 25 26 27 28 29

98

Across

1 Conflict medal doctor's hidden in his clothes (8)
5 Troubles seem to overwhelm tenant (6)
9 Headache for one old King in a state (8)
10 Suddenly leave community in moist conditions (6)
12 Puts down old songs (4)
13 China's adjusted rent for big retail outlet (5,5)
15 Let those tiles suffer damage? Ban these! (8,5)
19 Hear soldiers are blocking reserves in drainage zone (9,4)
23 Does he throw in coins in hope of recovery? (4-6)
25 RAF ordered old hairstyle (4)
28 Here the French eat cold dripping that's frozen (6)
29 Antenna covers heart of Chertsey, carrying main traffic (8)
30 Pleasant-sounding rock (6)
31 Start to slowly break down and seethe with emotion (8)

Down

1 Cunning member brought in nun's headgear (6)
2 Bury managed to control good game (5)
3 Lift front legs and back (4)
4 In Irish legend her wailing has been dreadful (7)
6 7's first to finish, so get your stake back (5)
7 Thus artist supports a poet, like neighbours, say (4,5)
8 English papers put in standing order for drink (8)
11 Crack appears in returning Spitfire (4)
14 TV aerial in Germany is on top of house (4)
15 E.g. Sputnik: all see it spinning over Thailand (9)
16 It finishes just before eleven (3)
17 He's greatly admired lady's ring (4)
18 Milk supplier's in medical support, looking angry (8)
20 Whence we get blended teas? (4)
21 Doctor met 17 to produce formula (7)
22 S. African settler ate the Italian chicken (6)
24 Joins and marries fencing novice (5)
26 Mate ignores last of bacon cooked in fat (5)
27 Dandy in part of Tower Hamlets, say (4)

99

Across

1 Novelist's written about policeman; printer produces it (4,4)
5 Brother kept wild bear; he'd cut you and charge (6)
9 Doctor unable to comprehend very variable colour (4,4)
10 Disorderly artillerymen joke about front of tank (6)
12 Part of Alsace-Lorraine after it was returned (4)
13 Michael can, playing 12 in *A Midsummer Night's Dream* (10)
15 Narc was rather put off by permission to enter (6,7)
19 Dress injured brother to accept medal in warplane (7-6)
23 To a great extent all agree to differ about S. Carolina (5-5)
25 English detectives back risk (4)
28 Actors' union quite upset at closure of play (6)
29 Downhearted daughter thrown out (8)
30 After a short time, most people collapse and fall (6)
31 Our silly display's like a mirage (8)

Down

1 One left country wanting food (6)
2 Put up bar and have lots of fun (5)
3 Young fox on top of earth, one of 25 perhaps (4)
4 Foreign couple collect note for French composer (7)
6 Muslim commander elected once more (5)
7 Wash a rich invalid and transport him in this (4,5)
8 To gain control, get a rule formulated (8)
11 Who's organised exhibition? (4)
14 Hang around and serve food (4)
15 Sweetener in the form of 3 usually (5,4)
16 Centre of activity in Inner Wheel? (3)
17 Steal English garment (4)
18 Rich worker catches virus within borders of France (8)
20 Sway Gibraltar (4)
21 Leo will suspect source of fuel (3,4)
22 Stupid delay calling in doctor at first is lethal (6)
24 Speak highly of contents of next Olympics (5)
26 Begin trotting round first few bars (5)
27 Study all but southeast in country (4)

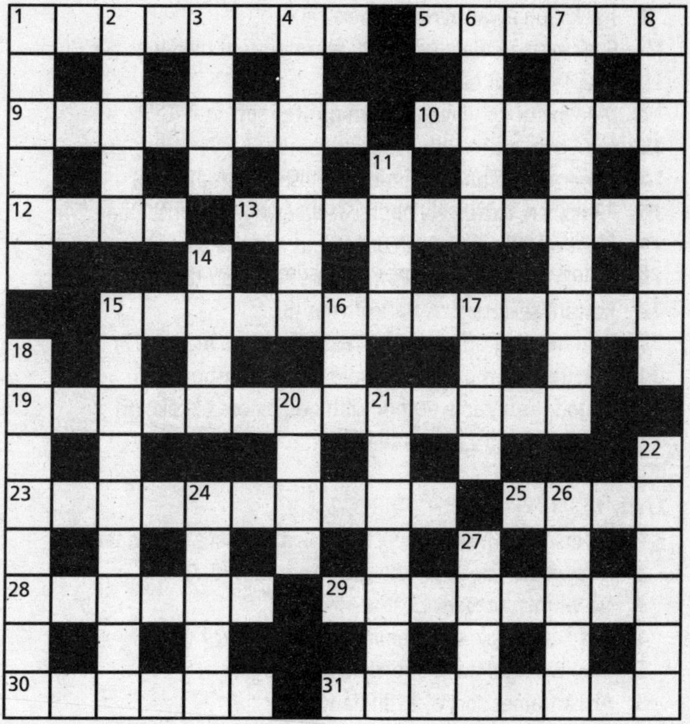

100

Across

1 Lack beans, nuts and half of ceps (7)
5 Writer's got terrible rash describing bog (6)
9 Tracks run away across Illinois (7)
10 Businessmen welcome 2000 for important meetings (7)
11 Rear layabout (3)
12 Dine in strong wind, consuming very soft fruit (6,5)
13 Faint colour no good in neckwear (5)
14 General prohibition restricts English vegetable (5,4)
16 Rhino, say, extremely happy in otherwise cramped cage (9)
17 Plant part displayed in Louvre, but not rare (5)
19 French devil grabs Sir Patrick? It's not important (11)
22 Reward secretary at start of year (3)
23 Zulu heading off at night? What his wives may do (7)
24 Drink knocked back in one old urban transport (7)
26 Festoon venerable author with odd pieces of cake (6)
27 Ray, Sean and 11 wrestled (7)

Down

1 A person from Dubrovnik hosts British circus performer (7)
2 It suggests Coe must change into trunks (8,7)
3 No women present (3)
4 Get first couple of pyramids mixed up here? (5)
5 Give wrong data to short girl in class (9)
6 Artist frames sort of 11 in dance (5)
7 Serve him up tripe, chopped – he should succeed (4,11)
8 Like the Navy leaving harbour behind? (6)
12 Poem, say, written in cathedral city (5)
14 Following complaint Kate's cooked rump (9)
15 Chauffeured bird across river (5)
16 Previn's beginning to hate his platform (6)
18 Bliss here – it could, with love, make you smile (7)
20 The first woman to adopt commercial dodge (5)
21 11s take power in strikes (5)
25 Manage ladder (3)

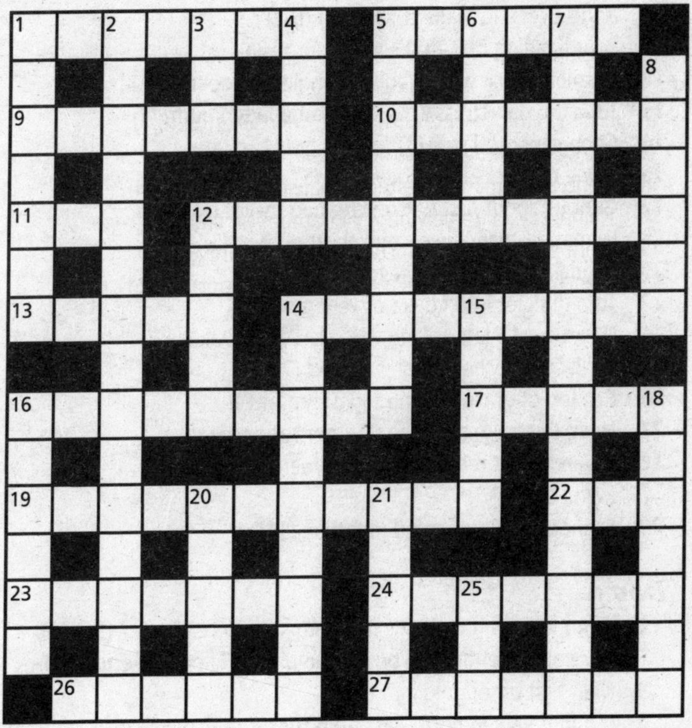

101

Across

1 Pal refusing to work in part of Arabian Sea (7,4)
9 I am returning pound to a government post-holder (7)
10 Adult Greek to make confession (5-2)
11 Bear heading off? That sounds surprising (3)
12 A sailor's back with rubbish, banging on door (3-1-3)
13 Tank top on actress Kate's not large lady's outfit (7)
14 Chop crown off tree (3)
15 Some big rocks rolled over dog (5)
17 Curious about first person creating racket (5)
18 Dominant theme in second short quarrel (5)
20 Politician: "Cut energy everywhere!" (5)
22 Turn director into object of veneration (3)
24 Unsettled 15 left, taking wife like Annie Oakley (7)
25 For instance, the recital is flawed (7)
26 Cut top of grass, leaving top of grass! (3)
27 Need to secure a bishop's authorisation (7)
28 Where to get refreshment in moderation without awful din? (7)
29 Scandalous figures clad in tatters (11)

Down

1 What left-wing council's decorators do to celebrate? (5,3,4,3)
2 Boringly repetitive old boy in trio played Chopin overture (7)
3 Melt first bit of gold into bar (5)
4 It might vary in north-east from sunset to dawn (5-4)
5 You have a point perhaps: it's supposedly perfect (7)
6 Where rich young female students learn Polish? (9,6)
7 Region of Italy or NE England once (not North) (6)
8 Lack of interest in a track at end of motorway (6)
16 Controller raised pistol at soldiers (9)
18 Parrots' parent makes sound of a crow (6)
19 I'd get into fights weekends (7)
21 Remove head in Chalfont somehow? Very much so (3,4)
23 Very attractive doctor, English girl (6)
25 Bizarre old worker in charge (5)

102

Across

1 The new article about oxygen is based on supposition (11)
9 Train up revolutionary Protestant (7)
10 Improve English Channel – it's nearly all busy (7)
11 Vehicle's about right (3)
12 Find old word processor during that awful canal walk (7)
13 Material in advance about incomplete article (7)
14 Harry Enfield clutched money (3)
15 It's sticky in Cyprus dancing topless (5)
17 Doctor on old ship's rubbish (5)
18 American woman's escort (5)
20 Shake coins, producing sound (5)
22 The Roman way through (3)
24 It's diabolical in S. America and it can spread (7)
25 Contract at beginning of bridge, not end (2-5)
26 It's a bit of a spoof usually, on reflection (3)
27 Revealing clothing needed for climbing hills (3,4)
28 Turner imprisoned by British? Nonsense (7)
29 Harry Lauder spoke – using this? (11)

Down

1 How Rocky initially won the title maybe? He didn't do this! (5,2,3,5)
2 Catches parents in trouble (7)
3 Big cattle farm managed church (5)
4 Immediately after a small number set up over here (9)
5 Having put her in mixed school, held firm together (7)
6 Working on clever hunch, OU sent in meal ticket (8,7)
7 Like some young faces, small and silly (6)
8 Stones that belonged to Ms. Reid? (6)
16 Ignoring rector, doctor resurrects therapy breaks (4,5)
18 Like remaindered stock left in sound condition (6)
19 Gironde author's poem (7)
21 Reduce breadth in copper nail (3,4)
23 Entertain high hopes for a part of church? (6)
25 Steal book leaving aristocrat (5)

103

Across

1 Insect in eerie West Sussex town, I hear (6-6)
8 Record poem about island event (7)
9 Cow flu spread to black wild animal (4,3)
11 Shades girls following wildebeests heading west (10)
12 Loud melody that's quite good (4)
14 Leading animal's good for Scots, say, holding party (5,3)
16 Read story again about archer (6)
17 Heads of Welsh Electricity Board's network (3)
19 Like scenery in capital, for instance (6)
21 Harry Walker holds degree as legislator (8)
24 Even pudgy lady's clothing isn't 12 (4)
25 Purcell has managed to become gloomy (10)
27 Cut-back led overwhelming tension at high level (7)
28 Colt kept here in run-down hostel at rear (7)
29 Fine marionette shaped by normal process using mould (12)

Down

1 Vital energy one worker injected in wine (7)
2 Writer's up till one mixing special skin creams (10)
3 Naughty wee shop offering glimpse of porn inside (4,4)
4 English poet welcomed in Moscow perhaps (6)
5 Rod's drink has unknown contents (4)
6 New mums do it at night nursing a crying tot at first (7)
7 Signs on staff – it's crucial to add form of ID (3,9)
10 All Marburg's out to welcome a king; it rings bells (7,5)
13 Liver and lime scattered over cold pasta (10)
15 Large lump? That's too much for hair preparation (3)
18 Old Russian woman's British, alias host of president (8)
20 Mischievous elves gather silver in strip of cloth (7)
22 A tinker trained to be maker of nails (7)
23 "Burglar alarm" clue wife left to get strong tissue (6)
26 Nuclear material at heart of bomb (4)

104

Across

1 Sort of holiday that's all tied up? (7)
5 French novelist in dreadful stupor (6)
9 Terribly silly way to get drunk (7)
10 Don't do chorus (7)
11 Arctic explorers cross it (3)
12 Fit of pique in the CAA sadly produced disaster (11)
13 Courageous chap guards back street (5)
14 Run into it abroad for nourishment (9)
16 Very tiny microphone follows U-boats at sea (9)
17 Add up 3 (5)
19 Environment-friendly energy with each vegetable (5,6)
22 Delve into ground primarily (3)
23 Surrounded by a peculiar song in mountain (7)
24 Revealing clothing in which driver sets off (3,4)
26 Risk having an accident on one foreign piste (3,3)
27 Senator gets punished for crime against the state (7)

Down

1 One in former Chinese capital reaching top (7)
2 Cook able to cook beef with fine glossy tome (6-5,4)
3 Sally impresses everybody (3)
4 Last three in strategy exercises somewhere in N. Africa (5)
5 Living on Capri, it's a shambles (9)
6 Having taken top off, chest becomes tender (5)
7 Doctor with depressants shows intelligence (5-10)
8 Nun dashed around bishop's place, out of sight (6)
12 Weep with pity in odd places in vault (5)
14 Position of "refrain" in Cameron's address? (6,3)
15 A piece of virgin territory in Bury (5)
16 Morse, for example, is striking (6)
18 Some Roman soldiers confined king in shackle (3,4)
20 Check up about government banker in Africa (5)
21 Conspiracy involves international guide (5)
25 You and I possess nothing but unhappiness (3)

105

Across

1 Copy half of verb and tick off (7)
5 Engraving on tomb of female's grossly overpriced (3-3)
9 It's necessary to end fuel shambles (7)
10 Plant all gone to seed outside … (7)
11 … used to be cut back (3)
12 Tom's rioting out of control in lounge (7,4)
13 Only bananas store oxygen? That's insane (5)
14 Charlie Brown, that is, replaced by a quack (9)
16 Sounds as if county swallowed gag (9)
17 Fighting's bitter in outskirts of Bristol (5)
19 Sick troops collapse round cold places they visit (5,2,4)
22 What people do regularly in repasts (3)
23 Award title to posh guy in centre of Henley (7)
24 Creepy guy moves lower in public relations (7)
26 Time lapse creates panic (6)
27 It's not affected note (7)

Down

1 Irene Walker's housing extension (7)
2 Coppers enrol sundry enforcers handling small media event (5,10)
3 Old fellows on holiday (3)
4 22 entertaining 150 in showy display (5)
5 Suspend new curates who take up Italian (9)
6 Car crash – priest called (5)
7 Red sympathiser left Orwell dubious about French composer (6,9)
8 Flower part meant to burst after start of spring (6)
12 Ohio supports States' authority (3-2)
14 Display coat, say, for driver (9)
15 Liberal sacks artist for defamation (5)
16 It's great hosting prince for evening meal (6)
18 Large retail complex means exactly what it says (7)
20 Rose, sozzled, grabs top of bottle? She's not this! (5)
21 Middle East writer's tree (5)
25 Love exercises, yet plump (3)

106

Across

6 CERN chap is surely not about to change his subject (7,7)
9 Class a lecturer as stiff (6)
10 European Community is in free fall – it's final (8)
11 Some let temperature control this dish (8)
13 Disturbingly, there's anger over in cathedral city (6)
15 Wisdom of William the Conqueror, for one (6)
17 Mean-spirited, cold bird (6)
19 It flows in violent surge around Houston primarily (6)
20 Intrepid UN assistance covers half of Africa (8)
22 Priest exercises in Spain playing wind instrument (8)
24 Showed signs of exhaustion as new day broke (6)
26 Third note in requiem Dave's arranged, very short one (14)

Down

1 Doctor must earn income outside? That's not in keeping (14)
2 Turn over computers in fraudulent scheme (4)
3 E.g. cage bird eats old bit of cloth, ejecting this? (6)
4 Hear tick everywhere? Maybe not after receiving this (5,3)
5 River exists twice (4)
7 Boat guide's more flushed if I'm on board (6)
8 101 disgusting, sneering, erratic road designers, say (5,9)
12 Stagger lunch, losing heart for recipe (5)
14 Lunar vehicle drove round houses (5)
16 Pilot maintains it disappeared, somehow avoiding pad (3,5)
18 Food for assorted luminaries (Iran backed out) (6)
21 Safe place in yard in a run-down area (6)
23 Chief cut 9 (4)
25 5 block road that's undulating (4)

107

Across

1 Disease that may produce ulcerous bits (12)
8 Discontinued port on holiday (4,3)
9 Hit plug that's defective to provide illumination (5,2)
11 Pressing items maybe Jeremy's mates sorted first (5,5)
12 Dull poet retired (4)
14 Odd Balkans aristocrat in event at Cape Canaveral (5,3)
16 Its mama evolved with regular helpings of milk (6)
17 Flight over Germany starts in dense cloud (3)
19 Purpose of new job etc. (6)
21 It helps to stop estate car parking these days (5,3)
24 Peer into underwear, lingerie etc. (4)
25 Top Mafiosi ordering 17's death get run in (10)
27 Isolate cryptic clues editor rejected (7)
28 Fancy writer appearing in translation of "Enigma" (7)
29 Typical butts of jokes: man in mortal sin dancing with wife (7-2-3)

Down

1 Welsh river swallowed up flimsy stuff (7)
2 Helpful chap kept old Tom's broken brush handle (10)
3 Rabble repeats musical phrase with different one (8)
4 Map in middle of Bude shows high ground (6)
5 Our guy's extremities visible in riotous party (4)
6 Provisional trendy expression describing Italy (7)
7 Craftsmen who profit from inflation? (5-7)
10 Footballer ran round two backs first, finished unevenly (6-6)
13 When in suburbs of Bangkok ballet dancing's a sport (10)
15 Thief observed pinching chain (3)
18 Gift fair displayed Banksy's work (8)
20 First person in France to lead foreign choir in ME town (7)
22 Papers initially write critique of early performance (7)
23 His purpose? Exuding power affectedly (6)
26 Sum up husband's face (4)

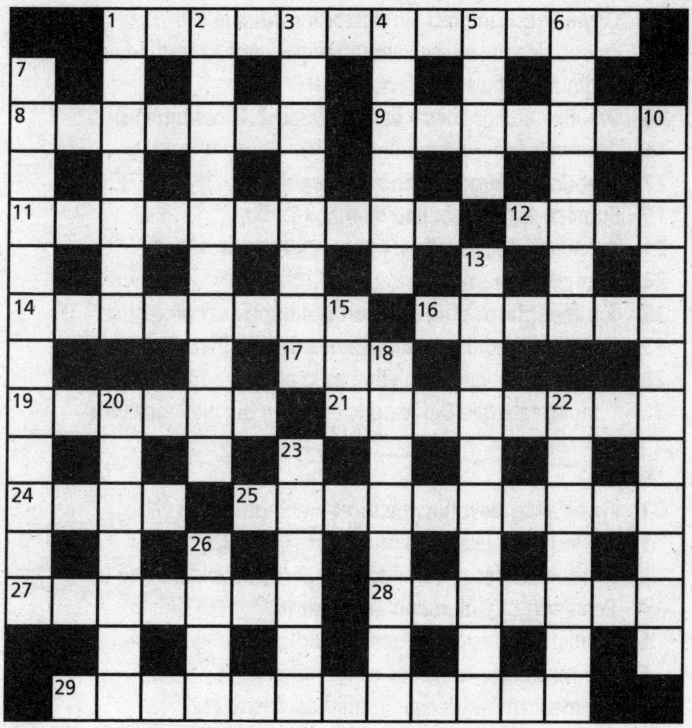

108

Across

1 Keep up with inflation? It's good fun for kids (6,6)
8 Fancy tailor pins middle of flannel in front of bench (2,5)
9 Unwell, rush to grab old doctor for lozenge (7)
11 Query data misprinted about recipe – one of four annually (7,3)
12 Slight lack of clarity in speech (4)
14 What examiner does wearing glasses? About time (8)
16 Country's former US airline ace (6)
17 American's forgotten name for cattle (3)
19 Subject covers right line on map (6)
21 Contents of food in fancy bakery's almanac (8)
24 Take out fruit (4)
25 Address Mayor thus with sort of flourish, keeping quiet (10)
27 Call about regular reward somewhere in Berkshire (7)
28 Poor Del's thwarted, making little effort … (3,4)
29 … with talented Del happily enjoying big audience (4-8)

Down

1 Gives away best flounders, retaining other fish (7)
2 Undecided – like users of 1 Across? (2,2,3,3)
3 Swift describes it – well-known person book omitted (8)
4 Pen's sort of pink round tip of ear (6)
5 Sunlight makes ozone gas primarily, creating pall (4)
6 Flower's liable to wither with hole in it (7)
7 S. American invader spent quid on Castro (12)
10 Murderer likes rare novel about evil (6,6)
13 Just one in company dined out (4-6)
15 State succumbed and yielded initially (3)
18 Arch supporter in old Hollywood studio (8)
20 A cat chewed into fine energy biscuit (7)
22 Rotten boy keeps duck in shed (7)
23 Sweet not containing sugar essentially (6)
26 Motionless, timeless slab of rock (4)

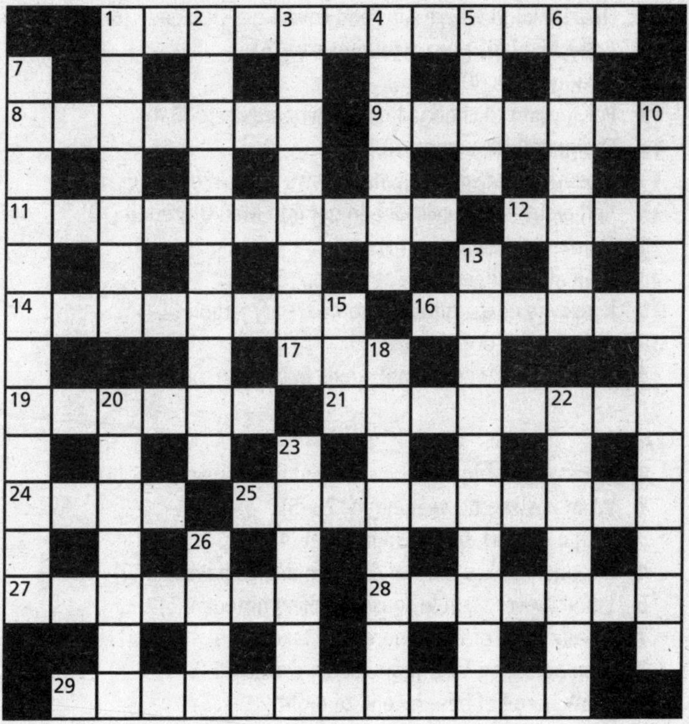
1
2
3
4
5
6
7
8
9
10
11
12
13
14
15
16
17
18
19
20
21
22
23
24
25
26
27
28
29

109

Across

1 Weird tale about this place but not in this world (8)
5 Exhausts would be identical back to front, in reverse (4,2)
9 Oval building where slips and covers get changed? (8)
10 Collect curious person touring area (6)
12 Arrange type (4)
13 Poly opting to change lots of keyboards here (6,4)
15 Ordinary little tremors (2,5,6)
19 Violent threat secures what pirates were after (8,5)
23 Red plant – trust odd one to get into Man U ground (10)
25 Finished six deliveries (4)
28 Animal in Guiana I put at the top (6)
29 Ring wife or daughter for some trendy jargon (4,4)
30 Colonist left out compiler (6)
31 Time of year when female goes to buy rare outfit? (8)

Down

1 Reveal what biggest show in Kent might be called? (6)
2 What kestrels do in Hungary, 25 (5)
3 Turn over part, by the sound of it (4)
4 Anyone ill takes drop of diamorphine as painkiller (7)
6 Small flower stem in season lacking nitrogen (5)
7 Unruly tykes grab diamond and take off (9)
8 Stop adjusting leap years (Spain excluded) (8)
11 Drink barrel of beer by end of night (4)
14 Booting up computer game takes for ever (4)
15 Rewrite men's duets – it's unavoidable (5,4)
16 Seaweed held in great respect (3)
17 Take notice he'd pasted round base (4)
18 Substitutes back tax in seating (5-3)
20 Broadcast proper ceremony (4)
21 French cleric's clothing no longer in fashion? This is (7)
22 I'd dropped in to fight Robinson's man (6)
24 It's turned up in Jean-Luc's bones (5)
26 Shakespeare girl's gripped under the chin (5)
27 Perhaps Alexander's last letter found in vehicle (4)

110

Across

6 Distraught poetess in Spain reveals unsuitability (14)
9 Expedition in South Africa managed to avoid Cape (6)
10 PR fuss: "Film bear besieging large youth hostel!" (8)
11 A skipper's sadly lost power in Zermatt party, say (5-3)
13 Tonight's not about hosiery (6)
15 Writer's stated English attribute (6)
17 A copper and his team show sharpness of mind (6)
19 Needle old writer (6)
20 A piece cut from Angelina's ensemble somehow (2,1,5)
22 Disparage beautiful woman hiding sex appeal – tons (8)
24 Tiny tart but you need lots of tissues for it (6)
26 Birth sign of St. Mark bears immature fruit (10,4)

Down

1 Girl's job's a let-down (14)
2 Thinks again about long story (4)
3 Old photos about Thailand in a row behind bar (6)
4 Fit and agile, like Charlton, for example (8)
5 Ambassador expressed nothing but grudging admiration (4)
7 Tender hearts perhaps inspire doctor's return (6)
8 Filming rural areas sitting on these? (8,6)
12 Throw out 10 in Peel reorganisation (5)
14 I'm replacing amateur in game, getting easy shot (5)
16 Check underground laboratory container (4,4)
18 Long and very thin cruise ship goes round America (6)
21 Flautist's missed top G every time (6)
23 I am in charge of Muslims primarily (4)
25 Partly consumed a mellow cheese (4)

111

Across

6 Sam and Paula Rogers managed backstreet business (7,7)
9 Tramp straight across outskirts of Dorking (6)
10 Superiority of writer's name in eastern church (8)
11 Alienate intoxicated sergeant (8)
13 Canvas covering perhaps an extension guarding north (6)
15 Element that is protecting Norse god (6)
17 Man abandons cunning plan to find work (6)
19 Get it from orang-utan or alpaca? Goat, actually (6)
20 It's improper to limit latitude to go up and down … (8)
22 … i.e. don't be foolishly toeing the line (8)
24 It's behind character in Shakespearian comedy (6)
26 16 miles I swam, getting old complaint (6,8)

Down

1 Easily led, am I responsible when let loose? (14)
2 Exploited American newspaper boss (4)
3 Tennessee controls state hostelry (6)
4 Poor time to suppress trendy repartee (8)
5 Sold one odd fruit (4)
7 French pupil's new team (6)
8 Offbeat wedding on a lake surrounding nunnery (14)
12 Some people wrangle here in Leicester Odeon (5)
14 It could be a volume in Christmas wrapping (5)
16 Want to own one, one under 7, so got smarter (8)
18 Sleuth solved fraud (6)
21 Entitled and expected to receive books on desktop (6)
23 Platform said to wobble (4)
25 Carry better system (4)

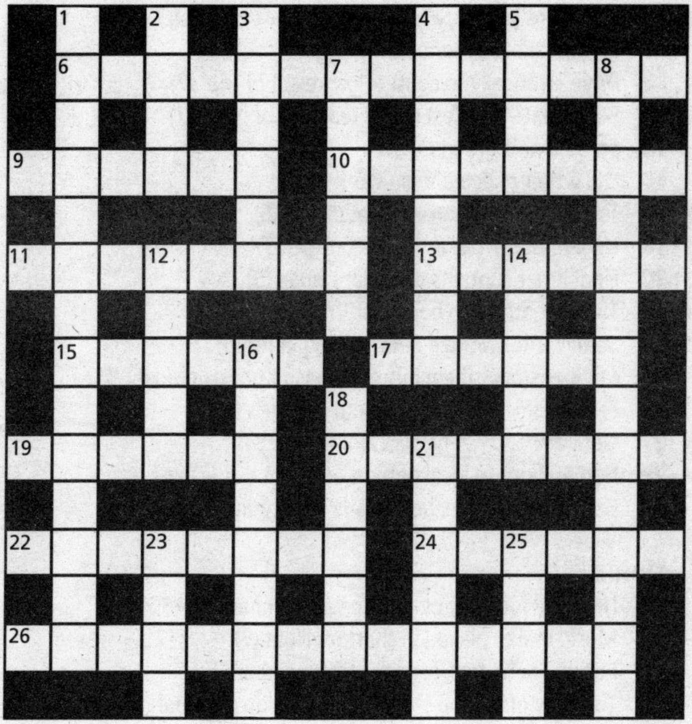
1
2
3
4
5
6
7
8
9
10
11
12
13
14
15
16
17
18
19
20
21
22
23
24
25
26

112

Across

1 It could be worth following rock group, but not far (6,5)
9 E.g. the Vatican hosts 150 in eastern body of church (7)
10 Musicians primarily refer back to heart of organ (7)
11 Prompt Scouser periodically (3)
12 Drive erratically to court to get result of trial (7)
13 Best meat's smallest round rear half of bone (7)
14 Some tennis group (3)
15 Old writer rejected main work (5)
17 Took out fruit before start of dinner (5)
18 Understood what a citizen controls (5)
20 Final letter contains ring that's huge (5)
22 There's nothing in books for Robert (3)
24 Sentimental woman gets nothing in return (7)
25 Milliner stocks them but sadly hasn't got paid oddly (7)
26 Female animal's done without nitrogen (3)
27 Get back and get better (7)
28 Half an hour in local getting tiddly on this (7)
29 Calm and sensible, he'll evade nasty editor (5-6)

Down

1 UN body foolishly cut no ice with Cyril and us (8,7)
2 Music-maker played in short raincoat (7)
3 Put up exotic tree, feeding it with carbon (5)
4 This way of filming shows mite develop on sepal maybe (4-5)
5 Ref's ultimate weapon in NE resort derby debut (3,4)
6 Orson proposed taking his away; it's been here for ages (4-11)
7 Pages, several shredded, not rare … (6)
8 … stuck together, odd title in crazy binding (6)
16 Dirty underclothes deterring the villain (9)
18 Wood finally altered quality of sound (6)
19 TV covers a live broadcast in Middle East city (3,4)
21 Stomach prescription somehow can't help out (7)
23 Abba's alternative setting for rock (6)
25 Almost the perfect place for lift (5)

113

Across

1   Temperature rise as passionate mum catches fever (3,5)
5   Pressure on musketeer's pitiful condition (6)
9   Wrongly advise taking extra teaspoonful as relaxant (8)
10 Roman orator exploited coercion on leaving (6)
12 Clever lecturer in Lincoln (4)
13 Very slow current small spaniel splashed across (6,4)
15 Call a kid Isaac? That's clumsy and lazy (13)
19 Did it do for weaving what a nodding donkey did for oil? (8,5)
23 Modified Cape accent gains favourable reception (10)
25 Part of ski-lift to be arranged on run (1-3)
28 Unsightly mark in new tablecloth et al is removed (6)
29 Broadcast is copied at intervals (8)
30 Head Office in real turmoil in Asian city (6)
31 They begin running first course (8)

Down

1   Cavalryman, having mounted, spots us going in (6)
2   Like big wave, it flipped boy who popped up (5)
3   Reluctant to put up left hand outside (4)
4   Salvation Army girl tours very grassy plains (7)
6   A young lady's wrong (5)
7   Under Henry I archery was organised in rank order (9)
8   We separately leave slow and evenly, getting dirty (8)
11 Old man is impressed in city in Italy … (4)
14 … in Tuscany, take a quick look (4)
15 Simple garment Colin's torn in three (9)
16 Tail, or its owner? (3)
17 Ruined Louis XIV briefly? (4)
18 City where I meet sultan who's crazy about Britain (8)
20 Not far from north-east Arabia (4)
21 Pat and Jock wrestled for big prize (7)
22 Female supporters entertain Church of England couples (6)
24 Front runner gives top-class service in publicity (5)
26 Emblem of Karlsbad, Germany (5)
27 Ruler, 25, governs Sweden, not Britain (4)

114

Across

1 Intimidate male, nearly 12 (8)
5 Surprise attack in the morning on ex-president (6)
9 Obey a lunatic in sanatorium to get source of protein (4,4)
10 Opportunity for women to host fashionable party (6)
12 It may precede storm in tropical Mexico (4)
13 Trio played series back to front for barbecue (10)
15 Negotiate over ground surrounding certain valuable find (8-5)
19 Decorators use it to line up 6 roughly (8,5)
23 Suffer punishment or accept non-stop therapy (4,3,3)
25 Attempt photograph (4)
28 Quote about cow brought back from abroad (6)
29 Mixture of endless rock and mud hides a French gem (8)
30 Very little's drunk (6)
31 Softie worried about freezing point in virgin snow (3-5)

Down

1 British independent religious group split in two (6)
2 True Liberal set nothing up (5)
3 First appearance out of uniform's a liability (4)
4 Very keen, a lot finish off in canal heading north (7)
6 Chap's retaining current source of power (5)
7 Layer of 19 maybe spread around etc. (9)
8 Being vigilant, we had arranged to tour island (4-4)
11 Complain bitterly about story-teller (4)
14 Charges into coffee shop (4)
15 Manoeuvre kart round M25, for instance (5,4)
16 Posh sailors' vessel (3)
17 Labour start to tax fuel (4)
18 Feeling intense when dancing tango (8)
20 Verne's captain picked up sign of things to come (4)
21 Deciding match in league with outstanding climax (4-3)
22 Eyesore across main road creates obstruction (6)
24 Woven fabric described in *Just William* (5)
26 Conceals what a tanner buys (5)
27 Young dog seizes Mike's shoe (4)

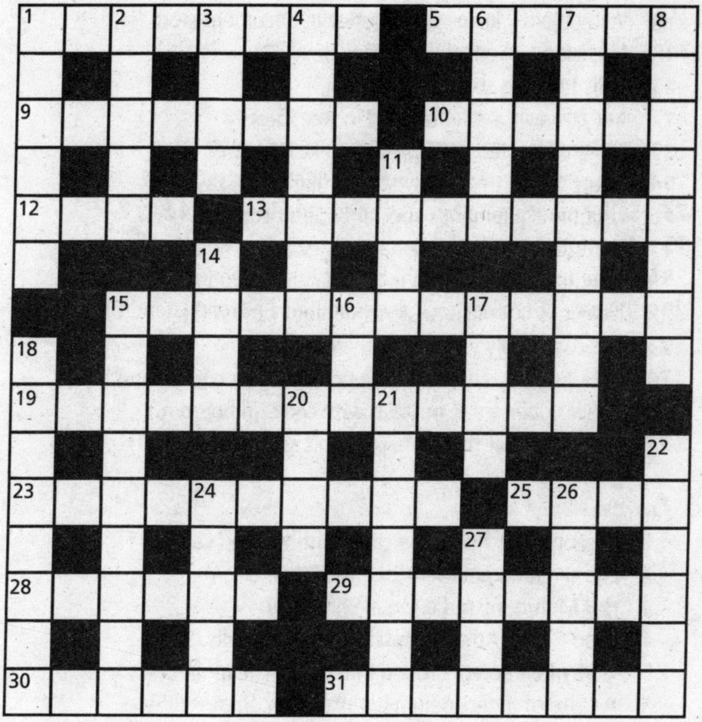

115

Across

1 Back-stage worker's kitchen furniture (7)
5 Intuitive feeling about a hip (6)
9 Vera stupidly keeps Greek letter in document store (7)
10 Musician is drenched in gooey paint (7)
11 Cells needing some renovation (3)
12 Cat and wily owl entangled in tree (5,6)
13 Money invested in RADA plays like this one? (5)
14 Pirate doesn't endlessly shuffle like Fagin, say (4-5)
16 Laundry equipment's special in Derry complex (4-5)
17 Statesman's wife's in Iona doing some rambling (5)
19 Countless trained men in blue surround gunners (11)
22 Novice is not unsurprisingly nervous at first (3)
23 Put case badly for drink containers (7)
24 Church group run disco around end of June at Exmouth (7)
26 Snowmobile is OK in crash with cook on board (6)
27 Executions for this perhaps aren't so widespread (7)

Down

1 Admonished, he's gone crazy with this red card (7)
2 End a remarkable sentence with this! (11,4)
3 H H Munro missed a run in winter (3)
4 People from Athens don't start nasty smells (5)
5 Tiddly Ben accepts round in time for cheap drink (5,4)
6 A taste of monosodium a milkshake contains? (5)
7 Posh twits turn up blushing in silly clownishness (8,7)
8 Having packed, Susan's first to get married (6)
12 Ring prince up for tartan (5)
14 What magicians said after they juggled with ropes? (3,6)
15 One is annoyed by this sound (5)
16 Bad-tempered son, 30, first to leave (6)
18 Granny bandaged injured knee in cotton (7)
20 Rocker's opponent owns a French pile (5)
21 Stay on end of seat using this in bathroom? (5)
25 Single working earl (3)

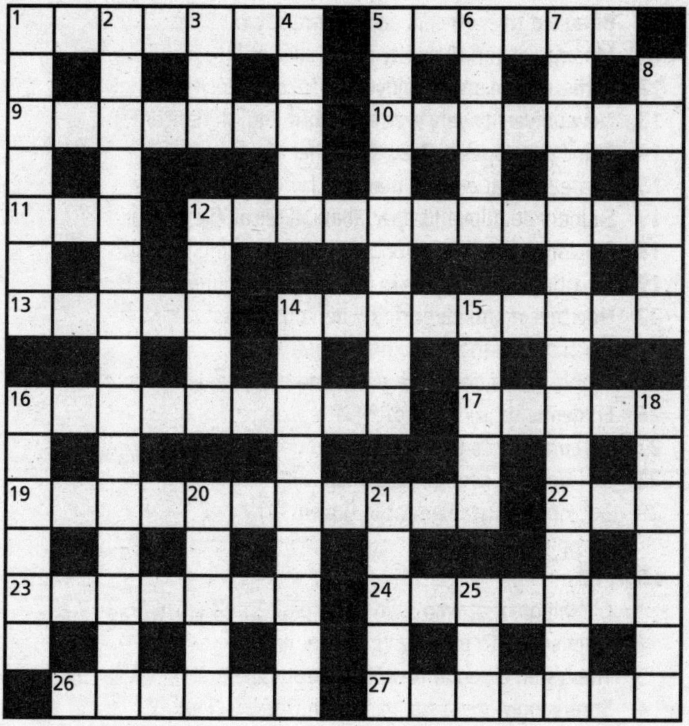
1
2
3
4
5
6
7
8
9
10
11
12
13
14
15
16
17
18
19
20
21
22
23
24
25
26
27

116

Across

1 Smart guy in British public garden keeps entitlements (6,5)
9 Distributed 11 fund as required (7)
10 Bring aid to engineers and depart, say (7)
11 Majority of Yorkshire city offers shelter (3)
12 A cherry confection enjoyed by toxophilites (7)
13 New university very worried about English dancer (7)
14 Enjoy the slopes in Zürs, Kitzbühel etc. (3)
15 Bar leader, little upset marquis, for example (5)
17 Sisters retain love for grammatical terms (5)
18 A number understand it (5)
20 Tautologous seal? (1-4)
22 Odd bits of shoddy turf (3)
24 Track of two snakes going to a yard (7)
25 Highly praise doctor of girl at end of therapy (7)
26 Epidemic spoils finish of 9 (3)
27 Suffer athlete's foot in rough ground (7)
28 Self-denying sect CIA broke up (7)
29 Booking adjustable seat in Rover (11)

Down

1 Cleaning agent who bred clean pig? That's crazy (9,6)
2 Alter sound to transfer virus over line (7)
3 There's no wood in Tinseltown tree (5)
4 Surprisingly green site in African National Park (9)
5 It helps control plane if no reliable part turns up (7)
6 Calm down! No one wants to see your chest (4,4,5,2)
7 Girl's obtained student's yearly records (6)
8 Doesn't touch tea, say (6)
16 This piece of timber makes 8 (3-2-4)
18 Beat NI party suppressing unionist females (4,2)
19 Approaching notice for visitors in hospital? (7)
21 Italian dish requires clever coaching, not advanced (7)
23 I decry changing source of "smoke" in theatre (3,3)
25 Tropical fruit found in Nicaragua valleys (5)

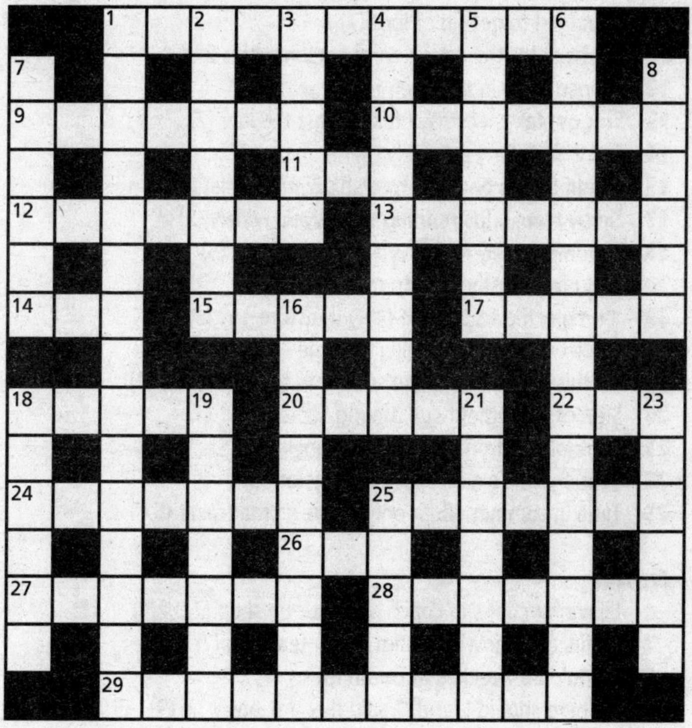

117

Across

1 Unwanted guest gets her car dented touring Austria (11)
9 Feeling shown in European subject for debate (7)
10 Managed to get rid of loot (7)
11 Put back for the attention of person who's 24 (3)
12 Expose team in the open (7)
13 Sick girl takes ecstasy? It's against the law (7)
14 Evil little fellow primarily (3)
15 Singer Simon backed Swedish philanthropist (5)
17 Derby team wins nothing but travels widely (5)
18 The French way in Turkey's more accurate (5)
20 This is all mostly used to make rope (5)
22 It's expected to provide early moisture, say (3)
24 I'd one old timer initially in charge – stupid (7)
25 Do this in order to make scorecard harder to find (7)
26 Sign of agreement still among Scots (3)
27 10 removed from 12? It's permanent (7)
28 Skating here's a bit nicer in Kingston (3,4)
29 Time in summer when only Lassie's broadcast? (5,6)

Down

1 Leave functions in coach and shut up shop (2,3,2,8)
2 Instinctive knowledge but not in teaching (7)
3 It could be wrecked in ocean (5)
4 "Where should I land?" said flier anxiously … (9)
5 … land awkwardly in woman's trainer (7)
6 RUC and Gardai are not trained in defensive tactic (9,6)
7 Concerning, say, revolutionary writer's life in cell? (6)
8 Does winter sport over heart of valley, showing talents (6)
16 Laurel shelters lilacs cultivated in a simple way (9)
18 Big families' elaborate rites involve bishop (6)
19 Hang around back ringing number to get vitamin A (7)
21 Shoes made of leather or false compound (7)
23 Yell from a topless Greek, maybe grasping essence of fluid (6)
25 French banker at home in Ely, for example (5)

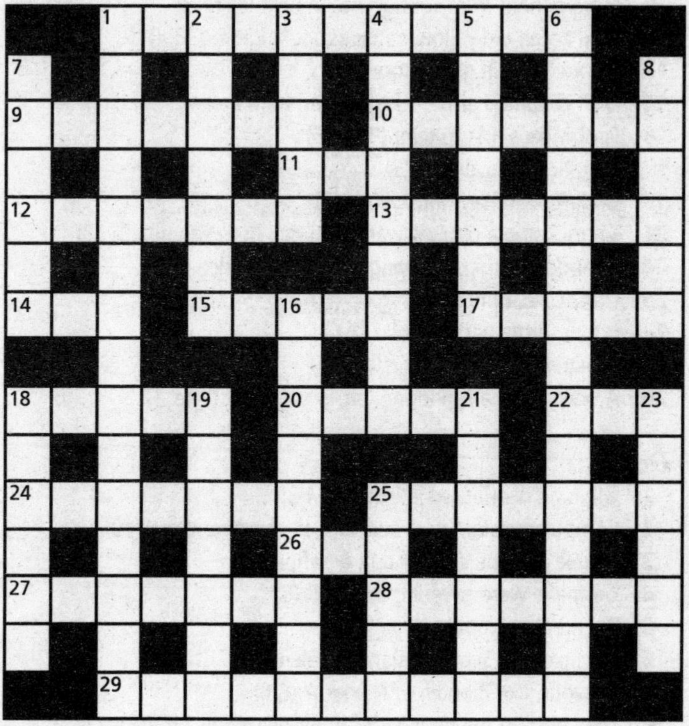

118

Across

1 Urban designers have place among leather workers (4,8)
8 Very big people occupy dilapidated semi (7)
9 Extra benefit from special shot in billiards (4-3)
11 He'd eaten old yellow bananas, looking tired (6-4)
12 Blended oils in grain store (4)
14 Fifth chap had also backed person from Balkans once (8)
16 Poor Mike's first to tempt fate (6)
17 Metal rolled over egg (3)
19 Undertake to sew loose ends (6)
21 Angry Zambia cut Botswana's energy in nation nearby (8)
24 Strange sightings by flying officer in America (4)
25 Our bellies rumble, acting up (10)
27 It hides little part of violin (1-6)
28 Evacuate former Greek island (7)
29 A wad of dollars, nothing left, wasted on starter (7,5)

Down

1 Get mail distributed in interval (4-3)
2 Computer system gets bad support inside and out (10)
3 Enable pi to be worked out, unrefined (8)
4 Germans were covering up result (6)
5 Pin number trouble (4)
6 House girl in Scottish island for element (7)
7 Nervous, like Blondin at Niagara? (6,6)
10 They pushed the boundaries in former tennis broadcast (12)
13 I put in a local bid for reconstruction – it's fiendish (10)
15 Comic, namely (3)
18 Its reels spin, showing no sign of fatigue (8)
20 Spies grab reserve soldiers heading north in Balkans (7)
22 Stick around fine English literature supporter (4,3)
23 Church worker has rector on edge (6)
26 Victory over Germany in gale (4)

119

Across

1 Sect, say, danced in sheer delight (7)
5 Depart after Conservative split (6)
9 Ladies and gents see in an immoral way (7)
10 Soldiers take a tour wandering round city in NZ (7)
11 Examine short piece of digestive tract (3)
12 Prolonged applause drowned Serb's funny remark (11)
13 Animal noise from half of those next door (5)
14 Formal admission of popular French duke into ground (9)
16 Guarded 4 in south-eastern Greek island (9)
17 Take place in our outstanding cricket club (5)
19 Waste time waging a strategy of patience (7,4)
22 Entice odd characters and others (3)
23 A Liberal to a degree becomes legendary hero (3,4)
24 Only unnamed MP and one adult in big London venue (7)
26 Go out, for example, with cut hair (6)
27 Site of Taj Mahal in faint drawing (7)

Down

1 Put some energy in – 51 volts between two small gaps … (7)
2 … blowing a fuse with 17s right in it possibly? (5-10)
3 Consumed 8 by the sound of it (3)
4 Yankees import old very large toys (2-3)
5 Cold game bird, head missing, killed with this? (9)
6 He appears briefly in "Sex Trafficking" (5)
7 Native Americans each support state plant (8,7)
8 Cathedral priest hosts navy big gun (6)
12 Colour of mineral found around Switzerland (5)
14 Sort of gelatine used in redesign of sailing ship (9)
15 Copy 151 (5)
16 Who cares who sat in different places? (2,4)
18 Engineer miracle and recover (7)
20 Picture that is covering publication (5)
21 Don't go near an empty space (5)
25 The old answer in the affirmative (3)

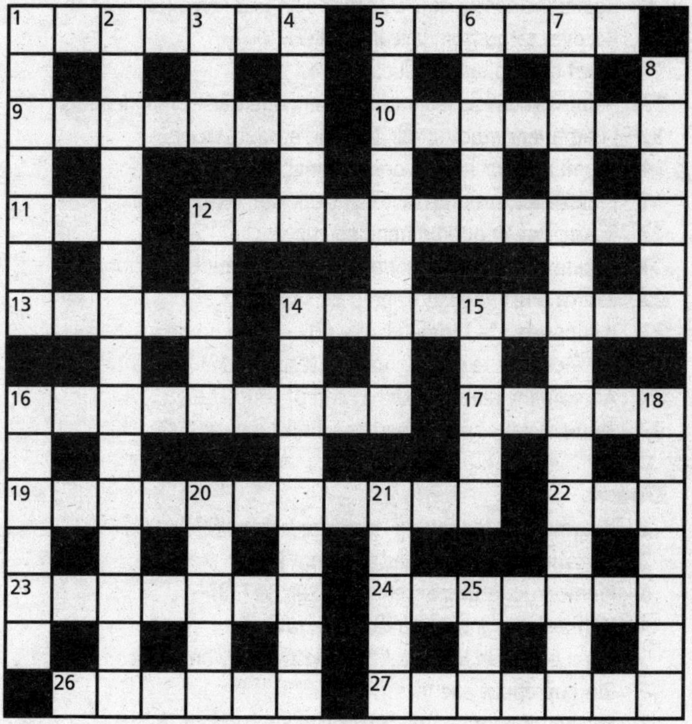

120

Across

1 Withdraw with spinal problem? (4,3)
5 Item of luggage from Savile Row? (6)
9 Roster includes a date by driver's annual levy (4,3)
10 Recover cargo from lake in wild (7)
11 What dendrologist collects (3)
12 Reform and resurrect moves to engage trade union leaders (11)
13 I had briefly stuck in oar, backing broadcaster (5)
14 Top man in yacht club or in cabinet, perhaps (9)
16 I fasten folds round baby's bottom, soft (6,3)
17 Spring flower lit up ground (5)
19 Unplanned internet changes secure commercial victory (11)
22 British artist's cups (3)
23 It supports 11s I forged badly (7)
24 Try tucking into green cocktail? It's swell (7)
26 Accompany revised score at end of concert (6)
27 Shout to rally hounds perhaps, firing rounds (5-2)

Down

1 He gets arrested during Hamburg larceny (7)
2 Gadaffi research worried diplomat (6,9)
3 Plump, suggesting absence of exercise? (3)
4 Half-a-dozen a time pulled up in rank (5)
5 Lay member in New St. Mary's inspired by archdeacon (9)
6 Ring up about one tree (5)
7 Special title for beauty constructed in harbour (6,2,7)
8 Frenchman has, say, to go back on (6)
12 Where rooks spend weekend on top of tree? (5)
14 Pry maybe into Gothic novel? Author's entitled to it (9)
15 Musicians get upset in concert etc. occasionally (5)
16 Scornful, if cornered by Stephen Fry at the margins? (6)
18 This neutral dose is sure, if mixed, to make a cure possible (7)
20 City in S. America erased Monte's tape (5)
21 70 not taking sides in contest (5)
25 Upstage snooty young lady (3)

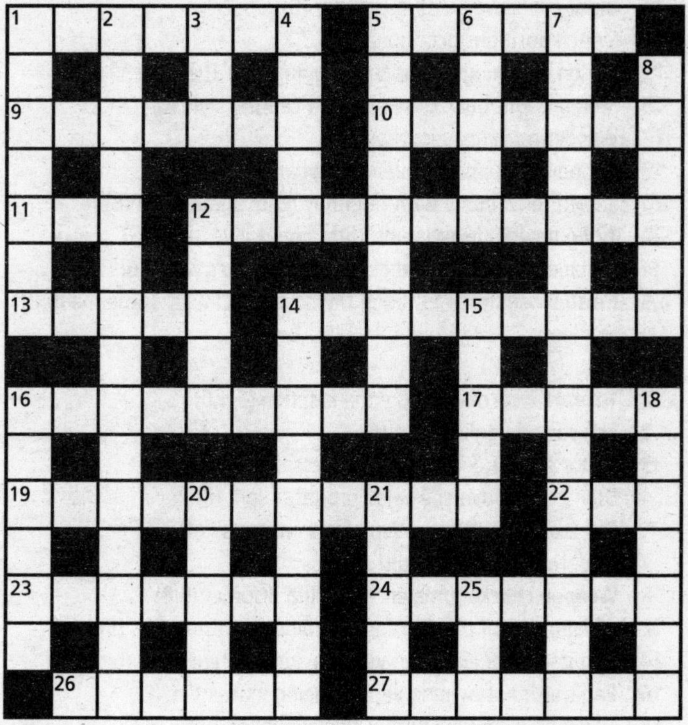

121

Across

6 "Peter Piper ..." et al, creating stuttering woes (6-8)
9 Make up popular opening (6)
10 Block explosive burst in October (8)
11 Switch positions occasionally (3,3,2)
13 Person watching TV has to struggle with "The Queen" (6)
15 Men brought back clown in 18th-century style (6)
17 Wandering varlet's journey (6)
19 A blonde trapped fellow in illicit liaison ... (6)
20 ... or this at home with Tiger having boundless fun (8)
22 17 bonus for clever Israeli with money invested (3,5)
24 EU chief recruits United Nations man who's weak (6)
26 He stirs debate, lived round Davos, worked with Catherine (6,8)

Down

1 Tolerate workplace and enter election (5,3,6)
2 Ken ruined English joint (4)
3 Editor supported Hearts, say, dressed formally (6)
4 Diana's controversial verse produces split (8)
5 Did it baffle earliest group of astronomers? (4)
7 God, New York's difficult! (6)
8 Weapon chucker on alert following disorder (6,8)
12 African capital city regularly accommodates leaders (5)
14 Last part of poem given voice to some extent (5)
16 Earl's into not owning vehicle, being inattentive (8)
18 Like a bowl bowled with a side, wobbling (6)
21 Vibration in Turkey, then more shaking (6)
23 Protective coat made from newspaper (4)
25 Smart old cattle (4)

122

Across

1 Child in pony hairdo maybe worrying about health (12)
8 Give different name to dance entertaining 17 (7)
9 Upstart never initially appeared in wild rave-up (7)
11 Worked together at centre abroad I'd controlled (10)
12 Discovery by boffin during excavation? (4)
14 Fabulous hybrid flower we developed … (8)
16 … never managed to retain the last thin layer (6)
17 Dance nearly upset research area (3)
19 Sort of messy and tense way of working (6)
21 Get very angry about disgusting fried cake? (8)
24 Long church behind short version of 28 (4)
25 Judge tackled a violent heroin-carrying cocky youth (4-3-3)
27 Extol golf played round Rhode Island at end of May (7)
28 Former old trap that is catching mice primarily (3-4)
29 Try motoring freely round Spain, navigating with this? (12)

Down

1 He has lost surprisingly rare place to keep gun (7)
2 Serial boozer vandalised pre-war club (3-7)
3 Salesman's unexpected visit about antique ring (4,4)
4 Bird's outstanding victim (6)
5 Bumpy ride's awful (4)
6 List that is covering difficult times (7)
7 Changing minds radically in war perhaps during beating (12)
10 Stand-in actors display rudest in lingerie (12)
13 Most enduring thing designed in molten steel (10)
15 Fine commercial for short-lived fashion (3)
18 He loves reading complex work in time of prosperity (8)
20 He's readily taken in, say, help (7)
22 It's fully in order to cancel (7)
23 Nancy goes off to tour old ravine in US (6)
26 Superficially wound some fellow in Gateshead (4)

123

Across

1 Cate Blanchett races off across river with a free hand (5,7)
8 Ridge hides edges of dowel in axle (7)
9 Agitate birds flying round you in Paris (7)
11 Feller to court daughter on sailing ship (10)
12 All the best volunteers appear twice (2-2)
14 Launder diamonds, proceeds of larceny (3-5)
16 I repair piano brought in, and loom (6)
17 There's little known about the place grouse display (3)
19 Book in which former American took overdose (6)
21 15 turned up to case new hotel for TV fund-raiser (8)
24 However you look at it, it's done (4)
25 Band look out backing pieces (10)
27 Withdraw do-it-yourself recipe for tongue (7)
28 Flawed genius collects old type of rock (7)
29 Flares fit me badly over uniform, not shorts (7,5)

Down

1 Groucho's brother Roy has no love for salad plant (7)
2 Absurd and ludicrous novel writer penned (10)
3 Final 15 value after audit (8)
4 Stories about a duke's women (6)
5 It's served up in the Smithsonian (4)
6 He carries gold and silver round Lima in this business (7)
7 When wash-days end – maybe round start of Easter? (3,9)
10 Angry grandpa and I block top man's flight permit (8,4)
13 Mail shot describing human objective (10)
15 Conservation body stores energy after deducting costs (3)
18 Cheer if mad king's put on top neckwear (8)
20 Late arriving in Dover, head to last fuel centre (7)
22 Could these 4, about 10, make Lotharios quiver? (7)
23 Excitement afterwards when husband comes in (6)
26 Plants do with insufficient liquid treatment at first (4)

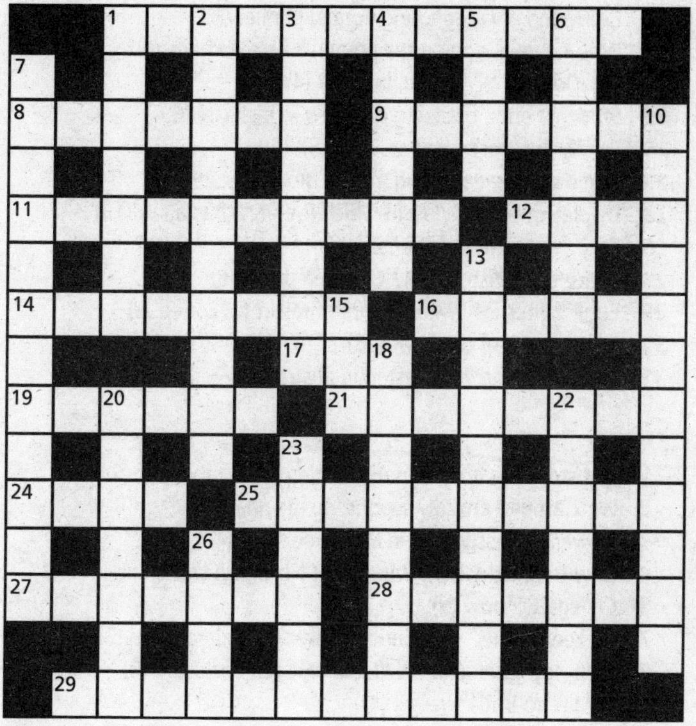

124

Across

1 It copies other works and it's cheap, jumbled up (8)
5 The world as reflected by Epsom society (6)
9 Beavering away, ignoring normal blather (8)
10 Writer enjoys sipping tea primarily here perhaps (6)
12 E.g. Doh, re, mi, fa, soh, la, doh? (4)
13 Students do it, breaking a US law in Irish city (6,4)
15 Family butcher's business? (5,3,5)
19 Like old films, excluding middle ground (5,3,5)
23 Display of comedic art in which everyone has a say (10)
25 Fury's not new in mountains (4)
28 Space on British vessel? Climb on board (6)
29 English journos invade centre of resort for coffee (8)
30 Score at top of dartboard (6)
31 Sort of income 20 invested in abstract nude (8)

Down

1 Flat stones in front of patio, having top scraped off (6)
2 Walk around proudly supporting member (5)
3 Flower endlessly bred in Dublin perhaps (4)
4 How to drink gallons when hot? Nonsense (7)
6 College window (5)
7 "It keeps time," said Zurich banker on underground (9)
8 Help, say, farm animals first in wooden enclosure (8)
11 Set fire to British vessel (4)
14 Humble writer beginning to entertain king (4)
15 Mabel and Alf worried about money that 11s readily (9)
16 Put on a big bra? (3)
17 Edge, with or without black on top (4)
18 Compliant, get into bed roughly about nine finally (8)
20 Approach new organ (4)
21 Festival with unruly local star (7)
22 Look, he's got up in audacious clothing (6)
24 Weight of diamond's an incentive, I hear (5)
26 A lad conceals ringleader's crime (5)
27 Region where a big bird loses height (4)

125

Across

6 Dorothy almost upset Charlotte about old cross in religion (8,6)
9 Note the right tie (6)
10 Coats of arms led Harry to be confused (8)
11 Using both ears, I hear you are in a lab at work (8)
13 Chinese dish is obscure, some said (3,3)
15 English speaker in Mexico going wild about king (6)
17 Reach a dry one at home (6)
19 Stopped once a sedative's swallowed (6)
20 Extended farewell by band on radio (4,4)
22 Naked streakers stupidly wasting energy (8)
24 Five republicans leave violent woman (6)
26 New choir rang agent for some church music (9,5)

Down

1 Explanatory missive protecting tenant? (8,6)
2 What engravers do with some pocket chisels (4)
3 Pore over old recipe that's not as rich (6)
4 Authorise a direct broadcast about Cuba (8)
5 Around Ullswater it's a bit boring (4)
7 Temporarily delayed on short vacation to Germany (2,4)
8 Sail round in magic UTV race at sea (14)
12 15's farewell said to be different around Ohio (5)
14 Chinese leader's wife takes one call from Siamese (5)
16 Gary and Ted fussed about good ingenious equipment (8)
18 Playful slap by mum? It's in her blood (6)
21 Abbey trainee and what she should display? (6)
23 Rare gas ruined old clothes (4)
25 Wander around capital, say (4)

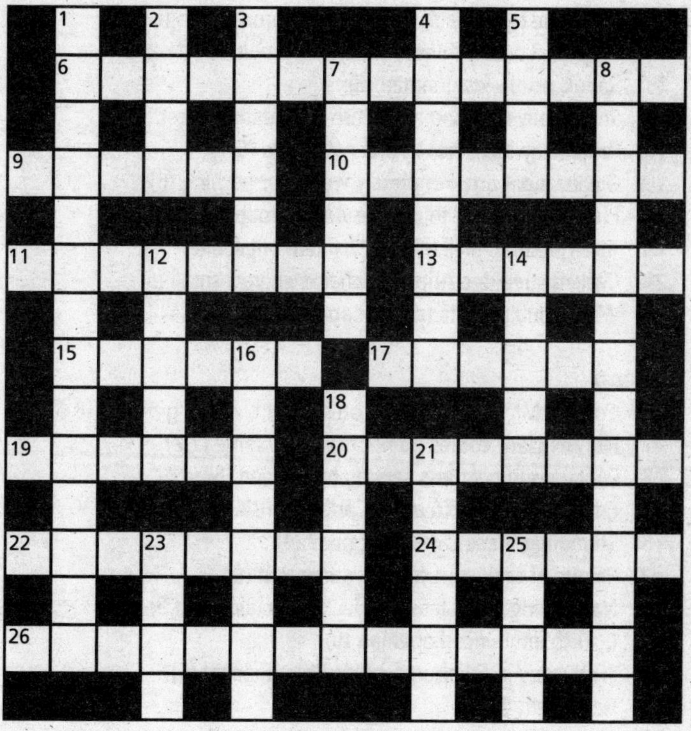
1 2 3 4 5
6 7 8
9 10
11 12 13 14
15 16 17
18
19 20 21
22 23 24 25
26

126

Across

6 Cleaner which manages somehow to control home (7,7)
9 Commercial about Clio perhaps was entertaining (6)
10 North-east gets back extremely generous savings (4,4)
11 Polite but unjust reverse in intercommunal strife (5,3)
13 Spook withholds gunmen (6)
15 Ship finally reaching a Scottish isle heading west (6)
17 People say it clashes in orchestra logo (6)
19 Government artist endlessly works for nothing (6)
20 Plaintiff isn't able to receive *Mail* abroad (8)
22 Told Foreign Office minder to move outside (8)
24 Christian led one Athenian character, very small (6)
26 What army recruits tackle – and starving diners? (7,7)

Down

1 Contest Mr. King must win on seafront, wearing these? (8,6)
2 Fibrous plant comes up not quite the same (2,2)
3 Fungus is almost less serious on women (6)
4 Employ wide one to enter Caribbean island? (8)
5 Stumbling horse casts right one? (4)
7 People of rank start to gain admission (6)
8 Nasty thing binds lens, producing nyctalopia (5,9)
12 C. Firth announced opening (5)
14 A chimney in Edinburgh holds British record (5)
16 Cast outfit (8)
18 Sharp accountant caught African dictator (6)
21 *Mail* implicates king in affair (6)
23 Approve sweet wine after top's removed (4)
25 Mackin abandoned coat in rubbish (4)

127

Across

1 Willing to tell what lies ahead? (11)
9 Slim, small supplier of mortgages (7)
10 Old vessel constructed in Longleat nearly (7)
11 Main notice, by the sound of it (3)
12 Allow yourself the pleasure of eluding reforms (7)
13 Americans wear it loosely interlocked? Lord, no! (7)
14 Do wheel-makers incorporate it? (3)
15 Lizard's oddly grey and cold, with fine back (5)
17 US lake where volunteers do some weeding (5)
18 Mention both ways (5)
20 Speak highly of section in index to literature (5)
22 Cruise to Malta (3)
24 Publicised extremely hungry youngster Ed brought in (5,2)
25 Girl makes jokes, say, and breaks down (7)
26 Opera doesn't include much activity (3)
27 English people allowed out for air perhaps (7)
28 Old boy in camps abroad making women's headgear (3,4)
29 Seen kid head off? Maybe he's playing this (4-3-4)

Down

1 Cook cheesed off with poem about recipe? That's right (7,2,6)
2 Signal to stop socialist song (3,4)
3 You can bet on it appearing in Bath or Sedgefield (5)
4 Stupidly forgot about article left in church gallery (5,4)
5 Served up chilli hotel rejected? It's not allowed (7)
6 Her straight wake disoriented huge fish (5,5,5)
7 Nurse ambition to achieve one ecclesiastical height? (6)
8 Old queen accommodated old flame in space added … (6)
16 … to palace designed to house queen – this older one? (9)
18 Fix shoe here, broken, edges of welt gone (6)
19 Like Neil Kinnock in more ways than one? (7)
21 Clearly written French articles about one in this country (7)
23 Is America stopping Middle East's harsh treatment? (6)
25 Like St Paul's, fated to forfeit love (5)

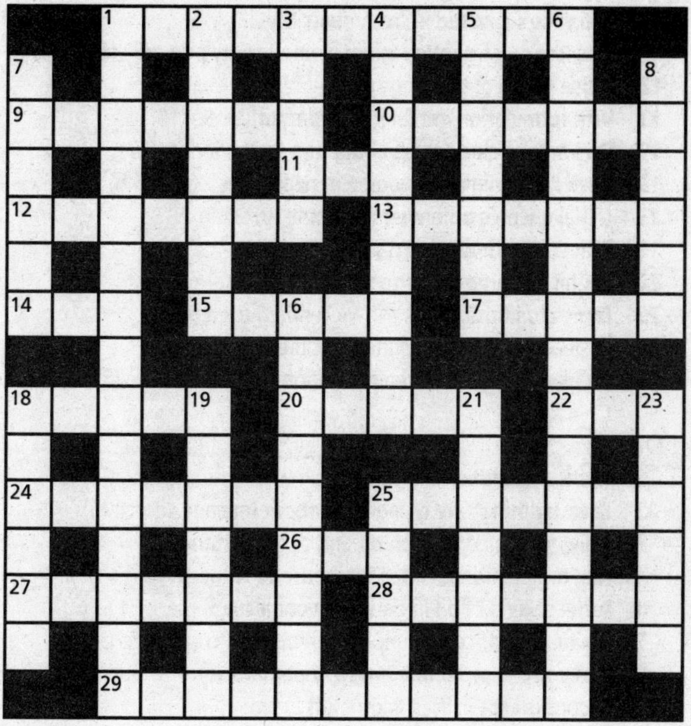

128

Across

1 Reduce cereal following penny discount … (3-5)
5 … at shop that's gone bust – pity (6)
9 Actor: he's covered in fresh paint (8)
10 Persecution of ghetto residents or minority primarily (6)
12 Loose group of gun dogs (4)
13 Nice formulation in tablet, popular antibiotic (10)
15 Very arcane clue solved about 'um in appliance (6,7)
19 Australian animal entangled in neat snare – pity (5,8)
23 A dull queen's otherwise peerless (10)
25 Officer interrupts an old singer (4)
28 In Chicago a teenager sports a beard (6)
29 Twice give up 3 points at Twickenham for it (4,4)
30 Mislead American person about the Spanish (6)
31 Drunk touring posh area of London left after sunset (8)

Down

1 Rustic refreshment in fruit (6)
2 The way things are going, care about revenue source (5)
3 Fully developed epitaph on end of gravestone (4)
4 Talk to union about each big house in France (7)
6 Perfect blend of oil in garlic mayonnaise (5)
7 His tough stance had impressed rabbi on cruise ship (9)
8 Many rise in order in monastery perhaps (8)
11 Record is kept in Washington (4)
14 Unpleasant and cold about king (4)
15 Old Vic's about a mile away: leave messages there (9)
16 Ran into New York opera house (3)
17 Food cultivated in east (4)
18 Mollified a French artist catching us up (8)
20 Pipeline turns back across big river (4)
21 Intellectual East Ender's description of facial hair? (7)
22 Plug here cost comic about a thousand euros (6)
24 Turn over mounted object (5)
26 Telling stories in bed? (5)
27 Love friend's stone (4)

129

Across

1 I had time during royal broadcast for worship (8)
5 US soldier in gaol designed as open gallery (6)
9 Familiar address for writer Sharples introduced (8)
10 In this condition drunk isn't permitted to return (6)
12 Maestro's youthful and to some extent promising (4)
13 Piano salesman's calm about hotel and private academy (4,6)
15 Ordering a TV briefly produces this extra cost (5-5,3)
19 Getting together around heart of Kabul for chat (13)
23 Sort of crime that I study in 13 (10)
25 Finished session at Lord's (4)
28 Act like a fool and clear off (4,2)
29 Deliriously happy individual's red box perhaps (8)
30 Smashing sight from Paris tower, they say (6)
31 Writer isn't able to defend husband's taste (8)

Down

1 Fashionable company's weak (6)
2 Monstrous creatures make some progress (5)
3 Spots number in winning card (4)
4 Guilty feeling about Rome's collapse (7)
6 The sort of nerve needed to see one behind bars? (5)
7 A French corps got encircled, not tossing explosive (9)
8 Fit, a Warsaw man wields power with axes (8)
11 Dashed off special edition (4)
14 People always include earnest request (4)
15 Clear victory on show (9)
16 Primarily a woodworker's little tool (3)
17 Gulf ruler's Queen takes note (4)
18 28 occasionally bolted in motorcycle event (8)
20 Fertiliser found in a river first (4)
21 Shake it when opening a barrier (7)
22 Not much space in trio playing in the East (6)
24 Poetry has always intrigued Kyoto union leaders (5)
26 Flower girl (5)
27 Heroic adventure of Peregrine Pickle? (4)

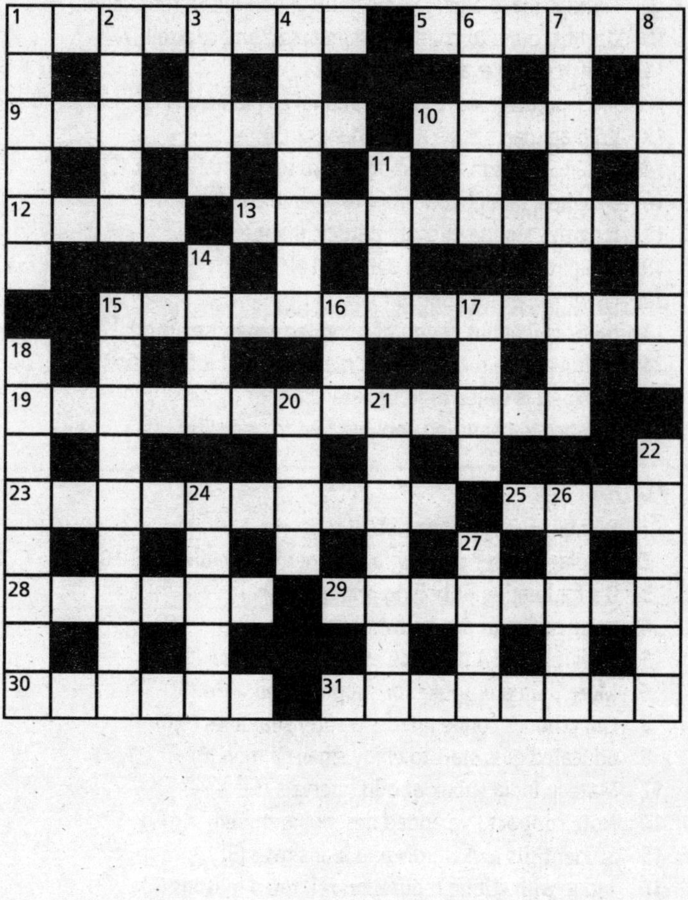

130

Across

1 Pig accepts new home one way or another (7)
5 Local area in European capital beside harbour (6)
9 Perhaps make a peer some genteel bonnets in retirement (7)
10 Dashes round to collect passport, say, and cocktail (7)
11 French water available in palace (3)
12 RA separately leaves international as planned (11)
13 Wild animal: has he any bananas? (5)
14 Detail a Territorial group to return to counter-attack (9)
16 Dejected, ploughed furrow for one in soil (9)
17 It carries stigma in characteristic manner (5)
19 Naughty movie is such a mess (11)
22 Oscar leaves on holiday (3)
23 Baltic city opens centre of booming Japanese art (7)
24 Instruction to machine user maybe, one of lots in Texas (3,4)
26 IT expert is called in to update chief (6)
27 Finishes transmitting, moving first to back (7)

Down

1 Bomber wrecks latest hotel (7)
2 Bipolar sufferer choreographed permissive dance (5-10)
3 It's for heating or boiling primarily (3)
4 Seize centre of power with ease (5)
5 Mail former SA province after child's arrival (9)
6 More than one spoke for supporters in arms (5)
7 Old school's condemned – a sorry shambles (9,6)
8 Educated girls start to enjoy small salmon (6)
12 State in India shook at odd intervals (5)
14 Note contract I've added describing myself, say (9)
15 Student sits awkwardly and leans over (5)
16 Judge with strong reputation reformed masons (6)
18 Hugs and fondles when distressed (7)
20 Former PM has formerly accommodated Spain (5)
21 Snooze topless out in bracing air (5)
25 Cover unfinished open-air pool (3)

131

Across

1 Distribution of cash in Turin not generous (11)

9 Doctor cares about province's poison (7)

10 Sort of underwear that has male in lather possibly (7)

11 He's a little fellow primarily (3)

12 Catcalls increased, I heard, in pub spree (5-2)

13 Disease in quiet deserted street (7)

14 Still no end to the abominable snowman (3)

15 Ensure king's ignored result (5)

17 Boat at end of quay 8 in Hamburg (5)

18 Object's not fully reserved (5)

20 A traveller's fragrance (5)

22 Employ American English (3)

24 A tanner for our star at Palm Springs? (7)

25 The call's put out: she's a fierce woman! (7)

26 Several periods are recalled (3)

27 Having joined EU, I find it's in chaos (7)

28 Stand on insect – it's scary (7)

29 As mentioned, ordered revisions to text (11)

Down

1 Change one's kit and run 24? It's not cricket (15)

2 Meet Catholic on even ground (7)

3 Go over again about EU farm policy (5)

4 Ignite forest – it explodes with energy (3,4,2)

5 Under perfect conditions, I trade extremely luckily (7)

6 Data analysts' colder teeth? (6,9)

7 Cobra wriggled at end of very big bottle (6)

8 Press fail to win in court (6)

16 Rushed headlong to make impression on editors (9)

18 Democratic Unionist puts up fight (4-2)

19 Understand Israel thrashed Spain (7)

21 Is this tempo legal or wrong? (7)

23 Turbulent Ireland's heart's intact (6)

25 Normal practice is a tad hard at first (5)

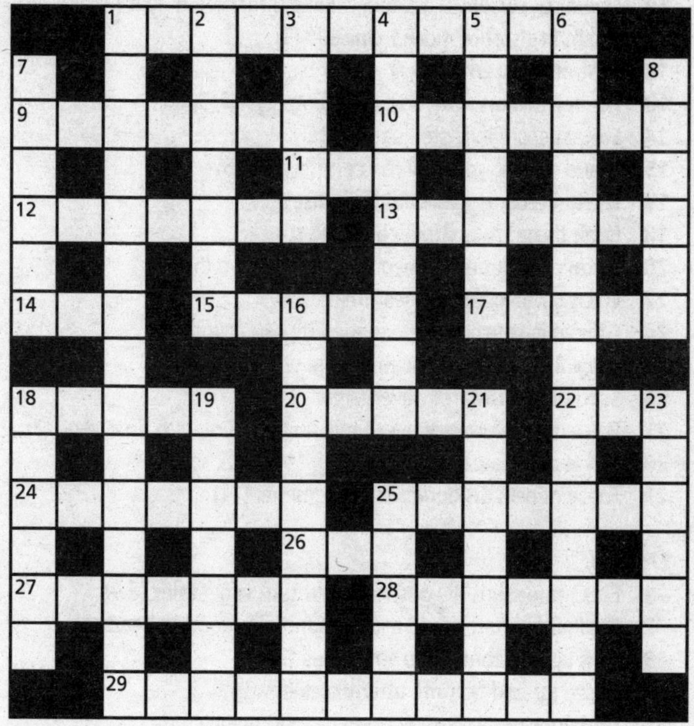

132

Across

1 13 broken adzes all over the place (6,5)
9 Not an annual sum disbursed by old boy (7)
10 One duck swallows another – kid's transported by it (7)
11 Old man's sort of music? Unlikely (3)
12 Desires wrecked lives (7)
13 I'm in Newport after, say, indulging myself (3,4)
14 Lowest score in Ulster league (3)
15 Island making minimal tax contribution (5)
17 The old records make painful noises (5)
18 Bank there keeps America united (5)
20 Boxers knock out ten people in Cape Town (5)
22 What cattle usually digest first? (3)
24 Official in court or one engaged by councillor (7)
25 *Daily Mail* etc. cover posh people with no money (7)
26 See it in the Antarctic everywhere (3)
27 Poles invest currency over time, tiny amount with no charge (7)
28 Old explorer's back having caught Virginia, say (7)
29 These miners dislodged tiny fragments (11)

Down

1 EU Commission HQ gushes about rare vegetables (8,7)
2 Realm of generous old monarch initially, good at heart (7)
3 Turn up box containing small files (5)
4 Speed up and tear off, utterly reckless (9)
5 Two unknowns have old logo redesigned in study (7)
6 Display Nile crustaceans – 5's one of them (7,8)
7 Gun-toting Arab unable to shoot (6)
8 Greek primate's source of wine (6)
16 Thresh thin barley, wasting energy? You'd get lost in it (9)
18 Outer layer on wall opposite (6)
19 Old money scattered in raid (including euros) (7)
21 Trip and fall after school (7)
23 Autocrat's son arrested in store (6)
25 Queen supports favourite saint (5)

133

Across

1 Quite anxious yet strangely even happier about son (12)
8 Plane supplies most of Airdrie with work (7)
9 Dull genus of roses in photograph (7)
11 Trouble spot in a derelict shop in Flint (10)
12 Sikh leader's returned from Uruguay (4)
14 Performers sit back having a fitful rest outside (8)
16 Large partner's league title disputed (6)
17 Polish rugby ball at the start (3)
19 Successfully handling stones on wall (6)
21 Graceful style of English angel sculpted on church (8)
24 Certain odd bits of squirrel (4)
25 Demand duties are endlessly improved for accuracy (10)
27 Insurance protection not starting? It's too old (7)
28 Person giving commands or controlling road before (7)
29 Imbibe spookily unreal art that's miraculous (12)

Down

1 A milk supplier's up to date (7)
2 Buying up rising new chains in suburbs of Reading (10)
3 Regiment picked up boxing trick for company, say (8)
4 Finish entertaining cross old man and spread out (6)
5 He wants to pass his exams, second two complex (4)
6 Television covers copper (Cardiff man) climbing bridge (7)
7 Old money invested in various casinos in US city (3,9)
10 Famous trial in which beer-case clue's solved (5,7)
13 Putting book last, bring in German article file (4,6)
15 Girl to take action (3)
18 Want to enter fight as precaution in wartime (8)
20 Upstart in normal meeting place, lacking finish (7)
22 Impartial doctor learnt to govern unit (7)
23 Visiting medic would be next ruler if name's dropped (6)
26 Group of convalescents' farewell (4)

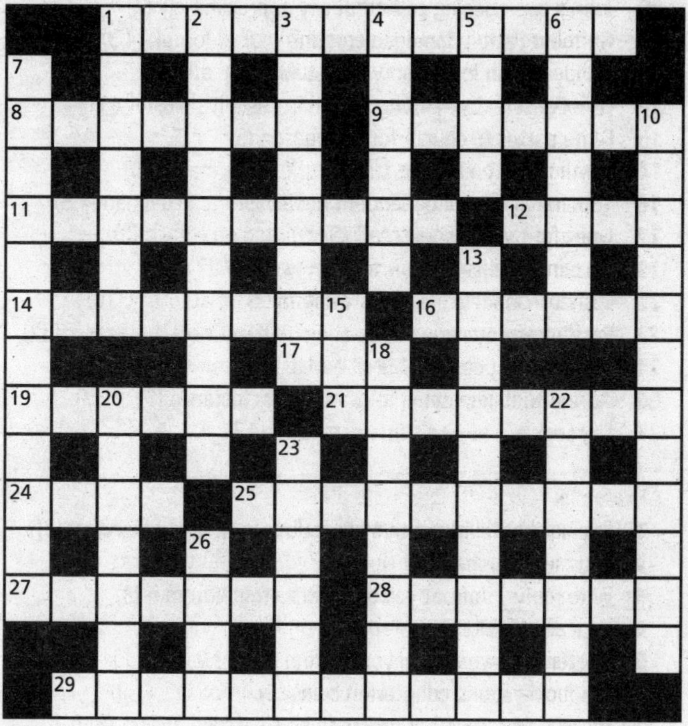

134

Across

1 Find American in ship unconscious (4,3)
5 Become stiff and cross if you're eating it (6)
9 John's approaching cathedral city approximately (7)
10 Garment Patton damaged crossing rear of Tobruk (4,3)
11 Annoy church in Glasgow after taking top off (3)
12 One Conservative among fifteen in cast? It's wasteful (11)
13 Female goes to church for this reason (5)
14 Having chewed hot taco, man suffers this maybe (9)
16 Voucher in good independent newspaper to Scotsman (4,5)
17 Lines "set in the silver sea" (5)
19 Do cartwheel vigorously to keep warm in it? (4,7)
22 The main leaders in south-east Asia (3)
23 Pacific zone managed once again without new government (7)
24 Thwart new peer and MP at end of parliament (3-4)
26 Agrees to delete name in property, for instance (6)
27 Lay sock out as bird's first container (4,3)

Down

1 I hear what Billingsgate traders do is in their own interest (7)
2 Legs, as brought by 7? (8,7)
3 With money upfront you'd get extra metal from it (3)
4 Your old Middle East herb (5)
5 Doctor Foot won't ring you in rural area (3,2,4)
6 Producing sound counterfeit coins (5)
7 It's as if Mrs. Thatcher dressed up as seasonal visitor (6,9)
8 Pet has ruined part of flower (6)
12 Group in container transport's not doing much (5)
14 Clever Kate's adopted a style for ready-made meals (9)
15 Dither and partially reach a verdict (5)
16 Lizards are small, fine, and about, say, to climb (6)
18 Final one in Community's showing flexibility (7)
20 Dwarf starts to have a pleasant peaceful Yuletide (5)
21 Women at home these days show embarrassment maybe (5)
25 Peggy hauled up fish (3)

135

Across

1 Parking notice cut short in field (7)
5 Edinburgh pageant that husband's missing as well (6)
9 University in Bremen condemned food additive (1,6)
10 Eve's first to allow people in where she's happiest (7)
11 At intervals reveal catch (3)
12 Talented pal designed denture (6,5)
13 Cat whose tail frightened baby (5)
14 London CID's mark of approval for standard measure (9)
16 Risks had damaged about 500 storage devices (4,5)
17 Bring back drink fit for a king (5)
19 A regent feigned sigh of relief for his brother's grandson (5-6)
22 Second person's portion of carry-out (3)
23 Told what your 19 is to 22 (7)
24 Dave stupidly collected 13 and left (7)
26 Funny thing doctor did to youth leader (6)
27 Drink for forwards at Twickenham? Pity it's off (7)

Down

1 Spurious excuse for priest to send message again? (7)
2 Labour rebel led new department, e.g. Marshall-Andrews? (6-9)
3 It goes with sceptre and gold book (3)
4 Sacred book in Algerian city supporting king (5)
5 Book of words Ruth uses in order to pen article (9)
6 Silly guy wept uncontrollably about end of affair (5)
7 Vital software needed to run theatre efficiently? (9,6)
8 Stark display involving bit of exhibitionism (6)
12 Teetotal poster for wood spirit (5)
14 Dry eyes at broadcast of a Beatles' song (9)
15 Bad-tempered woman who's mostly clever (5)
16 Some of the giraffes in early flight from Mecca (6)
18 Where to clean French articles, first 3 of 12 (7)
20 People in Rwanda like Dustin Hoffman film, I hear (5)
21 Spots where bees live (5)
25 Former police picked up dog (3)

136

Across

6 Like young minds and sealing wax? (14)

9 Taxonomic group of fruit having high yield at first (6)

10 Lose account in simple confusion (8)

11 Poor lines offered in bank by the Spanish (8)

13 Empower Emperor Napoleon initially on his island retreat (6)

15 Wizard's falcon (6)

17 This country and America return, having to solve puzzle (6)

19 Hip bones found in Mediterranean island (6)

20 She hired a French fly-by-night to lie on beach, say (8)

22 Top groomer from east London to improve image (8)

24 Monk's religious books bringing about change (6)

26 Seedy nightclub for all? It allows all kinds of turns (9,5)

Down

1 Good bonus earned by top-flight diplomats here? (4,10)

2 Old friend's a gem (4)

3 It bores me sitting in the back (6)

4 French author cut top off bride's clothes etc. (8)

5 Follow guy from Sri Lanka who's lost money (4)

7 Figure of speech is picked up at some distance (6)

8 Governing body's writer in neighbourhood (5,9)

12 Belt round here – it's a right shambles (5)

14 A traveller's fragrance (5)

16 Moving fast, Harry got involved with uni (2,1,5)

18 A complex maths problem demonstrated by wheeze? (6)

21 Native American annoyed Joan touring Virginia (6)

23 Group of pretty girls drink, ignoring Victoria (4)

25 Victory after tense match (4)

137

Across

1 Dusters left to fester around castle automatically go off (4-8)
8 Malcolm retains a right to it in marriage (7)
9 A small number at night clumsily make love (7)
11 Come and look everywhere round big car where kit's kept (6,4)
12 There's some welcome nutrition in bill of fare (4)
14 A riotous mob secure vault for WMD (4,4)
16 Badger, leveret with no tail, and donkey (6)
17 Observed cutter (3)
19 Take over when birds return (6)
21 Terrible fate limits Ark Royal developing here (4,4)
24 Not very far in Switzerland (4)
25 Seizing land, Queen's about to claim one tax return (10)
27 Harry learnt about union not taking sides (7)
28 Head of state, correctly seated, calms down (7)
29 Forgetful man's in debt unfortunately to editor (6-6)

Down

1 Wind circulating in Morocco rises (7)
2 Landlord Bob receives first of mail, a nasty package (6,4)
3 Old broadcast beats the blues (8)
4 Praised old heartless deity (3-3)
5 Engineers install computers etc. in ceremony (4)
6 E.g. Big Ben's a monster? Not really (7)
7 I am not prepared to support silly Malaga merger (12)
10 Bumpy US greens include a few giving cause for terror (12)
13 Double-edged, like some strokes at Wimbledon (10)
15 Awful poet forfeited right (3)
18 In West Indies skater trained to do another sport (5-3)
20 Give up diced cucumbers without sign of hesitation (7)
22 Forgot to include word for "glove" in dictionary (7)
23 Funny tale about new king's leg decoration (6)
26 Genuine ceasefire excluded 100 (4)

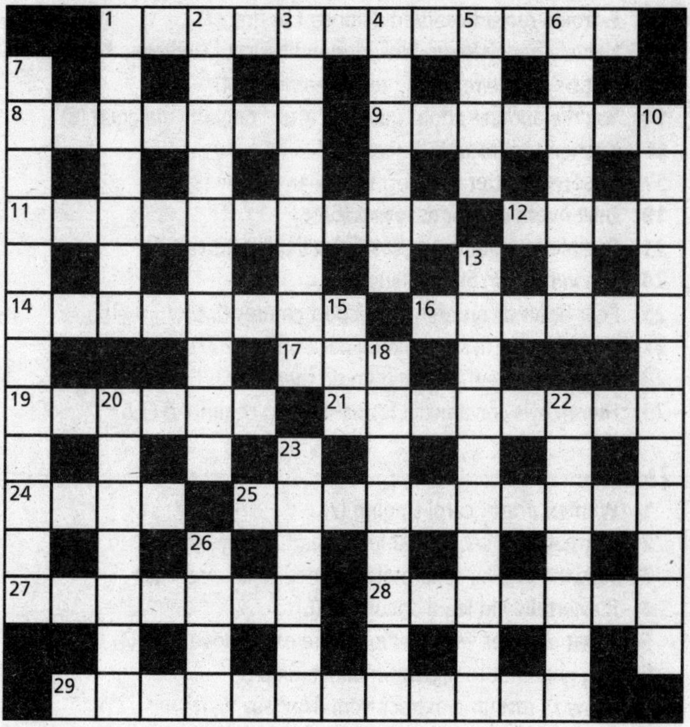

138

Across

1 Admiring sounds from low wits with flesh displayed? (4,8)
8 Feels aggrieved at unopened gifts (7)
9 Extreme racist unsettled democrat at first (7)
11 Naively happy Ringo looked round heart of Hollywood (6-4)
12 Notice female returning to get earnings (4)
14 You'll elaborate about question after company dialogue (8)
16 Kitchen tool sounds bigger (6)
17 The French start to invest European money (3)
19 Dry? Avoid sun for days in June (6)
21 Perform song about potatoes? It's brilliant! (8)
24 Second judge released suspect (4)
25 Peer bows as ordered by support centres (5,5)
27 Rock fragment, say, holding back half of 2 (7)
28 Regular aircrew followed Arctic sheet (3,4)
29 Hierarchy's constant in former Beijing command (7,5)

Down

1 Women attack carol singing (7)
2 Normal hunt sabotaged for around 29 days (5,5)
3 Was the fuel he separately dumped to no avail? (8)
4 It's certainly in legal document (6)
5 What changes when temperature rises above zero (4)
6 Beg chief not to appear in ballet jump (7)
7 Crowd's insulting extract from *Mail*, say (5,7)
10 Suspect resists charge for stealing from this in shop? (4,8)
13 Hybrid smashed BSE records (10)
15 I accept the old shilling (3)
18 One MEP got annoyed after I put in complaint (8)
20 Provoke National Front in angry email (7)
22 Nearly offend a king by being stand-offish? (7)
23 Scattered melons in grave (6)
26 Resist change in US (4)

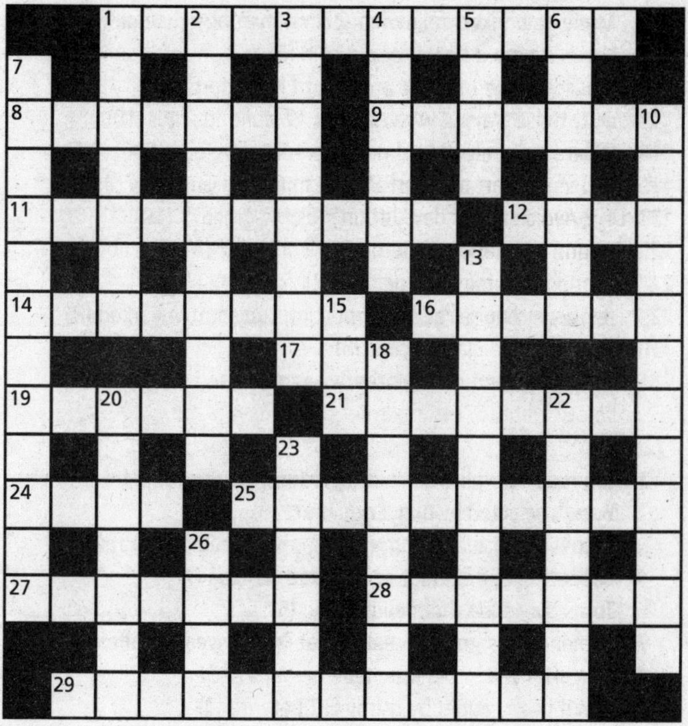

139

Across

1 Exercises power in America after newspapers (5-3)
5 A fraction of stature, top to bottom (6)
9 Many go bonkers following second marriage custom (8)
10 Harris returned home for old coin (6)
12 In his work he may use a chunk of Rochefort (4)
13 Duty nurse trained with director as stand-in actor (10)
15 Where every element is nearly predictable (about 10) (8,5)
19 Papers for one stranded abroad touring strange city (8,5)
23 A question to a sailor: "What's bluish-green?" (10)
25 Dental examination? (4)
28 Tension in spine damaged part of foot (6)
29 Its name changes at speed of light, subject to meaning (8)
30 Push board round harbour (6)
31 Sexy, small and no use otherwise to you and me (8)

Down

1 Big road's purplish-pink at the edges; it's the stone (6)
2 Bond's selected by him, Eric's mate (5)
3 Mensa geniuses welcome this knowledgeable person (4)
4 Pepper's prepared first and cooked on time (7)
6 Turns over slide that needs fixing (5)
7 Somehow a shrub concealed that French weapon of old (9)
8 One with yen to dip into hebe perhaps (5,3)
11 Has it been caught by canny E. Tibetans? (4)
14 Extreme left-winger overturned legal infringement (4)
15 Forerunner comes up again in two rivers (9)
16 At regular intervals Derry doesn't serve alcohol (3)
17 I ignored Italian city's performance (4)
18 New boxer's fist's bandaged – he's in the last round (8)
20 Some ground with fruit growing up one's missed (4)
21 Gather in very small space in cold unit (7)
22 Lousy ship cuts ... (6)
24 ... runs into Middle Eastern set unfortunately (5)
26 Secret Romans' clothing recalling former style (5)
27 Criminals are behind these watering holes (4)

140

Across

6 Doctor came and met egotist when Bill's discussed (9,5)
9 Sensitive offer (6)
10 Mabel managed to acquire single fertiliser (8)
11 Air can somehow absorb Idaho's pollution (4,4)
13 Irritable guy is keeping steak for you, I hear (6)
15 Spies probe Alf's weird beauty treatment (6)
17 Ghost of artist with skirts (6)
19 Within a month Leo trained wild cat (6)
20 Exhausted individual combining many features (3-2-3)
22 Wet air is bad for climber (8)
24 Lower position to cure eye irritation? (6)
26 Wildly imprudent, I call for smashing machine (9,5)

Down

1 Nice conceits, if elaborated, make literary genre (7,7)
2 It's in the centre or near the end of pyramids (4)
3 Is it among the easier ranges? (6)
4 Blend of green tea for young person (8)
5 Time-wasting couple (4)
7 System of pipes Yank installed around wine store (6)
8 New GP sent a letter round hospital: "Be courageous!" (5,3,6)
12 Double over cape belonging to nobleman (5)
14 Political group's swelling without a leader (5)
16 A foot extra roughly? That's the bottom line (5,3)
18 A woman in one African country or another (6)
21 Pretentious amateur performed in US city (2-2-2)
23 Time to embrace gangster (4)
25 Letters distributed in Lima (4)

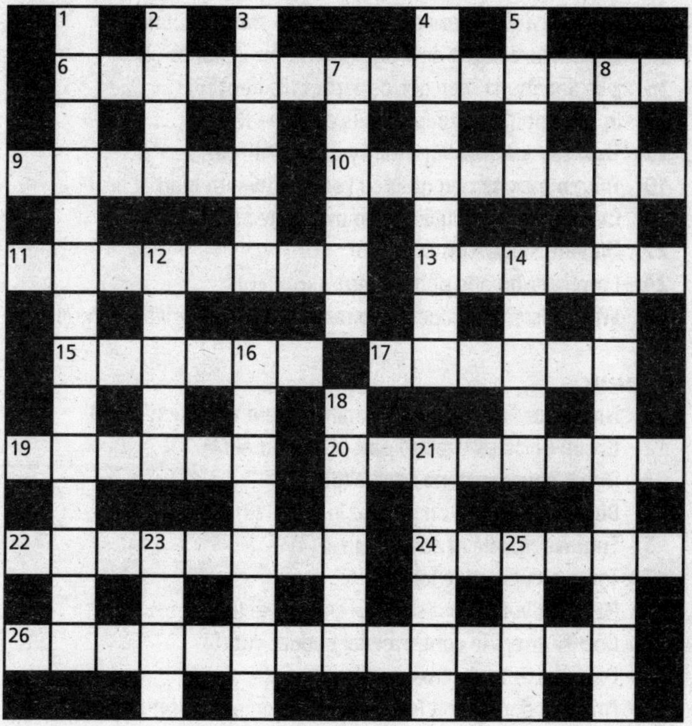

141

Across

6 Even Irish types can be extremely touchy (14)
9 Humble church leader impresses writer (6)
10 To make a prognosis doctor hopes to snoop around (8)
11 Harry heard about new-age bowler, for instance (8)
13 Like Sandhurst marcher, or part of his boot (6)
15 In recession, say, keeps books at home (6)
17 They say S. American country is hot stuff (6)
19 This country turned good fun somehow into martial art (4,2)
20 Disgust and unease at being mistreated (8)
22 Queen's station (8)
24 Comment on one of the gospels (6)
26 10% wasted not a penny to raise new 300th celebrations (14)

Down

1 Firm boss: "I've supported main current reduction" (5,9)
2 Group of chaps explore part of cathedral (4)
3 Dutch house with no stove? (6)
4 Bowl over and sit on ground in wood (8)
5 Engrave middle of socket chisel (4)
7 Top man was once forward (6)
8 Resident vet set out stake in enterprise (6,8)
12 Rectify errors in controversial budget cut (5)
14 Dicky loves to do crosswords (5)
16 One wanders round Turin, misbehaving a little bit (8)
18 Prisoner elected to last position on board (6)
21 Like boring book, French one about a duke (6)
23 Understood Italy abandoned diplomacy (4)
25 Neeson picked up paper (4)

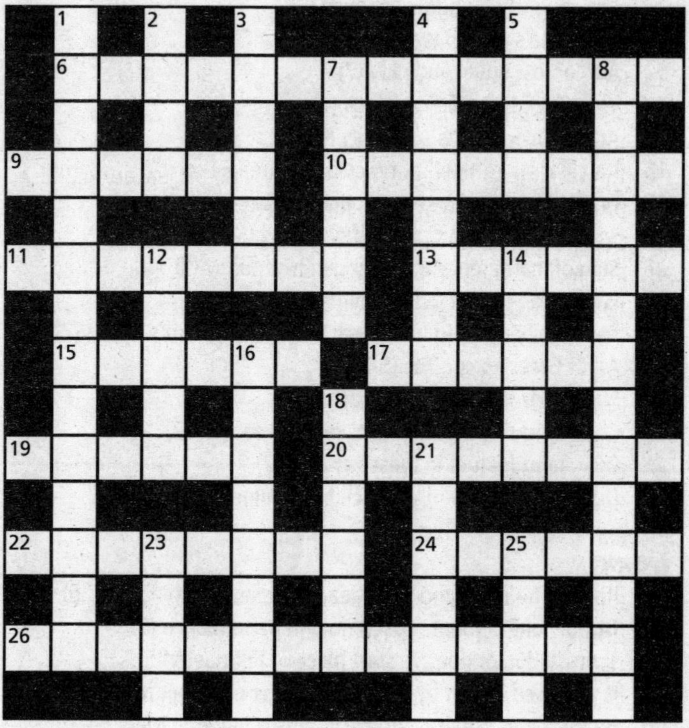
1
2
3
4
5
6
7
8
9
10
11
12
13
14
15
16
17
18
19
20
21
22
23
24
25
26

142

Across

1 He's mourning after treatment in private hospital (7,4)
9 It's used to copy letters from irritated clients (7)
10 Any thug can be badly behaved (7)
11 Cleopatra's poison was contained in it (3)
12 Author lost novel and play (7)
13 View duck then clip its wings (7)
14 Age of Queen Anne originally (3)
15 It's clear it's somewhat ridiculous on reflection (5)
17 Understood diplomacy surrounding Italy (5)
18 Source of Sanskrit signs half obscured (5)
20 Sign of indifference appearing in Irish rugby (5)
22 English king collected 50 animals (3)
24 Part of score played with Bach's last and Mozart's Third? (7)
25 Adult Greek to confess (5-2)
26 Inlet starts in Rhode Island area (3)
27 Quavering solo trumpet puts out this sound? (7)
28 Prominent feature in West's engine (7)
29 Doing the laundry in yacht club in Leningrad maybe (3-8)

Down

1 Require trained hand with treadle for sewing things (6,3,6)
2 Out-of-tune clarinet missed note in performance (7)
3 Scottish doctor doesn't start piece of marquetry (5)
4 It was used in plot by German prisoner-of-war in Neath (9)
5 He examines pupils customarily, busily ignoring Mary (7)
6 Dreadfully clannish genetic crime of Balkans war (6,9)
7 Fly groups during half-term (6)
8 Extremely canny gannet rejects an immature bird (6)
16 Cuban leader's got old; the Italian offers remedy (6,3)
18 Obtain situation outside, where it should be (2,4)
19 Hurried, therefore tucked into hot food (7)
21 They're in soup in Rome or Cochin cooked after midnight (7)
23 Captain's heading off for fish (6)
25 Ray's third letter from Athens (5)

143

Across

1 Complaint from Asiatic rotten with cold (8)
5 Bun, say, in musical party (6)
9 Flood could give us a treat otherwise (8)
10 Attractive woman goes to work for lump (6)
12 Satellite's low on horizon at last (4)
13 People yearn inwardly for their possessions (10)
15 Doctor, angry, confused, loses rag initially with green (13)
19 Doctor Nicholas urges self-analysis (4-9)
23 Agree to keep alternative trade mark in mixture (10)
25 Middle East ruler provides energy to space station (4)
28 The incomplete ethnic group in old country (6)
29 Vehicle second to tractor sadly forfeits time (5,3)
30 Person who writes cheque goes back for profit (6)
31 E.g. balloonist devised a route round North America (8)

Down

1 Open this, it's said, to enter seed plant (6)
2 Some paint rooms and bars at the outset (5)
3 Exhaust, say, or other part of car (4)
4 Middle-of-the-road gemstone (4-3)
6 Forward note in a record (5)
7 Slackening fast during harsh reign (9)
8 Facing work on river location (8)
11 Dominant old London district (4)
14 Our responsibility and where it lies (4)
15 It secures joint, maybe curbs increased pinching (4,5)
16 Former police force raised dog (3)
17 It implies silence for god (4)
18 Inquire about king in Far East shambles (3,5)
20 Girl rings royal host (4)
21 Suggest traffic deterrent's not introduced (7)
22 Conservative rises to support doctor in attack on House (3,3)
24 Come up again about 16 (5)
26 Hundreds fill Middle East area – this city perhaps (5)
27 Game in swimming pool (4)

144

Across

1 Strong words assist retired family (8)
5 Article by sibling helps to a degree maybe (6)
9 Celebration's flying start in the summer in US (8)
10 Signal to warn pilot in old airline trick (6)
12 Run into police gathering first bit of evidence (4)
13 Man, thespian, arrests female criminal (10)
15 Collapse and pine about unhealthy oviduct (9,4)
19 Cold axed new activity plans about start of Yule events then (8,5)
23 Non-European catechism is disputed, causing split (10)
25 5-to-4 against first exam (4)
28 Bruised crania? Get plant extract (6)
29 Parasitic growth, one in fine fruit (3,5)
30 Elegant English liner with no water about (6)
31 Disease is physical, releasing calcium, degenerating (8)

Down

1 Fed up with writer following a slander (6)
2 Passage is swamped by drink (5)
3 Drops artist at home (4)
4 Well done securing commercial! It shows courage (7)
6 Spotted one in Kenya maybe, heading off for hotel (5)
7 They can make easy cutters, pruning thorny ends (9)
8 Red top forgets words for various items (8)
11 Type of house millions possess (4)
14 Someone from Serbia, say, docked menial worker (4)
15 Can a chef perhaps hold teaspoonful? Not a hope (3,6)
16 Reward secretary at end of May (3)
17 Strangely, Hanoi's not got one original skipper (4)
18 Author took dips here in tanks rebuilt at Land's End (8)
20 Where to sell up urban transport (4)
21 School look into reserving first of March (7)
22 Stroke alarms beginning to last (6)
24 Gets rid of bags (5)
26 Drive mile the wrong way – parking's restricted (5)
27 Frame made from first bit of soft wood (4)

145

Across

1 Minister's Irish gear (7)
5 Cryptic clue about unknown male in theatre, perhaps (6)
9 Tattooist perhaps solved murder involving money (7)
10 Torn denims: teenager's primary train of thought? (7)
11 Tree has decayed (3)
12 Poor report has everyone with overdraft backing OPEC money (11)
13 Huge amounts of money but not for melodies (5)
14 Cyrus briefly wears eyeglass doing tricks on this? (9)
16 Cash collection with trendy circular (9)
17 Man from Copenhagen hosts sort of square old poet (5)
19 Dutifully meet them and a biologist working round north (11)
22 Policeman returns to seize ring? That's him (3)
23 Stretcher – last one in our community (7)
24 Pudding, one in a pot, stirred around (7)
26 Doctor hears about oxygen on beach (6)
27 Serious crime and its central cause (7)

Down

1 Intensely happy, Nadia melted in Rupert's arms (7)
2 English composer developed via Mulligan and Shaw (7,8)
3 Odd tot (3)
4 Bird in Spain, large, not adult (5)
5 Made fun of boy carrying on in silly poem (9)
6 Roman consul defended new section of 17's work (5)
7 Scotch uncles of cousins not easily embarrassed (15)
8 What some may do if all but start of harvest's devastated (6)
12 Model's tough question (5)
14 Eat so much it gets in a mess? (9)
15 Gives up some choice desserts (5)
16 Stiff and awkward on stage made of 11 (6)
18 Give reasons for former scheme I had (7)
20 Reach slum Henry abandoned (3,2)
21 Group turning up in concert etc. occasionally (5)
25 Regularly spoiled dish (3)

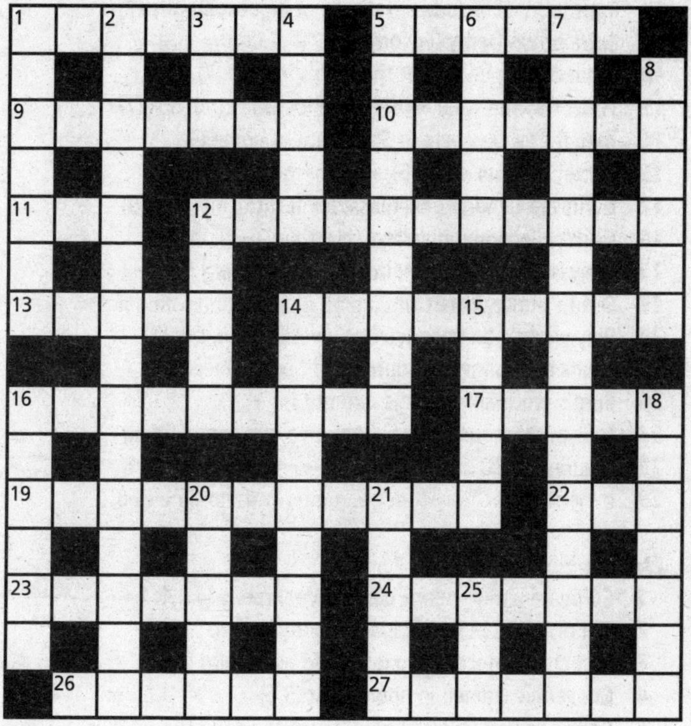

146

Across

1 Drink mineral in a nice jug, stirred? (6,5)
9 Teach me to fly in chopper (7)
10 International includes everyone of highest stature (7)
11 Extra run in Derby (Epsom) (3)
12 It guards the finger but the limb's injured (7)
13 What US men wear loosely interlocked? Lord, no! (7)
14 Take the waters here in Spain, not at home (3)
15 Blimey! Soldier's pet (5)
17 Dodgy salesman holds recipe for fish (5)
18 Writer is absorbing extremely special religion (5)
20 Imagine mother entertaining army regiment (5)
22 Song's atmosphere (3)
24 Playwright's on holiday after investigation, say (7)
25 Trains here, showing support for Spurs' chief (7)
26 Euro's precursor to some extent (3)
27 Toils away around Central America, not complaining (7)
28 Maureen is 10 and wet (7)
29 In general, picnics often get ruined with no time (3-8)

Down

1 Cultivate a nine-ounce bloom? Very rarely (4,2,1,4,4)
2 Old distiller's retort: "I blame faulty carbon" (7)
3 Last chunk of iceberg overturned water bird (5)
4 Get Jennie trained in power unit (3,6)
5 Chilli's served up less hot? It's not allowed (7)
6 Geocentric metal fluctuates in this sort of field? (15)
7 Old strikes created terrible mess across Italy (6)
8 Houses here and trees scattered around square (6)
16 Peer loved unfortunately to demolish and rebuild (9)
18 Where jewellery's kept, in the event that … (2,4)
19 … Monica has top of hair all done in this style? (7)
21 I'm upset doctor provided female diaphragm (7)
23 Mind gift being unopened? (6)
25 French writer raised tree (5)

147

Across

1 Income from it keeps *Mail* in the driving seat perhaps (11)
9 1930s' fashion ruined trade with small firm (3,4)
10 Rich fabric used in British version of timeless 9 (7)
11 Occasionally strike match (3)
12 Yankee typefaces cover top-of-the-range underwear (1-6)
13 Maybe Keats returned to drink a quiet cuppa here (7)
14 It ensures fish reproduce in odd places in Rhone (3)
15 Crop I found in Hampton Court attraction (5)
17 He introduces many comedians fully (5)
18 Do try to hold gang leader still (5)
20 Greasy stuff in weapon, say, after retreat (5)
22 Tree left in big space (3)
24 Learnt to dismantle front of neon light (7)
25 No one's upset after old tax gets huge acclaim (7)
26 Roadhouse's trendy name (3)
27 Rent-a-party jet? (7)
28 Dish colonial type before princess retires (7)
29 New rector drops in version of early Paternoster (5,6)

Down

1 Top 7 worked on treaty with top soldier (8,7)
2 Country where six million live round a volcano (7)
3 Grass too rich? These get pulled up near the middle (5)
4 Meanwhile, at home, Ben receives short message (2,7)
5 Is duck (sort of teal) in quarantine? (7)
6 Artist, in hedging prices, bankrupt illustrator (7,8)
7 E.g. person working in 26 with hen running round (6)
8 Shirley's place of worship (6)
16 Clever old Dean's intelligence enthralled island (9)
18 Scrub allowed in river (6)
19 Duck and swan? Perfect recipe for outside (4,3)
21 Demand fifty at very end? Spot on (7)
23 He's crazy to falsify main account (6)
25 It's bliss walking here when the red light shows? (2,3)

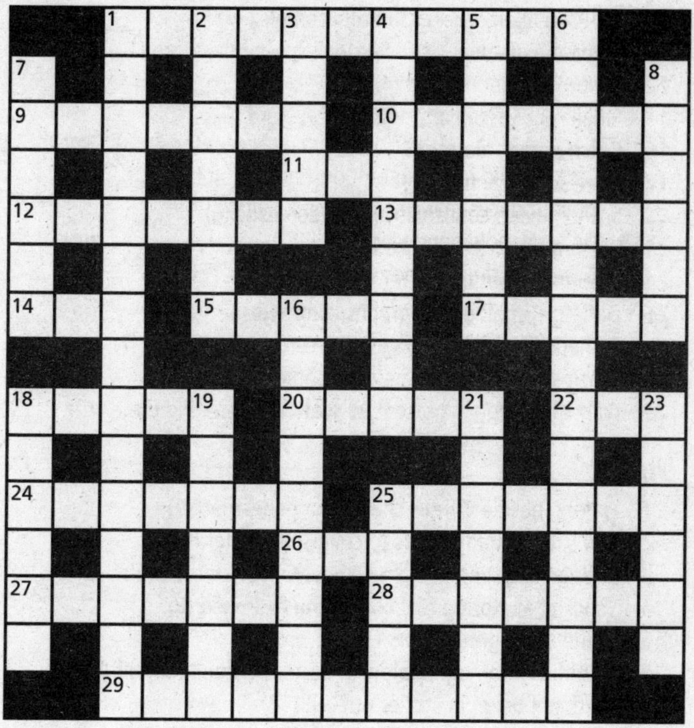

148

Across

1 New tutor's page includes ad about PhD course, say (12)
8 Perfect section of impromptu to pianist (7)
9 It's used in emergency in hotel complex (7)
11 In middle of speech evil Svengali spread the word (10)
12 Prison? It's about right (4)
14 Small rock tossed into Isle of Man ward (8)
16 Catch parent blotto (6)
17 Seize some cannabis (3)
19 Scandinavian country loses top domestic (6)
21 Eastern dish I take cooked with regular fruity contents (8)
24 Mountain goat in central Tibet's unknown (4)
25 Darling's small article probes controversial star (10)
27 Perhaps Muswell Hill vagrant secures one element (7)
28 It helps diabetic at home after endless abuse (7)
29 I'd hosted various presenters scattered here and there (12)

Down

1 Parking beside Cairo's chaotic for pedestrian (7)
2 Reg singing badly leads to childish laughter (10)
3 Strange lingo inhibits a new government nerve centre (8)
4 Shocked at storing fuel containing hydrogen (6)
5 Doing some group tours (2,2)
6 Potentially damaging blow in US for pontoon player? (7)
7 Irrational belief in stories put out (12)
10 Like shrieks from girl patients being massaged? (3-9)
13 An old tax on sibling? Quite the opposite (10)
15 It's meant occasionally to welcome visitors (3)
18 Living in church cooking nice beef (8)
20 Told fibs about having week's rest (3,4)
22 Helped adult live with a fractious daughter (7)
23 Son was entertaining MP in wetlands (6)
26 British president's personal transport (4)

149

Across

1 Small course organised as sweetener (7)
5 Puzzle's misleading in game (6)
9 Drive worried MEP wearing shabby suit (7)
10 First parts of speech in old radio broadcast (7)
11 It's at the door and is meant to be used regularly (3)
12 A bishop commandeers my workplace for general, say (4,7)
13 Hotel in Ruhr taken over by the French king (5)
14 Lee drinks unwisely and gets lit up again (9)
16 A small stake in Ascot goes wrong; he takes the blame (9)
17 Poisonous exotic confection zapping energy (5)
19 Thoughtful prisoners angry about odd parts of diet (11)
22 Either way, she's quiet (3)
23 Power failure across river creates extreme anger (7)
24 Anne and Henry, say, returned to hellish place (7)
26 Area multiplied by 10 in Egypt (6)
27 Made an arrangement and issued instructions (7)

Down

1 Over a short length hers somehow glisten (7)
2 Levy to cover computers etc. against a mistake left in (7,5,3)
3 Choose time after work (3)
4 Keep some horses stabled here (5)
5 Part of skull – I give it a thump during speech (3,6)
6 Error on table at home and on holiday (2-3)
7 US doctor mistreated mad Crimean exile (7,8)
8 Tusked animal seen in western Urals possibly? No (6)
12 A person from Athens almost gives consent (5)
14 President (Republican) loves to broadcast about Spain (9)
15 Gunpowder ingredient may be rendered inert (5)
16 Part of torn corset (6)
18 Order CND to store shells upside down (7)
20 Picture or representation of 5 Across with no name (5)
21 Leaders of a gang go round organising violence (5)
25 House 500 bricks in it? (3)

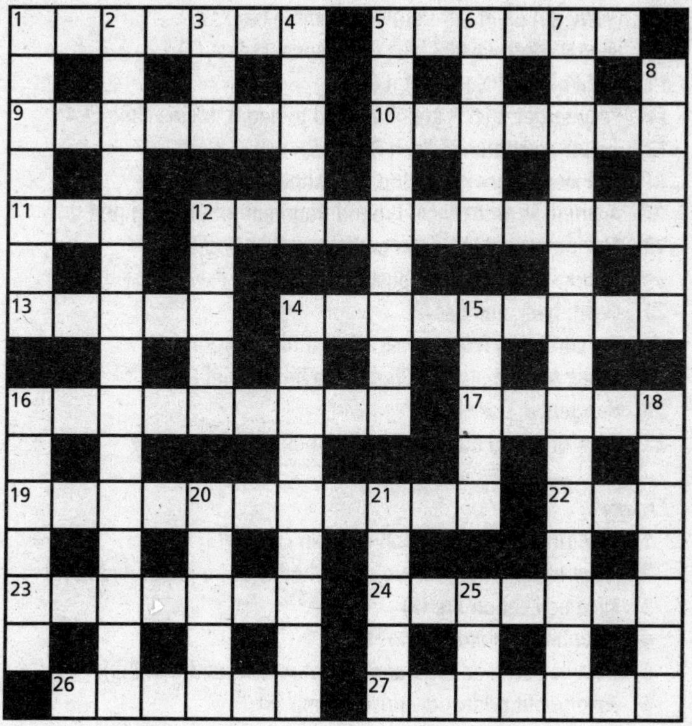

150

Across

1 Pair start to translate short verse (7)
5 Robust goods sealed bargain (6)
9 Feisty girl dealt differently with three banks (7)
10 Wordy controversial blue book appears first (7)
11 Spoil planet? Not all of it (3)
12 Easy target: Dick's gun managed to bag it, taking time (7,4)
13 Colour in stretch of Loch Restil (5)
14 Sail into eddies round top of Orkney alone in it (9)
16 A towrope gets tangled round Bournemouth launch (9)
17 Marine mammal's more exciting in East End, say (5)
19 Almost finish off GP's business supporter (11)
22 Catch back number (3)
23 It's correct to release tension in athletic ground (7)
24 Priest trained nurses (English) to bring relief (7)
26 Bangers in boxes (6)
27 Trick group to adopt new agreement (7)

Down

1 Pass ring to criminal mob in Asian capital (7)
2 After terrible thunder we're crushed with heat, poorly (5,3,7)
3 Nice bed set on fire (3)
4 How birds communicate? (5)
5 How to settle an argument about rotten tooth? (4,2,3)
6 Joke about oddly ugly prison camp (5)
7 Party with seven in it maybe, not computerised? (6-9)
8 Spent week installing a new sink (6)
12 Slander some loveless Arab (5)
14 Triangle I see LSO played touring small capitals (9)
15 Pain almost vanished inside a year (5)
16 Punch, for instance, set to entertain very quiet earl (6)
18 Withdraw duo, leaving trade route in chaos (7)
20 It's implied writer's constrained by discretion (5)
21 Billy Richardson owns theatre in Hammersmith (5)
25 Number not good for boy (3)

151

Across

6 "British girl hurt Daniel here!" seen on page 1? (6,8)
9 NASA in dispute with EU? It makes you sick (6)
10 Turn away a false story about Etna exploding (8)
11 RA members *in loco parentis* (8)
13 Right-winger persuaded no one to engage Cuba (3-3)
15 Find old furry animal trapped by the French (6)
17 It senses images in middle of 11, distorted (6)
19 Girl inhabiting strange land (6)
20 Act with subtlety, sacking trainee to cut wages (8)
22 County defeat American giant (8)
24 Snifters with or without rare ingredient (6)
26 Occupy unit, winning smashing prizes in tax-exempt area (10,4)

Down

1 A bad actor enlisted support on green for Booth's victim (7,7)
2 Where America's responsibility lies (4)
3 Gender of iron man? (6)
4 One in ten in step in operetta (8)
5 Extended family can include 50 (4)
7 Trained a horse and husky (6)
8 Patriotic song composed by Leo in Manhattan (8,6)
12 Lustrous substance found in new area (5)
14 It may make chair more comfy when its top's removed (5)
16 Section of church collapsed in ten parts (8)
18 At last you slim drastically eating energy breakfast (6)
21 Some lines may be hurried (6)
23 Bowling stint's finished (4)
25 It's played by top blower at regular intervals (4)

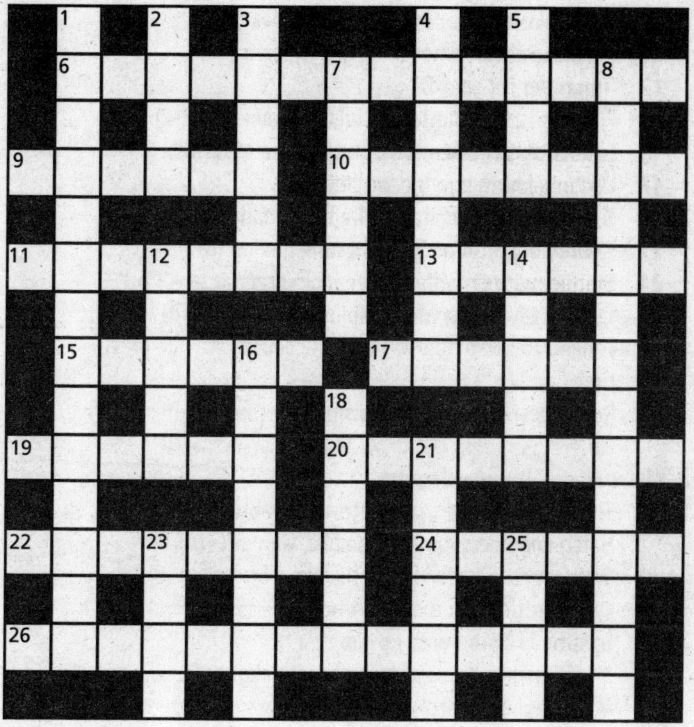

1
2
3
4
5
6
7
8
9
10
11
12
13
14
15
16
17
18
19
20
21
22
23
24
25
26

152

Across

1 Verge ought to have tougher covering (4,8)
8 Crowded together as comedian Roy went ahead (7)
9 Speak like an actor in medical complex (7)
11 Translate alien names of Pacific islander (10)
12 Firm order for car (4)
14 "Cheers" also entertained lots interminably (6-2)
16 Extract of gall takes some beating – almost (6)
17 Doctor's know-how's unlimited (3)
19 First-born in Leeds trained by team-leader (6)
21 Temporarily lose cycle in a simple mix-up (8)
24 Marine growth contained in zoological gardens (4)
25 Continually bothered to display due respect (10)
27 Longed to swap quarters when accounts are due (4-3)
28 First sign (7)
29 Rose doesn't fancy holding small part, cutlery item (7,5)

Down

1 Spanish gentleman kept secret gaol abroad (7)
2 Harsh engineers loaned a smaller amount (10)
3 Swedish comic keeps duck as minor attraction (8)
4 People suffer it in the gold trade (6)
5 Fortune in bottle with no top … (4)
6 … likewise aunt, say, shows sheer delight (7)
7 Man, unknown, accepts English mum's drug treatment (12)
10 Former heart-throbs repaired old amenities (7,5)
13 Cold cuppa's sent up with bent coin for hot drink (10)
15 Old monarch shows little sign of resistance (3)
18 Outerwear ordinary seaman has woven in silk (8)
20 Short degree comes across these days as lower quality (7)
22 Tropical insect's surprisingly not in LA (7)
23 Salesman drove off carrying note (6)
26 They provide access to low-lying islands (4)

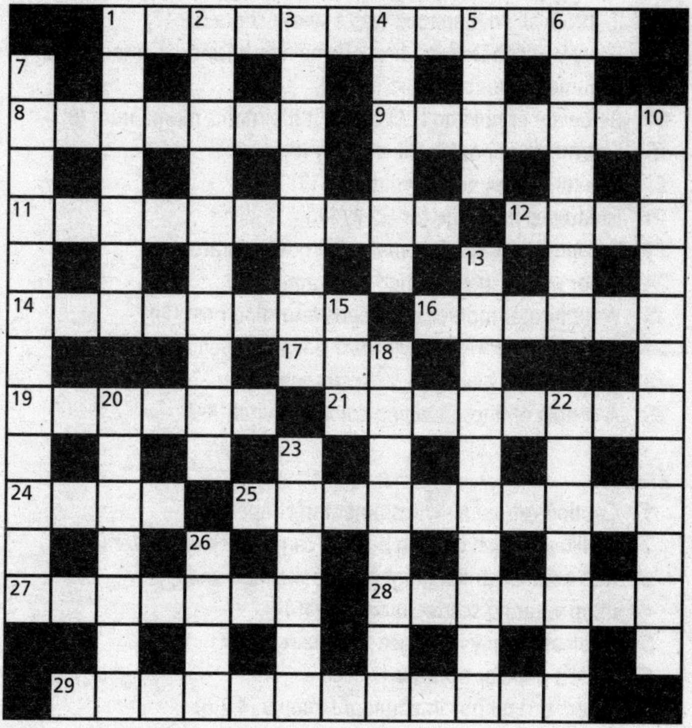

153

Across

1 What's played in Bach Summer in Cork initially? (7,5)
8 Aural pain returns to Algeria (not the very centre) (7)
9 In 2000, all I'd managed was a water container (7)
11 Harry went to Dorking first off, making business contacts (10)
12 Argument about small strikes (4)
14 Be aware of holding back hwyl: it maintains momentum (8)
16 Left article in pool in the country (6)
17 Cut stone gleams intermittently (3)
19 Isolated cryptic clue for Lily? (6)
21 I covered wounded woman who got separated (8)
24 Tenor nearly spent tenner, for example (4)
25 Westminster mother, say, keeps returning post (10)
27 My turn to tackle faulty radar? Sailors depend on it (7)
28 Lady's room, black one with strange odour about (7)
29 A couple of lines meaning colonist's vital (3-9)

Down

1 Cautious about New Testament in chapel (7)
2 He likes English galleon built to carry Greek character (10)
3 He's against striking highest snooker ball on (8)
4 Chap wearing scarlet in custody (6)
5 Unpleasant guy managed to obtain Lira (4)
6 State's popular princess (7)
7 Woodland fungus in abundant supply (4,2,6)
10 After main road, unfortunate hazard creates accident (12)
13 Carol's mad to take a tour working as opera singer (10)
15 Small light source was at the front (3)
18 Labour leader rejects N. Dakota Republican pressure (8)
20 Unforced 24 (7)
22 Main character's in bed, smoking this? (7)
23 Prepare for contest with weapon in the air? (4,2)
26 Munro initially seemed a kind individual (4)

154

Across

1 Fine hake is mashed with clubs into patty (8)
5 Artist works in tight space (6)
9 Disney's characters dance in writer's imagination (5,3)
10 Basket-maker's illicit affair (6)
12 What's left after drinking in Yorkshire city day out? (4)
13 Pseudonym in foreign menu has old MEP baffled (3,2,5)
15 Inn is wrecked with 11 and 12 automotive units (6,7)
19 Tibet pact held after relocating planned fight (7,6)
23 This scarab's horrible, but legend around Egypt (4,6)
25 Bacon supplier has time to put away … (4)
28 … meat dog's taking regularly (6)
29 Entry condition of a posh girl with sex appeal? I'm in (3,5)
30 Circle of light and smoke (6)
31 Tick off handsome chap entertaining Mike and Henry (8)

Down

1 Social group edit a film with happy ending (6)
2 Scorch part of housing estate (5)
3 What's the point in hauling up some lumpsuckers? (4)
4 Declared complete support for vital type of surgery (7)
6 Some go over to collect money for vagrant (5)
7 Wealth distributed with it could be ineffectual (9)
8 Cross party-goers note guards (8)
11 The landed gentry have an advantage (4)
14 Yours truly's quiet engagement? (4)
15 Note: wheel spun around, operating explosive device (9)
16 Shot by Lendl or Becker in their primes? (3)
17 Multi-millionaire Bill cut opening (4)
18 Moore's in blockbuster film that makes many ill (8)
20 Eat less in parliament (4)
21 Angry de Gaulle, ignoring union, made accusation (7)
22 Whip wag in school (6)
24 Ex-PM's name on forehead (5)
26 Primarily each musician in pit struggles to keep them (5)
27 Voice requiring some special tonality (4)

155

Across

6 What better tool for adjusting heater? (3-5,6)
9 Bigger billet housed one of the Desert Rats (6)
10 Rory misbehaved in extension, giving concern (8)
11 At end of eighties playwright penned Latin fragment (8)
13 Spoil writer's secretary, Irish (6)
15 What millions of bugs do in forest or elsewhere (6)
17 Wooziness of traveller let loose in fast car (3,3)
19 Deny food to a republican in shabby vest (6)
20 Rear of formal dress agitated a coal-tit (4-4)
22 Buy and sell bananas to English? Spot on (5-3)
24 Insignificant friend's 5 points at Murrayfield (6)
26 Missing curate found on ground clutching cycle (11,3)

Down

1 Manoeuvre put entire North off (5-5,4)
2 Try lifting clubs (4)
3 Keep notes in it, every one of them soaked? (6)
4 It's fruitless to play excellent vibrato (8)
5 Stop small Scottish river (4)
7 King misguidedly dared to entertain women (6)
8 Drilling nearby ruined local amenity (7,7)
12 Conclude there's no escaping hell (5)
14 First five of politicians spoiled trial programme (5)
16 Leek's not cooked to provide my support (8)
18 Sieve loose stones at bottom of mountain (6)
21 Fruit: apparently heaps I ignored (6)
23 Secure section of canal (4)
25 Officer keeps providing free ride (4)

156

Across

6 Management isn't worried when held in high regard (14)
9 Doctor's right about fungal problem (3,3)
10 Navy buddy steams away after me (8)
11 Series about new church conserving Italian grass (8)
13 A pile of snow's at the mercy of the wind (6)
15 For a Tory not taking sides, he's a good speaker (6)
17 Shirley nearly prepared piquant sauce (6)
19 Initially early February garden party is affected (6)
20 Account that keeps audience wondering what comes next? (8)
22 Small bed available without charge (4-4)
24 Major work takes time in circus venue (3,3)
26 Tiptop scanner designed for teeth – it's beyond belief (14)

Down

1 Wild speech in War Office rare for RSM, say (7,7)
2 Somewhat random Arab name (4)
3 Beat up in school robbery (6)
4 Various cameras catch royal superpower contest (4,4)
5 Cat chases a tiny particle (4)
7 A few stand round British grave (6)
8 Very impressive flour withstood cooking (3,2,4,5)
12 Head of Thames event leaving footprint, say (5)
14 Generate foul air over Kent and Sussex (5)
16 Like obsessive mind in sort of trance, fine outwardly (3-5)
18 A 7 in boat's wake (6)
21 14 states worried best part of larger group (6)
23 Very small beer in Australia lacks heart (4)
25 Barrier's not high in north London area (4)

157

Across

1 No more jumping golf balls lost here? (3,2,6)
9 Conservative MP's tall tree (7)
10 Cover for photographer's normal in nasty places (4,3)
11 Year abroad in Georgia and Portugal (3)
12 Genuine problem for young actress (7)
13 Managed a big orchestra first but not a winner (4-3)
14 Plan 11 with money for German (3)
15 Having a slight figure and somewhat self-interested (5)
17 There are blades on it moving in either direction (5)
18 Hard to penetrate, needs to be deciphered (5)
20 Harry tries to take paper again (5)
22 Top's cold apparently (3)
24 Characteristic of 12, came last in vanity perhaps (7)
25 Flooring which, in Paris, has some protection (7)
26 Drink imported in crate (Assam?) (3)
27 Butch girl lives in borders of Monmouth (7)
28 Technicians stop filming hairstyle (4,3)
29 Music style infuriated Lord Clark? No (4,3,4)

Down

1 He was, when working, no idle personage! (3,3,9)
2 No truce arranged, so thrash (7)
3 Falsify sweet stuff (5)
4 Old doddery pianist has left artist's materials (3,6)
5 He doesn't employ abstract nouns with hesitation (3-4)
6 UN top brass work circuitously with centre? Not half (8,7)
7 It's obvious: somehow I must allow in radical (6)
8 Prone perhaps to conserve energy, like Strauss? (6)
16 Shrub's soft and airy, dispersed around hospital (9)
18 Monday's no good for this bundle of energy (6)
19 Mournful European translated Gaelic (7)
21 Weapon in submarine or in specialised depot (7)
23 Crisp material brought up by Scot at opening (6)
25 Had a brisk walk, with due respect to director (5)

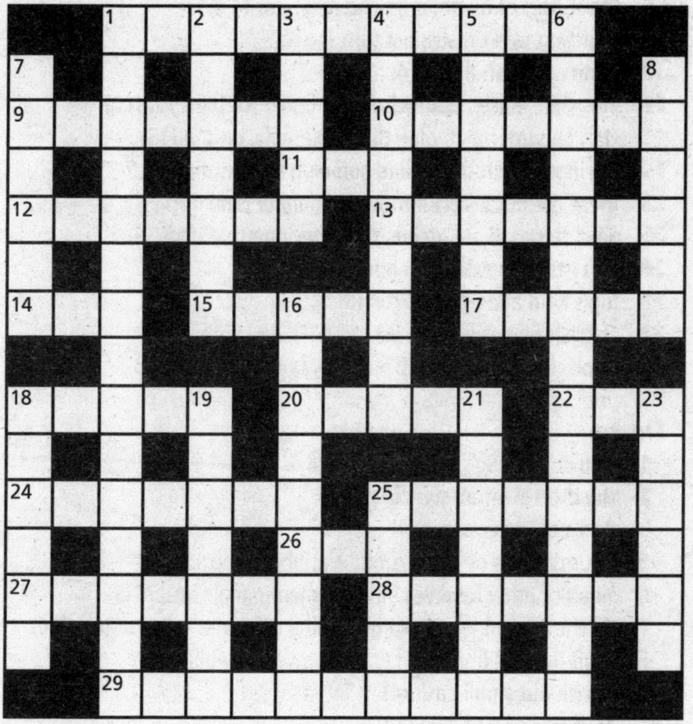
1 2 3 4 5 6 7 8 9 10 11 12 13 14 15 16 17 18 19 20 21 22 23 24 25 26 27 28 29

158

Across

1 Prompt action in Special Protection Area in channel (8)
5 Clever chap parks a vehicle in street (6)
9 Plant, sort of allium enjoying rare year (4,4)
10 Sanction raid on suspect (6)
12 Notice English agent (4)
13 This CEO makes photochemical liquid for the eyes (10)
15 Official statement: glue it, for example, on top (13)
19 Barrister wasted no clues pursuing NI university (6,7)
23 Water protects very soft part of larynx (5,5)
25 Hear it initially in orchestra before overture ends (4)
28 Girl lies nervously clutching old book (6)
29 Sign with a sting in its tail (8)
30 English flower festival (6)
31 Look closely at big ship – it may bring out pupils (8)

Down

1 Dull cul-de-sac's not complete (6)
2 Big drop in small swelling (5)
3 Rod's ten beer cases (4)
4 County hosts new plays and Caribbean music (7)
6 Head of army reserves held his men in main vessel (5)
7 Danger signal in marble hall going off: hotel's evacuated (5,4)
8 Awfully neat financial centre shows stickability (8)
11 Knock out small cask (4)
14 Fluff this sort of clue? (4)
15 A sport designed to involve bloody carnivores (9)
16 Mystery vehicle uses some biofuel up (3)
17 Queen's left feeling ill? No problem (4)
18 A sequel's planned, I gathered, to achieve balance (8)
20 A priest in church makes long garment (4)
21 A French girl swallows potassium? That's unfortunate (7)
22 Note singer's broadcast (6)
24 Spanish golfer tackles one riddle (5)
26 Child's melody in borders of Brigadoon (5)
27 Examination by dentist or a lecturer (4)

159

Across

1 Single woman cuts back short-term (8)
5 Second stroke produces illegible script (6)
9 Snack in the morning in Greek island area (5,3)
10 Press magnate cut off small river for dam builder (6)
12 Bank really lacks heart (4)
13 I am upset: nurse takes care of meat and 2 veg? (4,6)
15 Tall crop – a spear's length possibly (8,5)
19 A piano agent carries one fancy metal about (13)
23 Torch student has broken during escape (10)
25 Programmer has returned book (4)
28 Right to film fish in African country (6)
29 Protester adjusts limit on worker (8)
30 Referee endlessly goes off for a smoke (6)
31 Smile wryly about rioting mob – it blocks vessel (8)

Down

1 Make fast rescue after crash (6)
2 Perfect description of his job by croupier? (5)
3 All quiet in reservoir (4)
4 English pair of trees? Nonsense (7)
6 Mediocre doctrine's helping belief (5)
7 Notice very engaging star has no time for opponent (9)
8 Big son starts to show everyone generosity (8)
11 Churchman's heading off soon (4)
14 Woman's love for great man (4)
15 Enjoy sea air here – and a sleep perhaps (9)
16 Writer's supporting one point (3)
17 George, King of Spain, short-lived ruler (4)
18 Traveller surprisingly wary about ticket (8)
20 People in Dublin cut her (4)
21 Lack of faith in them is a failing (7)
22 Combatants potentially include Scot and this bird (6)
24 It shelters garden border behind hospital (5)
26 I'm 16, brought up in US city (5)
27 At first Ken is less obese, more than 2 lbs. (4)

160

Across

1 This Ulsterman's loud pattern (7)
5 Lets top off gibbet (6)
9 Brief account is said to be warm usually (7)
10 Sailor's allowed to eat sort of square little pie (7)
11 Protracted conflict with gunners in retreat (3)
12 Reorganise fresh rest-cure having got in sort of rut (11)
13 Rule's good when it's kept in check (5)
14 Mr. Dawson's trained to be someone like D'Artagnan (9)
16 She's one of the clan, like Nell Gwyn, say, but not grand (9)
17 A taste of tofu seems to be advantageous (2,3)
19 Hostile attack could be anytime once it's broadcast (5,6)
22 Yank suddenly starts taking up golf (3)
23 Mesmerise, then fancy really only now and again (7)
24 Joe's in pub being reasonable (7)
26 Some stars gather round head of state for prayer (6)
27 See exciting news on Sunday? It's covered (7)

Down

1 Port was rebuilt after 1945, say (4-3)
2 Irish anemometer could be a source of hot water (9,6)
3 Terminological inexactitude finally traps one? Nonsense! (3)
4 Twice you haven't finished with son's playthings (2-3)
5 Time to prepare for tea, hosting new cricket side (9)
6 Billy Richardson's too much for London theatre (5)
7 It may be a wet oscular mush after getting tiddly (6,9)
8 Some initially went wild guzzling royal spread (6)
12 Freshen up Frenchman at end of show (5)
14 Mark's monocle is broken (9)
15 Former SDP leader had no energy in flood (5)
16 Zoo employee sounds like crucial person? Not half (6)
18 Sail over into treacherous fens and swamps (7)
20 Measures, say, taken up to protect road (5)
21 Relative in Wales receives note (2-3)
25 Obtained green tea, say (3)

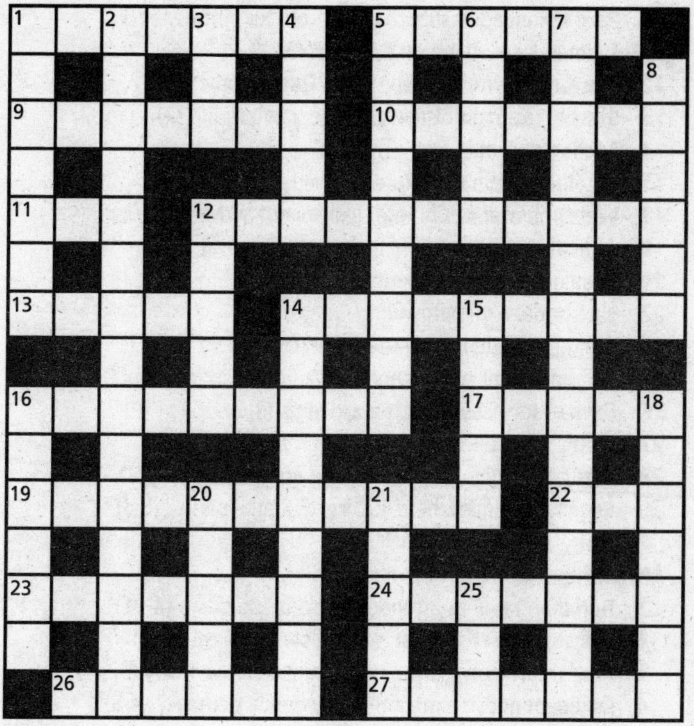

161

Across

1 Pity Mac's upset about article that's likeable (11)
9 Banking's third in line in retail development (7)
10 An oil blended in suburbs of Lincoln for ointment (7)
11 Woman loses daughter's deposit (3)
12 The King's awfully sleepy when Queen comes in (7)
13 Start of rattling noise in carriage going round (7)
14 Section of arable area (3)
15 Capital of Siam not entirely ruined (5)
17 Wet supporter of Chinese leader's not active (5)
18 Animal brandished horn – I'm impressed (5)
20 Rose nearly hugs students in big car (5)
22 Nap or doze primarily (3)
24 Changes made in a disheartened country school (7)
25 Self-important old member tucked into exotic soup (7)
26 Back or forth, some of it backwards (3)
27 Remit cheque to French pal for arty paperwork (7)
28 Less colourful way of working in Mediterranean port (7)
29 Registration mark here incorrect? Blame punter (6,5)

Down

1 No Texan families arranged personal check-up (4-11)
2 Illness with selfsame shivers fellow's shaken off (7)
3 Play's rewritten to mask tension in a suitable way (5)
4 Object of quest: extremely hairy gorilla perhaps? (4,5)
5 Instant rumblings about this childish outburst (7)
6 Colonel Lake is on route, I assumed; it'll end in crash (9,6)
7 Push strong cord into place (6)
8 He searched for 4 man on board (6)
16 Over fifty broke old record (5-4)
18 It's about a child's motive (6)
19 How to bowl six balls to a marine? (7)
21 Old African country in South Africa? No, in NE Africa (7)
23 Autocrat's son captured in warehouse (6)
25 Work? Smug young man's bound to appear (3-2)

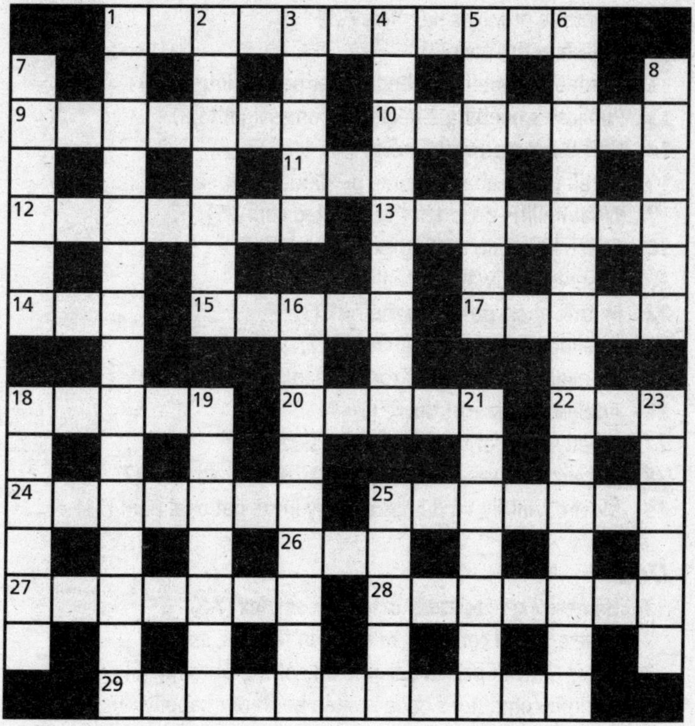

162

Across

1 Millions spread over Australia after firm British policy (11)
9 Old, I must somehow overcome women to win in pool (7)
10 Favourite granny's hairpiece? (7)
11 A bash in the past (3)
12 Trumpet maybe faded badly after perfect intro (4,3)
13 Publican's opening 2 beers; this one's light (4,3)
14 Unit concerned with energy (3)
15 Recall praise about Charlie or about Philip, say (5)
17 What bailiffs do when I've rejected court (5)
18 Coach keeps on getting extra money (5)
20 Observed ordinary journalist? (5)
22 Imitate short person in the nick (3)
24 Shaking a box for the Archers? (7)
25 Do over American workroom, heading off (7)
26 Adolescents start trouble (3)
27 Creative sort of thinking on the side (7)
28 A French Shakespearian king overcomes cold faint (7)
29 Most cowardly 14 dumps ecstasy in US national park (11)

Down

1 Homeworkers to study catering complex (7,8)
2 Wise old bird comes in to settle in Norfolk, say (7)
3 Actor Matt tipped to become one of the Drifters? (5)
4 Cockpit computer's dodgy oiltap holds out happily (9)
5 One million beans, for example, produce sudden urge (7)
6 Chap hands in rice maybe at end of June, using this language? (8,7)
7 50000 circle 500 in Caribbean cult (6)
8 It's still a part of theatre's tradition (2,4)
16 Funny cartoon about officer and singer (9)
18 Prankster Jeremy, parish official (6)
19 More than a few very nearly implicated in bung (7)
21 Actually died before old-time restaurant went up (2,5)
23 Have a go, starting with US writer's verses (6)
25 People and what they stand on, they say (5)

163

Across

1 TT rider, second to start race with 151 in the bag (12)
8 Um, rodent in charge is unpredictable (7)
9 A fool acquired new place in Belgium (7)
11 Are police clad differently for such a petty crime? (10)
12 Salvation Army man nearly gets the sack (4)
14 Finish tennis games with not much space in between (5-3)
16 Snow vehicle initially shows little advantage (6)
17 One of the 19 caught in traffic (3)
19 Crumbling fresco is compelling (6)
21 Herd cattle on ship, showing lack of sensitivity (8)
24 Increase in morale if officer's about (4)
25 Skin problem threatens to spread over top of leg (6,4)
27 Awfully rough time after variable dairy product (7)
28 A wicked habit hides a rare deadly sin (7)
29 Face sterling collapse taking this sort of holiday? (4-8)

Down

1 Bookbinder's covering old volume in untidy room (7)
2 It's got four feet to wobble around streetcar (10)
3 Radio this accountant to arrive after firm goes bust? (8)
4 Peer into the unknown twice every 12 months (6)
5 Many items in sale (4)
6 Compound found in minor planet heading away (7)
7 Brandish sceptre entirely with deference (12)
10 Adjust the lower step – throw clay on it (7,5)
13 Government refuse seating in centre for trendy celebs (10)
15 Rubbishy stuff that husband left (3)
18 Where to pass time in Scottish naval base (4,4)
20 EU free criminal who kidnapped German exile (7)
22 Removing all traces of opera singer? Not all (7)
23 Big gun in WW1 wrecked the bar (6)
26 Dragon's smoke (4)

164

Across

1 Sat around after food in China, Japan etc. (3,4)
5 Made of soil, they are almost falling apart (6)
9 Small number working 24 hours at hottest time? (7)
10 Return on investment by a busy group's outstanding (7)
11 Grass on road surface is back (3)
12 John misinterprets Carol's tweet (5,6)
13 Primate in Madagascar broke rule about money (5)
14 Dull mediocre journalist looked round Norway (9)
16 Made changes in Birdsong, tedious work … (9)
17 … taking into account established fact (5)
19 Court document ordered three changes but not name (6,5)
22 GP to perform at college (3)
23 University in Bremen analysed food additive (1,6)
24 Church is inclined to intervene and free of sin (7)
26 Half remember day without a fix (6)
27 Silly rule restricts current Queen's strong drink (7)

Down

1 One leaves distressed Fraulein in late ceremony? (7)
2 Emperor to mature abroad in ideal vintage conditions? (4,11)
3 Nearly ring up for help (3)
4 Secret meeting in country street (5)
5 Replica I'm rebuilding based on experience (9)
6 Two men and member of first family (5)
7 Sadly, any ad he receives is inadmissible in court (7,8)
8 Girl in South Dakota did some winter sport (6)
12 West Indian communist sent telegram (5)
14 In Hotel Paris fresh fish gets shock treatment (9)
15 Dark horrible thing (5)
16 You'll need one to enter dense wood? It's not hard (6)
18 Such power would be obscure if leaders were swapped (7)
20 Clark's talented in support of government (5)
21 Extra large label's said to be extremely good (5)
25 Part of the vice squad's formal address (3)

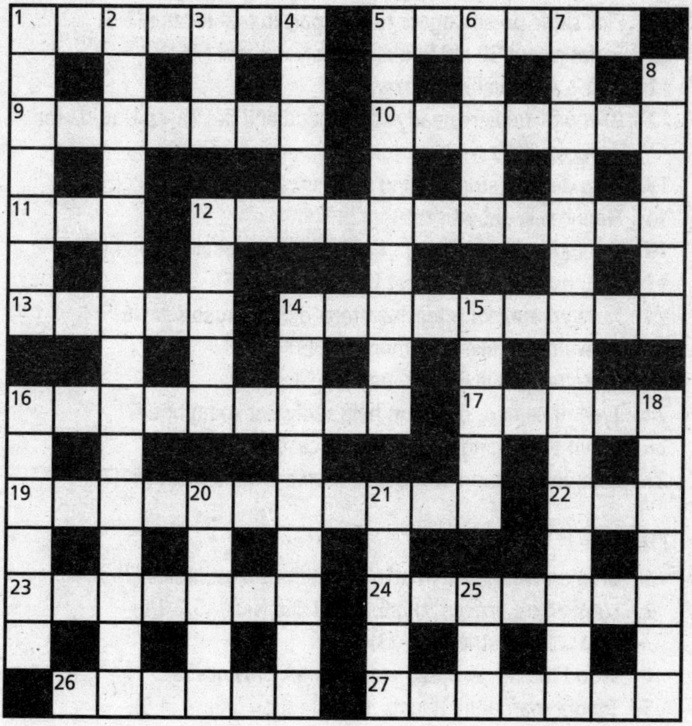

165

Across

1 Notice new gate at the back (7)
5 In retreat, Sting takes quiet walks (6)
9 Pick same person again to take part in free lecture (2-5)
10 Series about 50 old books makes you drool (7)
11 Wife's approval for cooker (3)
12 Group of soldiers nearly surrounded and destroyed Umbria for dovecote (11)
13 Boss doesn't stop making tactless remark (5)
14 Flounces in suburbs? (9)
16 Top Indian mum has not finished a drink over at hotel (9)
17 Ring back about 1 to get fragrant shrub (5)
19 Note where piano teacher starts girl, bourgeois … (6-5)
22 … sounding like duet moreover (3)
23 Pasta recipe Olivia prepared (7)
24 Type of camera offers no help sadly, snapping one (7)
26 Claim everything, say, at end of case (6)
27 Foreign seaman I introduced shows lack of 16 Down (7)

Down

1 Barman wears one in odd gripe about West Indies (7)
2 Look who's arrived to talk about Old Nick! (5,2,3,5)
3 First woman stripped 7 (3)
4 Wood that is uprooted in former SA province (5)
5 Try out marriage? It lasts no more than 5 days (4,5)
6 A traveller's scent (5)
7 Staff employed in marketing open accounts? (6,9)
8 US broadcaster inspires spirit and goodness (6)
12 Hurrah and farewell after 10 get sent off (5)
14 Goal of old bishop I've followed about in black (9)
15 14 Across made of silk and bit of tartan? (5)
16 There's more liquid in my storage facility (6)
18 Deadly disease caught Lahore ill-prepared (7)
20 Possibly lonesome, without men, unattached (5)
21 Local pharmacy secures top mark (5)
25 News about posh sister (3)

166

Across

6   They include speech and different varied comments (8,6)
9   Marks lines on compositions (6)
10 Person in theatre eats first of two fish (8)
11 Walls of Leipzig house one criminal all his years (8)
13 Like remote islanders, black in scarlet clothing (6)
15 Protect dilapidated ruins at one end (6)
17 Shrub or tree – try going in backwards (6)
19 Barnum & Bailey's first and last autumn production? (6)
20 Tiny tree's mistreated for a very long time (8)
22 Offering basic service only fills Ron with trepidation (2-6)
24 It pushed down charge for memory stick (6)
26 Stephen is very agitated when I go in, very touchy (14)

Down

1   Record on Rhode Island's threatening and biased (14)
2   It takes some bravery to make allegation in court (4)
3   Wall-painting in Corfe's vandalised (6)
4   Curtis Strange faces New York examination (8)
5   Self-satisfied dupes finish at the front (4)
7   Overhaul engines not having a starter as standard (6)
8   A4 reportedly referred to above (14)
12 Facilitate lecturer and art supporter (5)
14 It's picked up by not entirely notable conductor (5)
16 Spread story about boxer and fan of the monarchy (8)
18 Add spice to summer perhaps (6)
21 Bent wire snared a German insect (6)
23 Two kings held eastern English in bad odour (4)
25 Principal supplier of water (4)

167

Across

1 He comes out in different area around London (4,8)
8 Leave a group working (7)
9 We settle (about time) in marsh, for instance (7)
11 Bishop tolerated dreadful old racket (10)
12 John picked up place (4)
14 Cutter was not designed to have bend in the middle (5,3)
16 Coal, for example, has two names in smokestack (6)
17 There's nothing to be seen in Manila (3)
19 Henry dipped into a big book where he lives (2,4)
21 Put some spirit into drink, concocted purge (6,2)
24 Leading pairs in rugby league regulation (4)
25 Sportsman wears kit swimming in front of Queen (5-5)
27 TV cook's plant (7)
28 In France, 10 capsize in river there and rust (7)
29 Safe parents worried about new popper (4,8)

Down

1 Encourage female to collect oriental paintings (7)
2 Maid led men astray – it's her notable quality (6,4)
3 Person from Ottawa is able to entertain poor Diana (8)
4 Heading for the top on horseback, pull over (6)
5 Cheerio and thanks (2-2)
6 Pick up no one except for escaping (7)
7 Teacher went mad guarding a bishop in underground maze (6,6)
10 Berk loaded up convertible, obstructing street (6-6)
13 It's just a hint but somehow it eggs us on (10)
15 Worn in gale primarily it could blow off (3)
18 Vessel that's able to scramble if called in (8)
20 One of five elements nearly half gone, evaporated (7)
22 Wetter prince (7)
23 One artist has turned up in desert (6)
26 Pound up by 1p? It's a minor fluctuation (4)

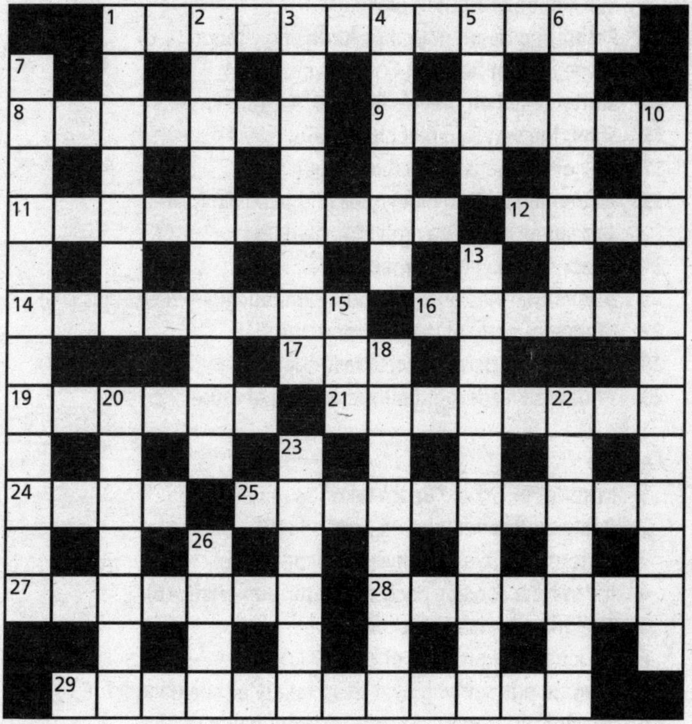
1
2
3
4
5
6
7
8
9
10
11
12
13
14
15
16
17
18
19
20
21
22
23
24
25
26
27
28
29

168

Across

1 Longest stretch of steel fence in ground (4,8)
8 You'll start off having set moves to market more (7)
9 Stack mine at front of plane (7)
11 Relocating board in Delhi's surprisingly tough (4-6)
12 Feline lives at home in Co. Durham, say (4)
14 Surrender when bread's finished? (4,4)
16 Show the way in credit crunch (6)
17 Part of Germans' U-boat or all of it (3)
19 Tory's managed to hide euros and pearls in it (6)
21 Abroad all get to pay road tax here (8)
24 Yawn during yoga, perhaps (4)
25 Arts master has posh, strangely limited audio-visual aids (10)
27 Model formerly of large proportions (7)
28 Porridge for Oscar at breakfast, say (7)
29 Widow's weeds, not uniform, as formal attire (7,5)

Down

1 Misprint in *On the Beach* taken as read (7)
2 Pirate, before foundering, tore off (10)
3 Furious A-listers seen flying in Scotland (8)
4 It's in New Yorker's pocket or in turn-up briefly (6)
5 The others at hotel eat out (4)
6 As a whim, limit price of cereal? (7)
7 Men go out working over there nearly all speaking it? (6,6)
10 Temporary supporter arranged street ballet (7,5)
13 Tiny distance left between main road and cut linden (10)
15 One of many seen primarily in regularly used track (3)
18 British do a lot at sea to secure a ship's cargo (8)
20 Treble gains out of arrangement of organs and pianos (7)
22 Do something about speech (7)
23 10 cross river in big bowl (6)
26 Odds on popular version of events (4)

169

Across

1 Single chap took in 500, then 500 more, as required (2,6)
5 US spies returned carrying Cruise bomb? (6)
9 Old soldiers start to march on Turkey's ground … (8)
10 … where most Anzacs were overrun in lines (6)
12 Old songs belonging to woman duke abandoned (4)
13 Fly-by-night ruined TV-AM pair hiding core of debt (7,3)
15 Finally, Oscar forced Ann to dance in front of everybody (4,3,3,3)
19 Being a chancer, operator left new units in charge (13)
23 Someone in planning department changed its targets (10)
25 Tool appears in A-to-Zed by mistake (4)
28 Book departure en masse (6)
29 Silly old men consume American energy drink (8)
30 Dredge river enclosure (6)
31 Toil away in building yard with skill (8)

Down

1 Refurbish room with centre of column in gold leaf (6)
2 Springfield's obligation to protect school? (5)
3 Come across gathering of horses and hounds (4)
4 Five enter magical Narnia to find happiness (7)
6 Tory oddly has hired out eccentric teacher (5)
7 In France my white wine has time to reach its peak (4,5)
8 Talk on Terry's personal possessions (8)
11 A group of careless pedestrians moved fast (4)
14 Old wound's almost frightening (4)
15 Unit has endless support, possibly deliberately (2,7)
16 She takes part in Annunciation (3)
17 A hot liquid taken in court (4)
18 Noticed duke under throne? It still needs explaining (5,3)
20 Strongly recommend a mouthful of beefburger (4)
21 Sent aid abroad as an alternative (7)
22 After church, disabled rely on sticks perhaps (6)
24 Chinese leader impressed by genuine peace agreement (5)
26 Bought and sold wood at end of August (5)
27 Game in swimming pool (4)

170

Across

6 Birders aren't twitching about old British bird (5,9)
9 Climb church covered in shifting sand (6)
10 Cheat wore mitt out (3-5)
11 Result of division's not quite worked out (8)
13 American beer Britain imported can be drunk (6)
15 She managed to ensnare disreputable men in trap (6)
17 Keep waiting at home after date's changed (6)
19 River takes sharp bend, so just out of the medals (6)
20 Creep slowly into different pubs for these (5-3)
22 It can land on snow and avoid small road (8)
24 Despot who goes in for petty ranting (6)
26 Harry enlists car pools to move fertiliser between plants (5-9)

Down

1 See pork course done about right using this? (8,6)
2 Competent to remove surface from fur (4)
3 Nervous diver's position? (2,4)
4 Like some rulers when playing at boules (8)
5 So-called snowman in yard with crumpled tie (4)
7 Heaney's occasionally written about bird's essence (6)
8 Small horses I planned to train she's corralled (8,6)
12 E.g. watch row about money (5)
14 Acre yielded sisal (5)
16 Chaps struggling with SNP showing some spirit (8)
18 2 is designed to descend quickly (6)
21 Cut front off suit of ugly West End clothes (6)
23 Illegally sell drink circulating with heroin (4)
25 Study grass, say (4)

171

Across

6 Big business retaining shy, engaging, penny-pinching man (7,7)
9 Female managed church across the Channel (6)
10 Loud singer group brought in as top vocalist (8)
11 Firm courage protects society in jam (8)
13 Conditions when I never take risks – Yuletide primarily (6)
15 Delightful GP may misguidedly stock ecstasy (6)
17 Thrifty West pulled out of Gulf War in disarray (6)
19 Poets love occupying stage (6)
20 Hairstyle potentially unkempt when let out (8)
22 Call him if grenade explodes round centre of Nîmes (8)
24 Seb keeps returning miniature wild dog (6)
26 Harry rated Bernard as leader of movement (8-6)

Down

1 To where merry Hood's few resort? (8,6)
2 Family's part in regional Caledonian uprising? (4)
3 Long narrow cruise ship tours area (6)
4 Bitter dispute arising over land borders? And how! (5,3)
5 Section of collapsed recess in church (4)
7 Presented with exceptional talent (6)
8 Subject to excite any hot ruralist (7,7)
12 TV adventurer Ray's last to start slanderous attack (5)
14 Dark, wild thing (5)
16 Avoid urban road, they say – you'll get abuse (8)
18 Unfolded drapes laid out (6)
21 Central parts of clue in novel (6)
23 Result of accident? Not half (4)
25 House in Selby or Knaresborough? Not far off (4)

172

Across

1 Imaginary fossil is nearly unique, covered in fur (7,4)
9 Uneasy feeling when touring island man's guarding (7)
10 Inject some energy into vulpine dancing (5,2)
11 It contains peas or dolphins primarily (3)
12 A Catholic nobleman's story (7)
13 Capricious girl's first seen in awfully filthy clothes (7)
14 Kate Adie's afternoon tipple? (3)
15 Look round eastern state for bird's nest (5)
17 It's difficult to hide ring in store (5)
18 Run across old car … (5)
20 … risky, sounding like old American car? (5)
22 Seaman reserves right (3)
24 Can dancer Fred dispel anger in card game? (7)
25 RC dignitary hosts British editor in royal office (7)
26 On her return, Queen eats old caviar, for example (3)
27 Daughter spoke out about temperature where PC sits (7)
28 Powerful oil spillage blocks opening (7)
29 Son gets up on a stone, surprisingly unprompted (11)

Down

1 Lavish mint sauce put out for these so-called pigs? (4,11)
2 Writer probes Suez manoeuvres concerning attack (7)
3 Clueless writer turns up in it (5)
4 Rich claims here if lodged correctly – about 50 (9)
5 I lead, given rocky harbour rail (7)
6 Teheran sends kid abroad, showing generosity (4-11)
7 Mark's seen (and heard) in Düsseldorf (6)
8 Sterilised one of a pack by the sound of it (6)
16 NE town's favourite way to welcome VIP? (3,6)
18 Go back and sow again, say (6)
19 Food's so dry in SA port (7)
21 Singer's time's wasted in Tokyo working on disc (4,3)
23 Meteor exploded far away (6)
25 County of both French and German (5)

173

Across

1 Parents wasted time in part of church (8)

5 Website chief employs IT expert (6)

9 Hotel in capital starts to employ educated old Jew (8)

10 Emotional problem? Put the phone down (4,2)

12 Get shot of outhouse (4)

13 Disloyal and in a huff until it's sorted out (10)

15 Help lop a tree round front of garden to make this? (9,4)

19 About 120° in humans, but could be fivefold in ISO (5,2,6)

23 Mail text of play: "The Afterthought" (10)

25 Have another go at decorating middle of fire door (4)

28 Old luxury car runs into farm animal, causing grief (6)

29 Hypothetical number, zero in Latin translation (8)

30 Improve quality of children, otherwise losing heart (6)

31 Bleach for every cow skin's hard going (8)

Down

1 Keyboard expert I spy working in middle of letter (6)

2 Wonder about a king not sleeping (5)

3 Dirty fuel's last to start (4)

4 Preferred to order nine grand in old German money (7)

6 Demand European levy's raised to include Cuba (5)

7 Pretentious, like pilot breaking altitude record? (4-5)

8 Rose climbs over it, displaying pearlies (8)

11 Pick up a small amount of information (4)

14 Winter transport slowed after old woman fell out (4)

15 Money man's foreign rate certain to rise initially (9)

16 Minister very nearly flipped (3)

17 Feel unwell after hot and cold shower (4)

18 Where skiing's risky in Fife's top resort (3-5)

20 Plant found everywhere round north primarily (4)

21 Beg for one more place inside (7)

22 Coal miner's tailless dog (6)

24 Philosopher who's resigned to interrupting thus (5)

26 Languid mood cut short in night in Paris (5)

27 Pit 3 with nothing at the bottom (4)

174

Across

1 Standstill as pack traps mature adult in retreat (8)

5 Top of the town's exotic headgear (6)

9 Drum's end battered in New Lyric (8)

10 Delay after this country backed another country (6)

12 Old Norse axes in stone (4)

13 House agenda: what to do if printer's empty? (5,5)

15 Strange goings-on in joke shop? (5,8)

19 Puppet show in gig patients arranged – I'm impressed (8,5)

23 Someone living permanently in a tin bath perhaps? (10)

25 Hindu teacher almost did the crawl, say (4)

28 A fine blonde's illicit relationship (6)

29 Witness finished describing Serb criminal (8)

30 It steers boat but ultimately not as well (6)

31 Brings back faulty stereos after start of renovation (8)

Down

1 He cures victim's heart, blocking opening (6)

2 Supporter accepts ring – bronze, for instance (5)

3 Join fifty thousand gathering at home (4)

4 Cuba really is in a bad way, without a doubt (7)

6 Take over rising insurance company led by America (5)

7 She has power to split responsibility for curse (9)

8 Senorita disputed what some solicitors do (8)

11 Would-be author employs dandy (4)

14 Irritating creature beat German up (4)

15 Gulf (Firth) turned out to be terrifying (9)

16 Ascent of Rock's very popular (3)

17 Republicans start to normalise country ... (4)

18 ... same country in past surprisingly ambitious (8)

20 Any key in scale of C except third? (4)

21 Having been given new order, I belong in base (7)

22 Sam heartlessly annoys and displays smugness (6)

24 Baron has cheese sent round to grease palms (5)

26 Western state to vacillate (5)

27 Wipes tyres, containing threat to livestock (4)

175

Across

1 Abandons final courses, not second (7)
5 It looks like 10 died horribly in compound (6)
9 Hide in some heartless Mediterranean island (7)
10 Sadly I seem caught between extremes – my downfall? (7)
11 Darwin oddly ignored bristle on 3 (3)
12 For poor, income is up surprisingly, union accepted (11)
13 Square-bashing doctor 22 (5)
14 Accused criminal nicked new pyjama top and stupid hat (6,3)
16 Trained actor got stuck into notes for top degree (9)
17 Nurse recalls time in church (5)
19 Reduced penalty to mum involved in fresh action (11)
22 Invoice doesn't start trouble (3)
23 Talk to institute about old man's bread (7)
24 One night's wasted gaining clear understanding (7)
26 Wayward header gets stick (6)
27 French marshal in violent demo, not 12 Across (7)

Down

1 When disturbed, birds run off and break up (7)
2 Deputy leader's possible clue for "O"? (6,2,7)
3 A taste of four-year-old port (3)
4 IoM town's taken up siesta (5)
5 In no way could this be said to be a sinless state (9)
6 Do men let loose malevolent spirit? (5)
7 I'd put up bracket, trying out about 50 in a worrying way (15)
8 Completely consumes American and English drink (4,2)
12 Accommodation up north has big-looking interior (5)
14 Director's materials oddly left out what playwrights do (9)
15 He was in jail a long time, having stolen 90 (2-3)
16 Extract by boiling in two short months (6)
18 Gave an account of what your cousins are to you (7)
20 EU eats fuel up? It's customary practice (5)
21 Local phrase is described in old manuscript originally (5)
25 Boy's shown odd letters (3)

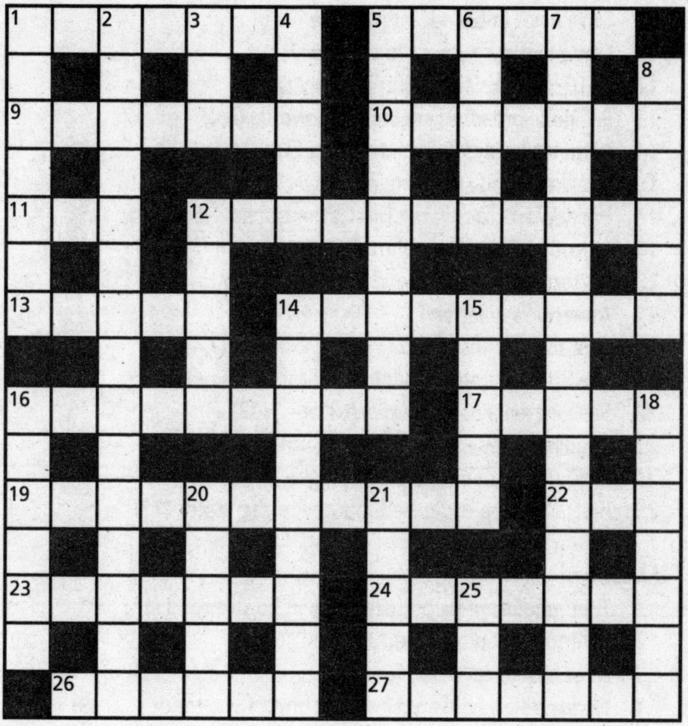
1
2
3
4
5
6
7
8
9
10
11
12
13
14
15
16
17
18
19
20
21
22
23
24
25
26
27

176

Across

1 One MP converted air miles in expansionist policy (11)
9 Is it truly crazy to jail team leaders? Absolutely (7)
10 Mike's not in broadcast passage (7)
11 Low pointless subject to debate (3)
12 In 10, tureen's surprisingly empty (2,5)
13 Pal kept spreading encouraging words (3,4)
14 Remains in Middle East hospital (3)
15 Murder melody with no intro? Tyroleans do it (5)
17 Harry West crossed river in tartan trousers (5)
18 Strand of DNA I found inside bottled spirit (5)
20 It's found in a church and may be initially dropped (5)
22 A marine's weapon (3)
24 Rest told stories about drinking whiskey (3,4)
25 The Spanish enter London hotel for sausage (7)
26 Sash appears in Holbein occasionally (3)
27 English scores in exam impress British boards (7)
28 A guard's trained on line in stages (7)
29 Fast, non-stop organised journey to the States (11)

Down

1 Their angle can be adjusted or can be swapped (15)
2 Offence in court tangled Jerry up (7)
3 Frost broadcast poem (5)
4 Dodgy oiltap holds out happily; don't fly without it … (9)
5 … to Spain, otherwise you'll get in difficulties (2,1,4)
6 Places to go so a regular spasm can be treated? (7,8)
7 Spain and UK are shaken by sound of Greek's triumph (6)
8 Arrange seats to cover start of Kentucky horse race (6)
16 Identified problem: lost power, no gas ordered in (9)
18 Old ship's kitchen (6)
19 He got ripped off holding self-indulgent display (3,4)
21 Try to shave a goat? Not all of it (4,1,2)
23 Ephemeral insect might pass quickly (6)
25 Sense location, say (5)

177

Across

1 Some chap with pot shifted pile in garden (7,4)
9 Golfer Fred's items (7)
10 Thinks about a boy soprano (7)
11 She's opening Individual Savings Account (3)
12 Accountant probed strange deeds for many years (7)
13 Offensive racket overwhelms old mike (7)
14 What pigeons do, or waterbird nearly (3)
15 Some music or fun in Greek island (5)
17 Formal announcement's somewhat predictable (5)
18 Mollusc shed edges of its covering in week (5)
20 Unusually small conflict between Germany and France (5)
22 Stewart travelled on horseback endlessly (3)
24 Like some nails? Ring now to get in order (7)
25 May lets in bishop; she's said to be looking for him (2,5)
26 Expected someone in synagogue by the sound of it (3)
27 Play about church? Not much change for old Greeks (7)
28 They must shine at Sandhurst to restore gap (7)
29 Confess to being in want? It's sensible (4-2-5)

Down

1 Harry changed for lunch, it's established (6,2,7)
2 Emcee introduces cracked oldie that's tuneful (7)
3 Rock group not often seen in Sahara (5)
4 Scary creature, thanks to natural evolution (9)
5 Woman picks up travel permit, avoiding trouble (7)
6 Tiny picture, sort of Hogarth promo pic (15)
7 Sour, like East End Jewish mystic, say (6)
8 Rise like US money (6)
16 Corroded tanner, dud, not needed (9)
18 Bizarre guy's wet hairdo that's almost ignored (6)
19 Stir wok now with hot contents, showing skill (4-3)
21 Predecessor wasted energy in refrain (7)
23 Hate extremely defensive cricket match (6)
25 Little more than a yard surrounded by lime trees (5)

178

Across

1 Use soldiers to replace one in unit that's not working (12)
8 Thrilled to be mentioned after former lover (7)
9 Repudiates rackets involving pig (7)
11 Check ransacked room has a bit of DNA (10)
12 Fuel that's somewhat undervalued (4)
14 Lawyer's work: complex deals with a small company (8)
16 Mother's addicted to fruit (6)
17 Shelter somewhere on the Solent (3)
19 French fighter or Russian one limits gunners' base (6)
21 Desire just in an unrestrained way (8)
24 Catch sight of head of Estonian undercover agent (4)
25 I'm clever, having cooked 51 cake decorations (10)
27 Pay mines back before closure (7)
28 Old parish priest is in French frills, like a dandy (7)
29 She had bra fixed at Rye after accident – using this? (12)

Down

1 What wine waiter does in Irish city in baking sun (7)
2 Scrawled note on terribly gloomy wildlife study (10)
3 Base is crudely plastered except rear (8)
4 Dropsy's described in embargoed email (6)
5 It could be the most unusual scent, known originally … (4)
6 … for novelty in all quarters at least once (7)
7 Scavengers' risky cache hidden in e.g. Wellingtons (12)
10 Record view about something that happened to you once (7-5)
13 Fancy special trip avoiding school, past or present, say (10)
15 The beginnings of dawn's early wetness (3)
18 Female wears same fur designed as lug-warmers (8)
20 Right place managed to hold single copy (7)
22 Cancel university lecturers provided in New York (7)
23 Devoted bishop choked by tobacco (6)
26 Some of the best garden plants (4)

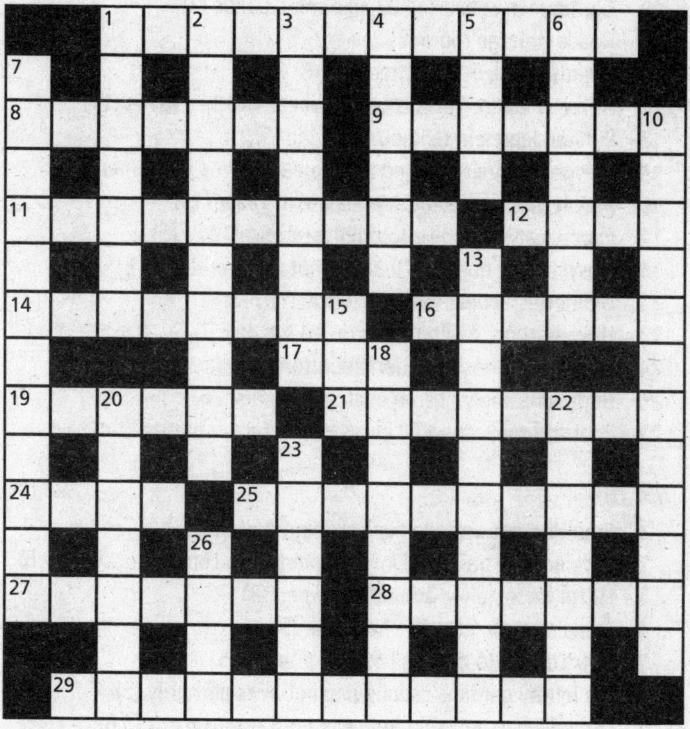

179

Across

1 Like black magic in South America, it can spread (7)
5 It's left to children, say, in clay potty (6)
9 Continue in converted 22, like some bands (7)
10 House or large room (7)
11 What's drunk in late afternoon (3)
12 A new shop in Welsh county's where violence flares (11)
13 Pursue degree in religious doctrine (5)
14 Evergreen tree managed to hide each circus performer (4-5)
16 People who run company dispute its record (9)
17 Express a view, one about mathematical ratio (5)
19 Nosy, trendy question that's about visit abroad (11)
22 Diamonds appear evenly in circle (3)
23 High-spirited, having squandered full pay (7)
24 First bars to host 6 under laboratory conditions (2,5)
26 Birds amazingly absorb energy in rubbish (6)
27 Poor after investing 10 euros but VAT-exempt, say (3-4)

Down

1 Small decent arrangement exuding perfume (7)
2 Moving RAF gala held in new quarters in London location (9,6)
3 Hazel for instance overturned barrel (3)
4 Firms start to advertise hot drink (5)
5 Hair cut top to bottom? Start fighting (4,5)
6 It's left by gannets usually and not owls primarily (5)
7 Dubious bets incriminate member of government (7,8)
8 Mad research chief confiscated rubber (6)
12 Female smuggled cocaine and old money (5)
14 Sail loft's designed to hold large groups of boats (9)
15 Eat away in bar in centre of Peel (5)
16 Inane eccentric accommodates rabbi (6)
18 Look carefully at hybrid rose – it's ugly (7)
20 Conclude there's no avoiding hell (5)
21 Writer Dorothy swallowed one nut (5)
25 Make cross, very English cross (3)

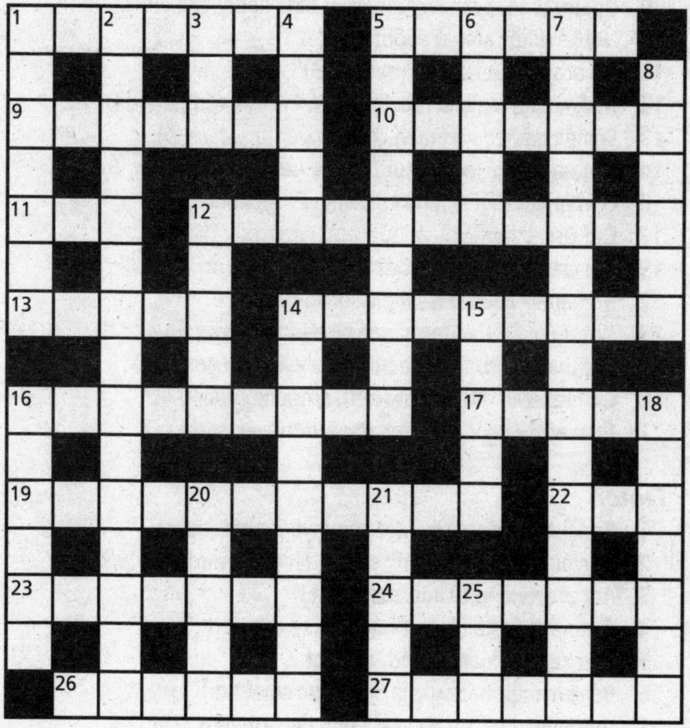
1
2
3
4
5
6
7
8
9
10
11
12
13
14
15
16
17
18
19
20
21
22
23
24
25
26
27

180

Across

1 Crossing Cuba, go and seek strange lizards (7)
5 Endorse proposal to transfer temporarily (6)
9 Doctor probes renal changes in old charity worker (7)
10 Noble wildly elated about kiss (7)
11 Go around dancing primarily? (3)
12 Make concrete and rebuild sty in Carlisle compound (11)
13 Some crazy zoo woman comes over in a daze (5)
14 Slate a Hindu sage? Mum finally goes for headgear (6,3)
16 Odd athlete's a smuggler during Prohibition (3-6)
17 Old Greek loft (5)
19 Cut class content maybe? It helps pupil's ability (7,4)
22 No goals? Even O'Neill produced it! (3)
23 Not quite first performance by head of government (7)
24 Old women in cheap jewellery playing on green (7)
26 Go higher in difficult descant, dropping tempo (6)
27 Go back? Eugene regrets in part doing just that (7

Down

1 Gas flickers in warm light somewhere in Scotland (7)
2 Doctor recommends any of, say, Noel Coward play (6,2,7)
3 Admit working to impress wife (3)
4 Grumpy? Certainly not hugging sweetheart (5)
5 Saccharin's financial inducement (9)
6 Behave ingratiatingly in slow movement (5)
7 Heavyweight's up and resisting nevertheless (15)
8 Notice opening in period before Christmas (6)
12 Decoy purposely trapped large rodent (5)
14 Butcher turned up riding cycle with a hole in it (9)
15 Chap's acquired energy and resources (5)
16 Price changes to cover European ingredients (6)
18 Officer's gone crazy in German city (7)
20 Beer bottles, four still with us (5)
21 It's maybe still hot at the end of three months (5)
25 Gain three-quarters of Burgundy, say (3)

181

Across

6 Courses here for crazy powerless yuppie inventors (4,10)

9 Second best person causing great amusement (6)

10 Does this hero join in jujitsu permanently? (8)

11 Obscure drunkard (English) appears in Morecambe (8)

13 Bank employee who relates to his customers? (6)

15 Joints where golfer receives gesture of respect (6)

17 How Hollywood star signs his name in gratitude? (6)

19 Cast rallies round, concerned about stars (6)

20 Posh dancer trained tenor to perform with restraint (8)

22 Split hairs: question head of divinity about new bible (8)

24 There's no space in London museum for prayers (6)

26 Old vehicles made from ten frying pans Henry brought in (5-9)

Down

1 Wide corsets are altered by uncle in odd places for dressing (9,5)

2 It's just old water (4)

3 Quiet talk to raise spirits (6)

4 Send chap Ted's replaced (8)

5 Emperor erected part of infrastructure (4)

7 Perhaps fly home with religious group (6)

8 Nauseous feeling in rickety van – it's reckless (6,8)

12 Borat played small drum (5)

14 Both sides contain a certain person who stays aloof (5)

16 Ploughed field will endlessly produce flora and fauna (8)

18 Separate socialist students' uprising (6)

21 It's no good beginning to haul in DIY craft (6)

23 Very thin body's normal for duke (4)

25 Opening fifth hospital department (4)

182

Across

1 How to revive two moths out at sea round end of Peru (5-2-5)
8 Illness is maybe terminal without second bit of treatment (7)
9 Ascetic Muslim's fuel is hydrogen (7)
11 Hope rowers can generate about 750 watts (10)
12 Smooth sound of car partly interrupted in reverse (4)
14 Score -1 at last hole in golf? (8)
16 French cheeses reportedly create wind (6)
17 For starters, some Italians prefer a small drink (3)
19 Stop talking and applaud Greek character entering (4,2)
21 Pressure's on busy ladies to host English stars (8)
24 Roubles are not often seen (4)
25 Many bribed corrupt person responsible for tots (4-6)
27 As surly youth his boy worried about blackhead (7)
28 Harry told me about one former dancing style (3-4)
29 Mad east German collects silver; he runs the show (5,7)

Down

1 Ernie's morning round, a journey that's 2 (4,3)
2 Rough flu outbreak round Tynemouth that's routine (10)
3 Mad Texas hobo lost old containers for his stetsons (8)
4 Lots of aimless scribbles start to disappear (6)
5 Time, say, that belongs to you and me (4)
6 Bitter dispute surrounds union's show of gratitude (7)
7 It could be anarchy with cards buying wholesale here (4-3-5)
10 Boundless care in doctoring style there? (6,6)
13 Cooked porridge traps excellent US rodent (7,3)
15 Pinch first of it back (3)
18 Make light of first of prizes lady won somehow (4,4)
20 A chap from Dubrovnik welcomes British circus act (7)
22 Exciting ride with dog could be more tricky (7)
23 Discover the meaning of deep-sea measure (6)
26 Ruler contributes to work in geometry (4)

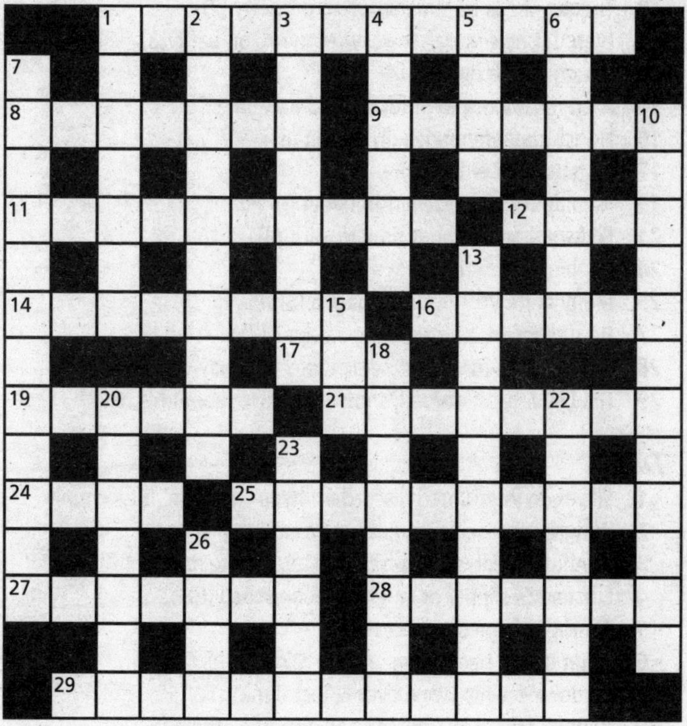
1
2
3
4
5
6
7
8
9
10
11
12
13
14
15
16
17
18
19
20
21
22
23
24
25
26
27
28
29

183

Across

1 Big hit for man could become addictive (5-7)
8 Big hit for American, Greek poet and French one (4,3)
9 The cat needs treatment, left in property (7)
11 Lynn C. Doyle understood what to rub on bat (7,3)
12 Struggle with opinion (4)
14 A lot must work to produce final amount (3,5)
16 Needy state depended on Queen (6)
17 Distant fliers return (3)
19 Harshly criticise attempt in larder (6)
21 I'd love a novel about time in joint (8)
24 26 harassed hero (4)
25 Big pets for VIPs in Copenhagen (5,5)
27 How to insert 21 in weeds perhaps? (7)
28 Old man's in run-down semi; there's no way out of it (7)
29 Hid coy orphan abroad, showing anxiety about his health (12)

Down

1 Silly moo interrupted discordant hymn – or him, for example (7)
2 Wily badger tackles pig; it runs round roof (10)
3 One fated sadly to be unable to appreciate music (4-4)
4 E.g. Lady's slipper or child left abandoned (6)
5 Average chap conserves energy (4)
6 What the S3 hear when writing about hotel (7)
7 Doctor loses hip twice over 6, just think! (12)
10 Primary school lessons? Snobs disparage them (5,7)
13 Marvellous but awfully rude during evening meal (5-5)
15 Short woman's boy (3)
18 Old German brought in to share time for prayers (8)
20 Refusal to replace Monday's leader at hottest time (7)
22 Incontinent men suffering loss of memory (7)
23 Tree has restricted lower part of trunk (6)
26 Leisurely individuals dived outdoors primarily here (4)

184

Across

1 Supply help, say, for US military prison (8)
5 I hear logo clashes with band (6)
9 Carpet has its wrinkles in church (8)
10 Everyone's mostly gone outside for several pints (6)
12 It's level and its centre's normal (4)
13 Michael can work like a robot (10)
15 It runs round the house avoiding table (8,5)
19 Big book: I'd a clean copy reprinted with English in (13)
23 General rules in food shop owned by flawed genius (10)
25 Back dictator's right to travel widely (4)
28 Bird nibbled tasty morsel (6)
29 Guiding light for sailor pursuing Europeans (4,4)
30 Big Apple has one goal: to reach a ripe old age (6)
31 Conductor's area in Heathrow (8)

Down

1 Holy area in outskirts of Sunderland (6)
2 Appaloosa gelding's more than enough for Native American (5)
3 High flier's kinetic energy primarily controls it (4)
4 Director is dispatched to withhold agreement (7)
6 Long time taken by planet to orbit sun finally (5)
7 Bacall frustrated Gardner in battle (9)
8 Dad'll mix with any one who takes in lodgers (8)
11 Butcher's cut damaged his nose at the front (4)
14 Metal quarried from quartz in Chile (4)
15 He runs church sanctuaries ruined after EU withdrew (9)
16 Even bits of bitmap can be quite a handful (3)
17 Make offer to European to stay (4)
18 Increase 8 with female around (8)
20 Old poet swallowed six in overdose (4)
21 Expert's not taken up English solvent (7)
22 A lesson in being unprincipled (6)
24 French material lifted poet (5)
26 In many cases one's confused putting feet in (5)
27 Ray's money supports old airline (4)

185

Across

6 I'd built centres designed to be durable (14)

9 It's thrown out of boats and planes in the morning (6)

10 Untidy drawer holds old boy's full set of clothes (8)

11 Pilot hearing cricket score (5,3)

13 High-flier in Attica rushed, fell and drowned (6)

15 Mathematician loves complicated recipe (6)

17 Beginning to use foreign wines? It's inadvisable (6)

19 Doctor lied about British energy source such as food (6)

20 Style of jumper, oddly long, kept in locker abroad (8)

22 Current fashion "New Tudor" (8)

24 It's about spring in Severn, although not all of it (6)

26 PR misleadingly represented marketing scheme (7,7)

Down

1 NYC is perceived to be rebuilding high US office (4,10)

2 They're offered on Derby Day sometimes at the start (4)

3 There's a few in Irish compound (6)

4 Arachnid and rat left conspirator to rot (8)

5 Story-teller upset bar (4)

7 Victory in danger? Go back to the start (6)

8 Job centre left a boxer angry, round the bend, with coins (6,8)

12 Dial controversial bishop for impromptu comment (2,3)

14 Get straight gain surprisingly, overcoming Liberal (5)

16 Take tricycle Katy left – it could be exciting (8)

18 Men lined up on board catch rare seafood (6)

21 Vivacious girl accepts 5 euros (6)

23 Biblical twin mentioned in thesaurus (4)

25 Check precipitation, say (4)

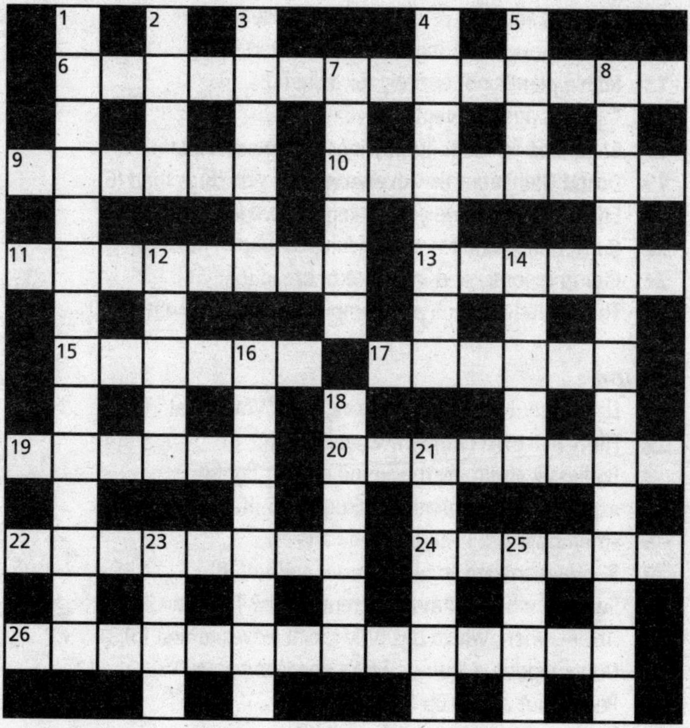
1
2
3
4
5
6
7
8
9
10
11
12
13
14
15
16
17
18
19
20
21
22
23
24
25
26

186

Across

6 Magnificent, like those men in their flying machines? (3,2,4,5)
9 Soft bed for sportsman (6)
10 Pinpoint and find yeti? That's nonsense (8)
11 Road through shifting dunes isn't diverted (8)
13 Edible plant's not entirely for a chef (6)
15 Careless agent accepts cut (6)
17 Stand beside a disc-jockey working round Italy (6)
19 Grand Old Party takes everyone for a ride (6)
20 Edward keeps three elaborately tied up (8)
22 Rocket and bananas – convenience food in India (8)
24 Plump tenor tucked into slice of bread (6)
26 They include speech and complex varied comments (8,6)

Down

1 Drink about two litres and sing out: "Vote here!" (7,7)
2 Filthy place accommodates one guy (4)
3 Endlessly afraid, by the sound of it, in fight (6)
4 A performance-enhancing drug, it's 6 (8)
5 Attempt to sell everything in Paris (4)
7 Rhoda managed to hide current coiffure (6)
8 Socialist workers have different needs? That's awkward (4-10)
12 Arrangement which has only radial leaves at first (5)
14 Unit supports a learner who's unaccompanied (5)
16 People put a pole up (8)
18 Tudors relocated somewhere in Gloucestershire (6)
21 Fish hauled up to dry (6)
23 Parliament regulated intake (4)
25 To doctor it's grave (4)

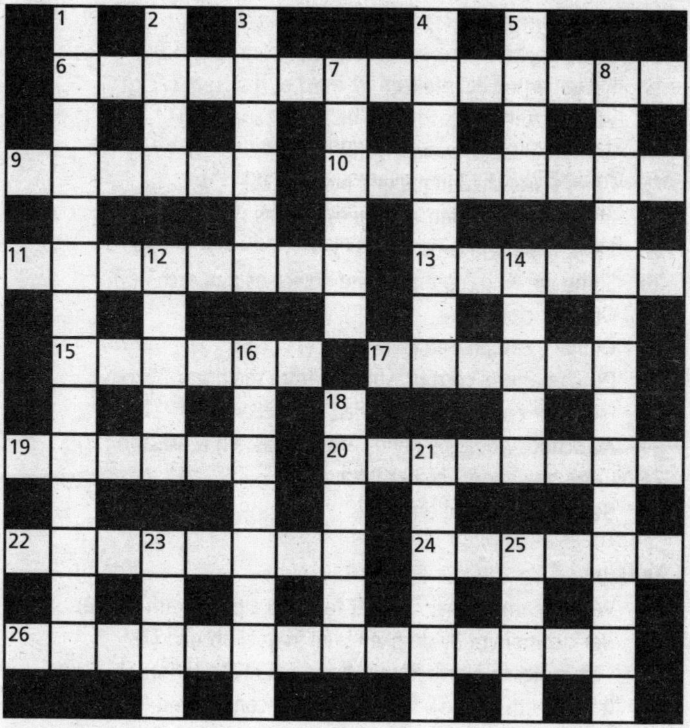

187

Across

1   Pilot's shaken about return of white bird's ghost (11)
9   Gives new title to prophet having chap's backing (7)
10 Don't vote and a crazy bat's elected! (7)
11 Small portion of cereal consumed in tea room (3)
12 It's governed by intellectual; most of it's great (7)
13 Why recruit King's soldiers first? That's lazy (7)
14 Definitely the ayes have it (3)
15 Chief's drenched in mineral pigment (5)
17 Increase admiration after priest leaves (5)
18 Confine muscle contraction (5)
20 Someone who regrets having novice as monarch? (5)
22 Object's close (3)
24 Old jar's camphorated contents (7)
25 Dutch native's corrupt, straying from the norm (7)
26 Friend or enemy? Their leaders will tell you (3)
27 RC school would be handy around eastern N. Ireland (7)
28 Catty one angrily blocks track (7)
29 Booking qualification (11)

Down

1   Writer learns cipher in order to make a point with it (6,9)
2   Back complaint by drunken bum in gaol abroad (7)
3   City in Hesse, North Rhine-Westphalia? The latter (5)
4   It has teeth where a leg should be reconstructed (9)
5   He provides cover for nurse working in Ireland (7)
6   Rewriting each letter in wild orientalist rant (15)
7   Dirty disheartened boy finishes food (6)
8   Foreign enemy seized unknown protein (6)
16 What's to come before father gets thrown outside (9)
18 Risk article dividing two churches (6)
19 Outstanding skill and amazing powers succeeded (7)
21 Pasta recipe Olivia concocted (7)
23 English come in third sadly, in state of indecision (6)
25 TV cook has time for one letter from abroad (5)

188

Across

1 Order ring for special soldier (8)

5 To do a favour for blog, I translated English (6)

9 Poor Dorothy's tailless cow's normal (8)

10 The whole or part of gluteus maximus clearly (6)

12 Batman's beginning to finish plan (4)

13 By overcoming every fault George made sand vehicle (5,5)

15 Tom, Norma and I come out for remembrance service (13)

19 One mad 1 Across keeps university college out of contact (13)

23 Glutton gets red somehow entertaining funny guy … (6,4)

25 … threatening different guy who has left (4)

28 Quits for tea, say (6)

29 Mechanic's plan (8)

30 Doctor hears about hospital's make-over (6)

31 Distorted legal document includes sheet to fill in (8)

Down

1 Endless routine work nearly all sung by massed voices (6)

2 Subdued rendition of Te Deum lacking energy (5)

3 Tiny fragment of demo tape turned up (4)

4 See, I break complex codes on base (7)

6 Publicity in book supporting rock band (5)

7 Distribute it in Congo using a false identity (9)

8 All, even Roy surprisingly, start to exercise (8)

11 Repeat eastern half of 1 Down (4)

14 I'm a Muslim leader (4)

15 Children tackle new play etc., riding bikes here (5,4)

16 People knock top off portentous sign (3)

17 Middle Eastern person in a bar in recession (4)

18 Remarkable ruling's redrafted to protect amateur (8)

20 Some ardour generated in "Basic Instinct" (4)

21 Extremely serious at home, unable to relax (7)

22 Extremely hungry bird's irritated and cross (6)

24 What's left after drink, say, in doctor's (5)

26 Single ampere provides dim light (5)

27 Writer's black ink runs out at the start (4)

189

Across

1 Various names etc. in the frame (8)
5 Head of college pours out complete works (6)
9 Oddly cold new curate's easy to understand (5-3)
10 Singer allowed to entertain pub (6)
12 I could swear it's hidden in boathouse (4)
13 Does cutting up birds seem wrong? Money's taken in … (10)
15 … family butcher's shop contents (5,3,5)
19 Dressmakers use them to alter shrinkage between legs (7,6)
23 Top quality former monk's room in French church (10)
25 Quartet in favour of retaining uniform (4)
28 Drops young student into holes in rock (6)
29 Stone a parish priest discovered in county (8)
30 Aim to change gear during races (6)
31 Columbus found it lower down maybe, missing nothing (3,5)

Down

1 Copper company hires fine upstanding migrant (6)
2 Line in bed linen (5)
3 Spoil English horse (4)
4 Waste hours in making up feed (7)
6 Hate platform with no front (5)
7 Thinks deeply about Open University – it's weighty (9)
8 Reject EU farm policy (3-5)
11 Topless ladies – good or bad sign? (4)
14 Some guidelines needed for food outlet (4)
15 Diversion replaces part in special kind of railway (9)
16 Fool a German bodyguard (3)
17 Sounds like an old South African pig (4)
18 Drug reduction's a blow (8)
20 Section of elevated flower-garden got bigger (4)
21 After ploughing, the acre becomes a larger area (7)
22 Pal's to finish after Friday (6)
24 Inaccurate story, say, about Belgian city (5)
26 Basket-maker's stockings topped and tailed (5)
27 Throw up small seat (4)

190

Across

1 Brag about doctor's pompous language (7)
5 Withdraw from dry, blissful place that has no end (6)
9 Boatman's cover of old silk fabricated at home (7)
10 Dash over to watch very famous dancer (7)
11 Success has influenced top leaders (3)
12 I did fine with gun, possibly looking foolish (11)
13 Competitor smashed rail, sealing victory (5)
14 Grew weak, heading off in great pain (9)
16 Formula One driver's speed flat out? (9)
17 Missile in east London school? (5)
19 Net earnings? They make OAP happy (4-4,3)
22 Extra run's so long (3)
23 When dancing, he lacks restraint (7)
24 E.g. runner allowed to appear in rescheduled heat (7)
26 Displayed for all like a herbaceous border (6)
27 Irritated one and worried about youth leader (7)

Down

1 Take the trouble to involve royal sibling (7)
2 It needs bottle and some fire for a riotous fling (7,8)
3 A British seabird (3)
4 Rotated with no resistance, as engines should be (5)
5 A guy's gone mad in place of worship (9)
6 Queen's pet in care of King George the First (5)
7 Big Brother lady baffled Yard in blatant overcharging (8,7)
8 Gave slip to editor after Dave turned up (6)
12 In Paris, a place to sleep in the dark (5)
14 It may go off if everyone steals sculpted marble (5,4)
15 Somewhere in Europe where the laity get mistreated (5)
16 Chemical fertiliser in container with tree (6)
18 Livingstone stopped tobacco from Friday to Sunday (7)
20 He walks for pleasure in Delhi, Kerala etc. (5)
21 Open space in Madrid or La Paz possibly (5)
25 Search for short vandal (3)

191

Across

1 Nation's 15 courts undergo reorganisation (5,6)
9 Facilitates former England manager losing his head (7)
10 Shoots harriers (7)
11 Heads to the opposite end, the tip (3)
12 Final moves on board need AGM to be arranged (7)
13 Look after child: organise bib, say, first of three (7)
14 The Scots know Livingstone (3)
15 Middle East city hotel provided boring articles (5)
17 Run away to marry Pole about end of June (5)
18 Unfriendly foal goes wild round ring (5)
20 Lowest point of dinar after conversion (5)
22 Bath underground's endless (3)
24 Film preview in caravan (7)
25 Public demonstration in favour of big game (7)
26 What doves do to lower temperature almost (3)
27 African city where robinia grows wild (7)
28 Health and happiness were keeping Alf busy (7)
29 Heart of the matter? Try tying it up over time (5-6)

Down

1 Big hand bearing eggs not raised without one (8,7)
2 Free straggling houseplant, having removed broken pot (7)
3 Hurrying, he's at ground (5)
4 Militant guy's cash in 1 Across supports brief development (9)
5 After treatment, I belong in base (7)
6 Harry overhasty in eating bad pear? It'll put him off (8,7)
7 Festoon place to sleep with even bits of teacake (6)
8 Set off twice and fly (6)
16 Urban centre's tiny and nicer in a strange way (5,4)
18 Get accustomed to a dry article in Paris (6)
19 Have an argument following end of innings? (4,3)
21 What badgers do at end of sett to find small branch (7)
23 E.g. goat that's sold in 22s (6)
25 Control with rope twisted around (5)

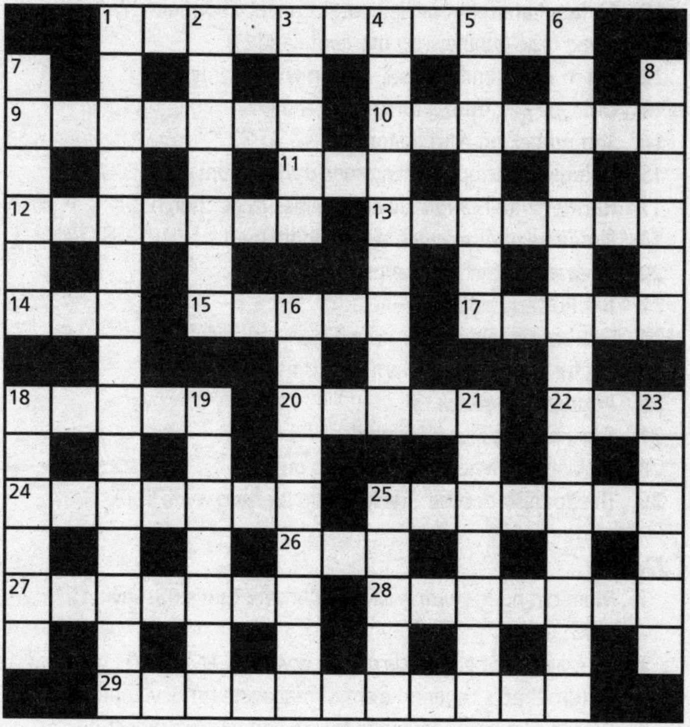

192

Across

1 It's practical and there's a ritual in it, funnily (11)
9 If such a strange plant emerges, it may have a … (7)
10 … familiar scent I picked out from fancy boutique (7)
11 Some urge equine with this command (3)
12 Put in water and simmer, stirring with energy (7)
13 Old type of clothing torn round end (7)
14 Second person who does puzzles? (3)
15 Is English bishop standing outside? Step up! (5)
17 Ravine at first gradually undermines large church (5)
18 It may be hard to catch winter sportsman (5)
20 Woman's taken over property (5)
22 Top EU farm policy (3)
24 Five bask in glow after Britain's brilliant display (7)
25 Doctor queries man's former address (7)
26 Appropriate attack (3)
27 She's a great first-class student (7)
28 Making call when cold shower's on? (7)
29 The Spanish decline Greek leisure for hard work (5,6)

Down

1 Mum cut no ice with Ivan when upset? That's not saying much (15)
2 He covers home with certain reservations at first (7)
3 Picture that is covering front of magazine (5)
4 Greece is supporting exotic bream and whale product (9)
5 Getting accustomed to 2's job when sun's out (7)
6 Even Uncle Louis and I managed what's simple but tasty (8,7)
7 Sculpture of Geoffrey is cast without Eros (6)
8 Bird in school gets sudden pain (6)
16 Naval base where a wolf pack cut loose under sea (5,4)
18 Power governs tube centrally – New York tube, that is (6)
19 Hubbard (Ron, not Don) developed dessert (7)
21 Spirit of Mexico quite widespread over Los Angeles (7)
23 Place on border makes promise (6)
25 Monarch receives article and number (5)

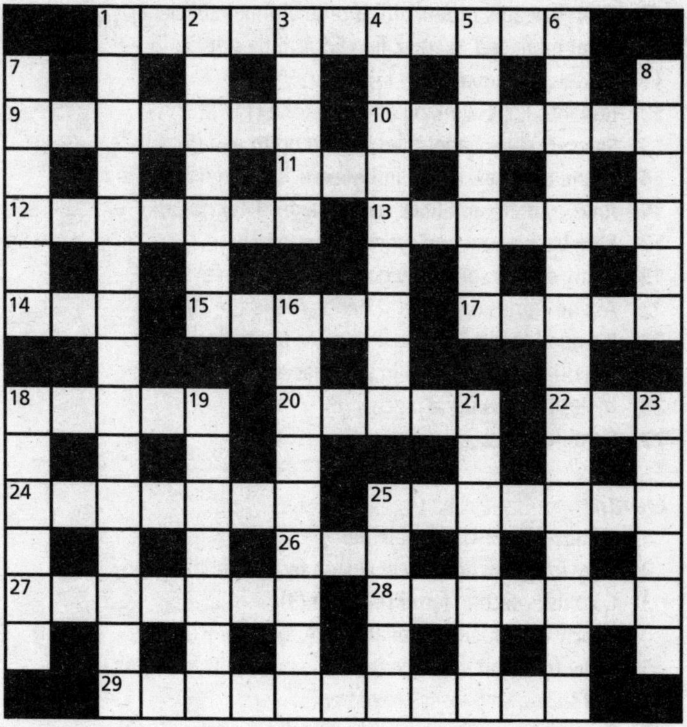
1
2
3
4
5
6
7
8
9
10
11
12
13
14
15
16
17
18
19
20
21
22
23
24
25
26
27
28
29

193

Across

1 Magazine includes exotic Bali letters in it (7)
5 I must change when rector comes in, that's obvious (6)
9 Sport's head's sacked? It's due to vitamin deficiency (7)
10 A cat managed to crack fine English biscuit (7)
11 Vessel in Uruguay navy (3)
12 Run into Pope working at a bad time (11)
13 Smooth, shiny vegetables beginning to end (5)
14 I have upset old union in Britain – it's my conduct (9)
16 Journey there and back could make 11 torpid (5,4)
17 Ring back about one syringa (5)
19 Henry's coins somehow go together perfectly (11)
22 Airline carries oxygen – it hangs round the neck (3)
23 It's good to put holes in iron plate for cooking (7)
24 Fan drier tackles damp in odd places (7)
26 Moles possess large pincers (6)
27 Continue to cause a fuss (5,2)

Down

1 25 queen is next to nobleman (7)
2 Fiery Toscanini hosts new Queen by lake, fiddling (15)
3 Colonist's second letter read out (3)
4 Hearty enjoyment's available in August only (5)
5 Army transport's second in line in posh port for repair (9)
6 Old sailing ship loses prow, say (5)
7 Second disputed beauty title for tall NY figure (6,2,7)
8 Measuring device orbits old falling star (6)
12 Peeved by bumpy ride around Cambodia (5)
14 Little people or tedious people having argument? (9)
15 Estimate worth of uranium in valley (5)
16 Give up dominance over society (6)
18 Doctor racing round hospital in embarrassment (7)
20 Garden boundary finished germinating, not all of it (5)
21 Sarah's son is ace in Air Corps (5)
25 Impair memory recall (3)

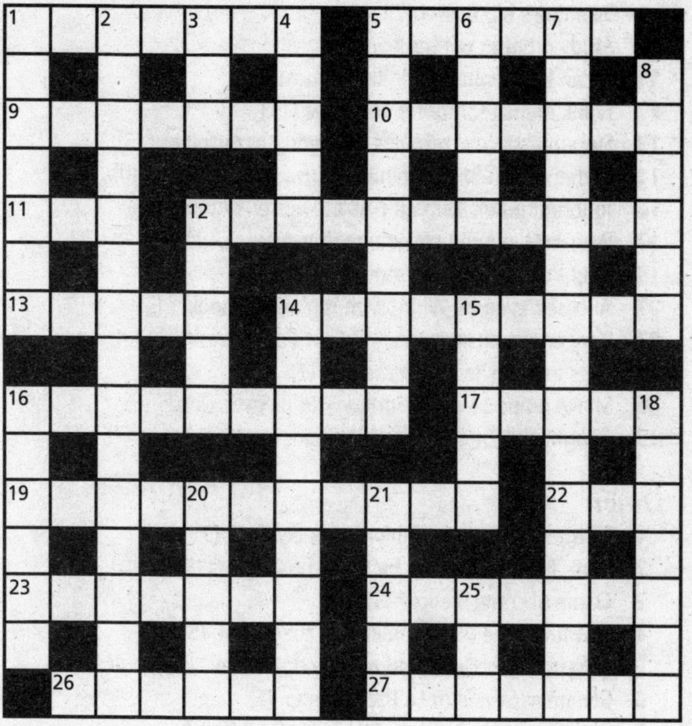

194

Across

1 Oxygen in small volume to heal damaged part of ear (7)
5 Tree that's liked a lot but not round university (6)
9 Womble's big flower (7)
10 Study pit after cut back (7)
11 It can be caught over in Leeds mostly (3)
12 Frank managed fight in marquee (11)
13 Delicious steaks' odd bits removed, try recipe out (5)
14 Perhaps each angelfish absorbs transformation (3,6)
16 Ignorant nitwit with gun on the loose (9)
17 Weekend in Aden spent completely exposed (5)
19 Emperor's always the same in East (11)
22 Accused even hit White with it playing snooker (3)
23 Very unresponsive model C. Cole I'd entertained (3-4)
24 Gets in boats to be overhauled (7)
26 Snake grabs 11 going round with its eyes closed (6)
27 Caught college heads coming back carrying goods (7)

Down

1 Fails to win in court – it's extremely tight (7)
2 She's lined crowns up for these posh idiots (8,7)
3 Game of convenience? (3)
4 A whiff of the unprincipled curtailed rising (5)
5 Ship in, say, collision traps conscript in navy (5-4)
6 Square in Seville or La Paz complex (5)
7 Active naïve lad's busy playing football (5,3,7)
8 Root crop'll reportedly be devastated by it? (6)
12 Romantic rendezvous in Bash Street? (5)
14 Spy kid hotel's let in for 17 swim (6-3)
15 Window fitting helps to make washing easier (5)
16 Ragamuffin grabbed by four Chinese (6)
18 Treated with manure, say, unlike 17 (7)
20 Serious complaint regarding English steak (1-4)
21 Jeremy's clubs (5)
25 Ate flounders for it? (3)

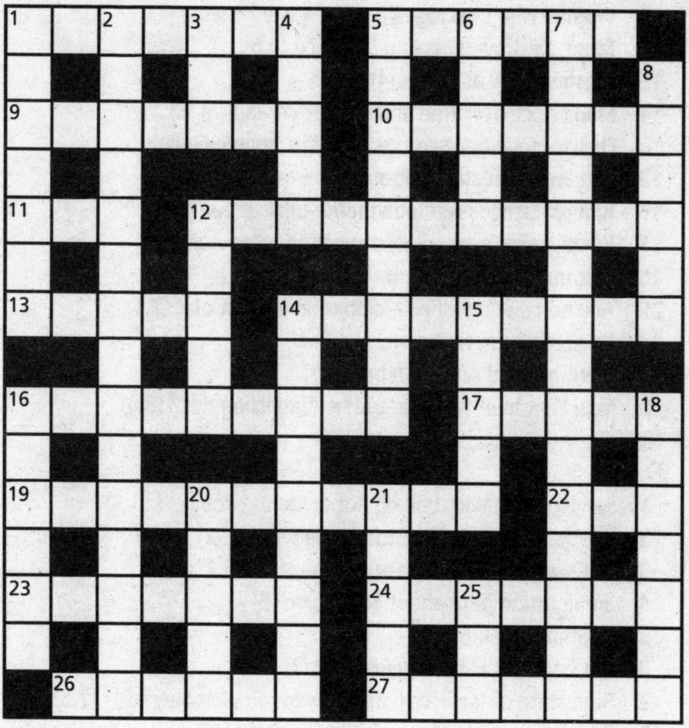
1
2
3
4
5
6
7
8
9
10
11
12
13
14
15
16
17
18
19
20
21
22
23
24
25
26
27

195

Across

1 Stormy sail crossings not good for small cutters (4,8)
8 Endure longer tramping a route around Wales (7)
9 Woman who's engaged in café wasted energy (7)
11 Target destroyed playing with Coe (4,6)
12 Finished spell at Lord's (4)
14 Mob knock over tree and dither over radical (8)
16 Persian governor captured artist in troubled past (6)
17 Fine work affected fellow (3)
19 Two old pence invested in fence post as oar (6)
21 Awful traffic almost stops Joe writing on wall (8)
24 Volcanic rock's strong, by the sound of it (4)
25 Tiny home PC crashed – smoke comes out of it (7,3)
27 An area to run round etc. playfully (7)
28 Mark trapped American bear (7)
29 New York men fixed central heating using this? (6,6)

Down

1 Serve up tart with boiling hot contents? You bet! (3,4)
2 Windows installed in entirely the wrong way with no skill (10)
3 Get rid of very loud violent roughs first (5,3)
4 Immigration data about 50 women (6)
5 Examine small tin (4)
6 Get back in car touring Ecuador (7)
7 High state of tension in music event on Wembley turf? (7,5)
10 Sing a triplet out of tune and very loud (3-9)
13 Husband's fallen awkwardly on boy in hold (4-6)
15 Start of frustrated attempt to climb in mist (3)
18 Concert is supported by Queen? He gives his word (8)
20 Actually faced up to … (2,5)
22 … current MP's every charge (7)
23 Happy here playing in city suburbs (6)
26 Sell wild fruit to king (4)

196

Across

1 Couple consider, say, paper in Nick's window? (3-3,6)

8 Nelson maybe back in fleet, upmarket (7)

9 A large number in factory working after one (7)

11 Harry needed pal round Birkenhead who's trustworthy (10)

12 He secures seats (4)

14 Can flu spread if confined? It's dubious (8)

16 Englishman in Mexico going swimming across river (6)

17 On which to perform a tumble, almost all stripped (3)

19 Mysterious phenomena half occupied officer (6)

21 Sweeper guards everything in Lyceum, say (8)

24 Famous office where tests are held (4)

25 Former Russian zone is rentable, surprisingly (4,6)

27 Dictionary has note about Queen's cervids (3,4)

28 Vegetable books written by amateur in jail (7)

29 Courses built specially for serious disease (12)

Down

1 Shane Warne imparted it in place around leg (7)

2 Naughty boys listen apparently! (10)

3 Blue plant – a good mature variety (8)

4 It's hard to understand silent ballet occasionally (6)

5 Part of small order sent up for some bread (4)

6 View old cogwheel (7)

7 Bride's attendant is a tart (4,2,6)

10 Representation of modern Darwin is prejudiced (6-6)

13 Urban transport? Yes, but out of order around 5 (10)

15 Where to light a Bunsen initially (3)

18 Skilful Attila manoeuvred with two corps (8)

20 Take tea inside mostly warm French castle (7)

22 They help wheels run smoothly in new casino (about 50) (7)

23 Bolivian leader in FARC seized current material (6)

26 Golfers everywhere took him to their heart (4)

197

Across

6 Everyone knows that very old course (7,7)

9 Dozing – please disturb! (6)

10 All to get in order to pay for entry here (4,4)

11 In first form exam included one drink (8)

13 Government due for shake-up round 2000 stuck together (6)

15 Herdsman gathers third of herd in port (6)

17 Fare badly – there's lead about in cheap house (6)

19 People follow a copper's keen sense of judgement (6)

20 First minister's on tablets for 11 film show (8)

22 Angry Zambia cut web broadcast in country nearby (8)

24 French author stored piano in university grounds (6)

26 Words reported in address behind roundabout (8,6)

Down

1 Theatrical event in RC church pioneered by Ford? (4,10)

2 Expert earns millions as peak of achievement (4)

3 Spent nearly 90p to get skittle (6)

4 Six lines on mature king, a character in Hamlet? (8)

5 All-male theatre's not finished (4)

7 Hat keeps dry just the tiniest part (6)

8 Rising men Dickie and David lost lead in old constituencies (6,8)

12 Good space for newly-wed (5)

14 Ottoman leader fit to work under Greek character (5)

16 Aim to have Le Bon controversially made a peer, say (8)

18 Optimistic Bishop dressed in taupe bizarrely (6)

21 Leak peace moves involving Sweden (6)

23 Security's essentially reliable in retirement (4)

25 Run into writer at the heels of the hunt (4)

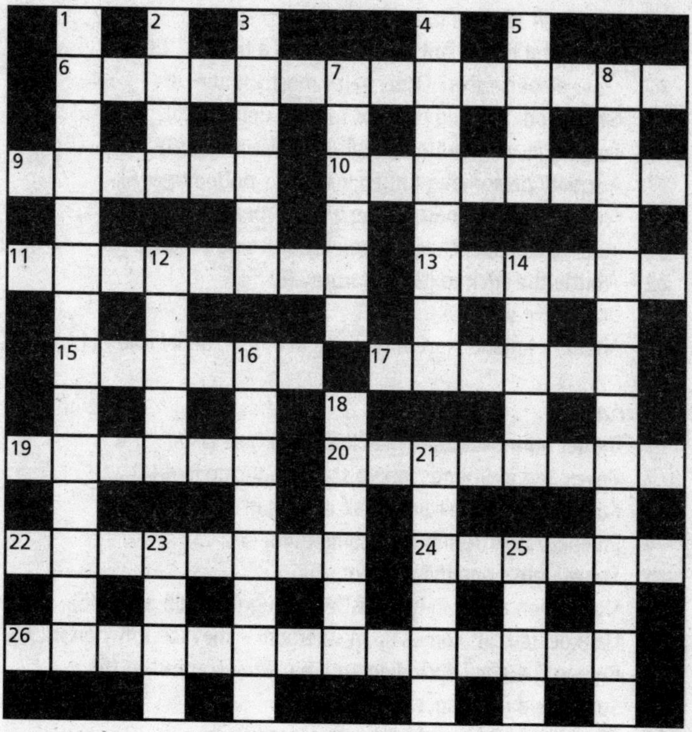
1
2
3
4
5
6
7
8
9
10
11
12
13
14
15
16
17
18
19
20
21
22
23
24
25
26

198

Across

6 Wild crew once seen mobbing National Front in press meeting (4,10)
9 Not much silver in lake (6)
10 It's helpful to put salt round bend on a track ... (8)
11 ... to disperse this? Other salt's mostly flown (8)
13 Getting on, I should perhaps remove uniform (6)
15 Country in union with Georgia and elsewhere (6)
17 A snooty person overturned institute's potted tree (6)
19 Problem: what separates the wheat from the chaff? (6)
20 In middle of speech it's extremely touching for all (8)
22 Whittle the stick to make it sturdy (8)
24 Dr. 5 wove yarn (6)
26 About 4, I made start in working in a managerial role (14)

Down

1 Dinner hour used to revitalise such people (14)
2 Wives and girlfriends last to start producing loot (4)
3 Rash groom came round, half lacking in zeal (6)
4 Prosperous watering-hole commotion (4-2-2)
5 The athlete's qualifying event (4)
7 No women about in Newcastle to snuggle down with? (6)
8 Unexpected gift comes up in saleroom – they identify donor (9,5)
12 Remap Danelaw excluding an area in the south-east (5)
14 Springfield needing a brush-up (5)
16 "Red Ken" is dressed in chamois, say (8)
18 Music group texts everywhere when touring Spain (6)
21 Organise Sting's mate to be put up endlessly (6)
23 Some psychics are smart (4)
25 Drops artist at home (4)

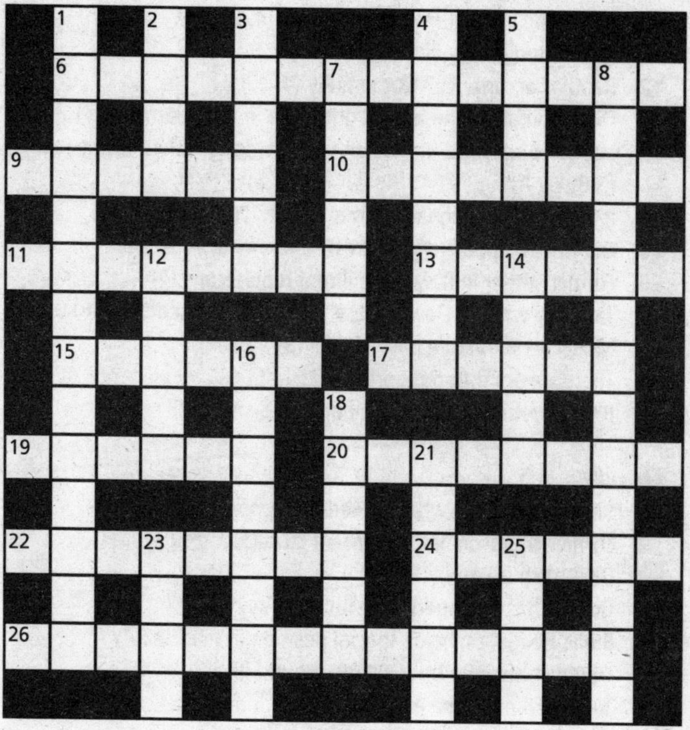
1
2
3
4
5
6
7
8
9
10
11
12
13
14
15
16
17
18
19
20
21
22
23
24
25
26

199

Across

1 He nicked a good poem adapted for part of website (4,4)
5 Model doing without one colour (6)
9 Attila and Co's strange formal wear (4,4)
10 Mistreated chesty old cropper (6)
12 Regular occurrence? Not entirely (4)
13 Dishonourable man has let grit loose in farm barrier (6,4)
15 Lucrative schemes by foreign spy in among violent Norsemen (5-8)
19 It may end in resignation over no-fees cut fiasco (4,2,7)
23 Old doctor apparently mistreated Tory with ache (10)
25 Former settler in Italy left militant republicans (4)
28 Tangling with 16 Down, these fools could be seditious (6)
29 Madly keen to store pink 18 fuel (8)
30 There's a point to this sort of match (6)
31 Pity my return route cuts suburbs of Sydney (8)

Down

1 Plot here to raise what's owed to support house (6)
2 Former NI prison houses current crop (5)
3 Deck stuff (4)
4 Cooper has managed store full of 2, say (7)
6 Sonic Hedgehog holds special position in market (5)
7 Obstruct institute on rent-free ground (9)
8 Too much medicine more than does damage (8)
11 Heartlessly precipitous part of staircase (4)
14 Found out about Open (4)
15 Alien rock emerges from remote time, miles away (9)
16 She's to take action (3)
17 Student body gathers old intelligence (4)
18 A classic way into getting trained for flying (8)
20 Get ready to fire farmyard boss (4)
21 Children 27 here in new Surrey complex (7)
22 4's customer maybe by hosting a king and queen (6)
24 Initially head overseas to enjoy leisure there (5)
26 Useless computer equipment has upset writer (5)
27 Concert's first to end in easy victory (4)

1
2
3
4
5
6
7
8
9
10
11
12
13
14
15
16
17
18
19
20
21
22
23
24
25
26
27
28
29
30
31

200

Across

1 Guarantee mad tyrant's guillotined after conflict (8)
5 Mostly worked with barrel-maker (6)
9 In teashop, a German fellow first produces drug (8)
10 Dozy agent receives shelter (6)
12 Odd number head off? Quite the opposite (4)
13 Police raid *Nuts* magazine (10)
15 Model Elle on the spot? Paps get closer with it (9,4)
19 12 is moving in personal property – it brings results (13)
23 Chopped up liver with lime to cover cold pasta (10)
25 Seven-piece group releases record: *Let it be* (4)
28 Brought up and torn down, say (6)
29 He connects caller to king after Tosca, say (8)
30 See round a small island without difficulty (6)
31 Again take on carefree MP, loyal to some extent (2-6)

Down

1 Evil, like a night light? (6)
2 Rebel leader starts life perhaps possessing this (5)
3 Top primate's unknown (4)
4 After 10 'e he got stuck into drink to get tight ... (5,2)
6 ... drunk usually well before it! (5)
7 Priest gets to embrace rabbi and other churchmen (9)
8 Exciting story about boxer and fan of King (8)
11 Monopolists store up crops in it (4)
14 Smart guy in fancy lace (4)
15 Welsh river waders' protection on boats (9)
16 Henry the Fourth's complaint? (3)
17 Finished deliveries at the Oval (4)
18 Cantankerous salesman comes up with poem (8)
20 Sure-footed climber in central Tibet chased by 10 (4)
21 Obscure bits of film found in middle of Greece (7)
22 Tale about maelstrom's origin in such weather (6)
24 Perfect ladies almost unsettled (5)
26 Write off to a lecturer, buying time (5)
27 Small amount for good sheep (4)

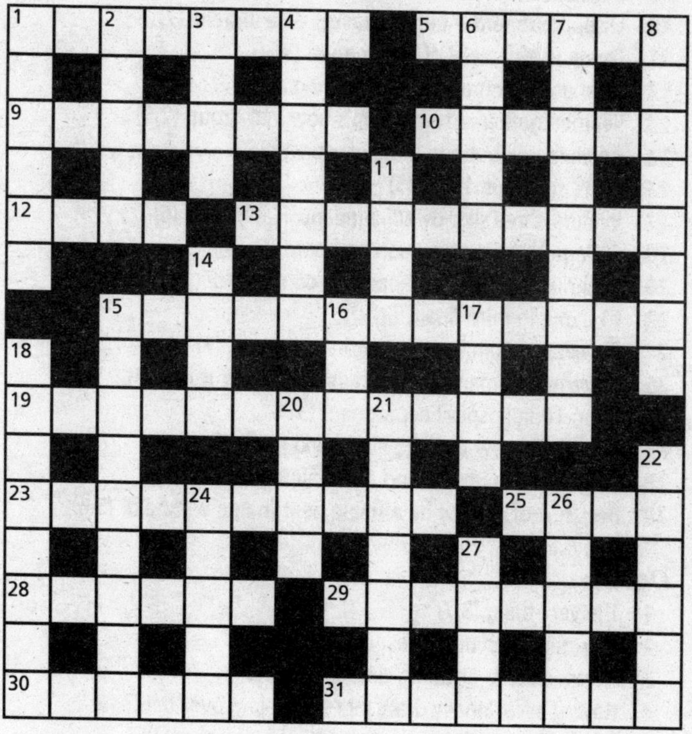

201

Across

1 Harry credited bishop with it in regular payment (6,5)
9 Denies violent features lack "Adult" designation (7)
10 Disappointment – terrible basket case initially (7)
11 Dump useful piece of information (3)
12 Strongly discourage runner veering a bit (7)
13 Seamen gathered round ship's bow in a group (2,5)
14 Consume all but odd parts of repast (3)
15 Bird's religious, 11 10 (5)
17 In Paris, three slightly adjusted musical groups (5)
18 College locks main person on board (5)
20 Odd-numbered pages appear in correct order (5)
22 11 came in third finally (3)
24 Element of humility's not entirely unusual (7)
25 Government managed tax outstanding for tramp (7)
26 Chop 10 in hospital department (3)
27 Hannibal's new place to stand and read (7)
28 King's feeling unwell and complaining bitterly (7)
29 Best sort of oil may be arriving next (name withheld) (5,6)

Down

1 The very thing (8,7)
2 Part-time Arab upset pest controller (3-4)
3 Actors start to examine class in India (5)
4 Having occasionally dicky pipes rumbling over time? (9)
5 Graduate put millions in that anti-slip device (4,3)
6 Strange rite in interpreting and rewriting letters (15)
7 Bird complaint (6)
8 Alpine sportsmen's dubious risks about end of race (6)
16 Urge to burn borders of pretty European state (9)
18 Ring youth leader about money, making no fuss (6)
19 Poet's clothing torn around end (7)
21 Developing energy-free egg and onion purée? (7)
23 Delirium tremens starts limiting old age? Exactly that (6)
25 Composer displayed drive (5)

202

Across

1. All animals except birds and mammals are heartless (4-7)
9. Old weapon given as mark of deep regret in China (7)
10. He oversees football supporter touring Rome perhaps (7)
11. What's boring? Everything, by the sound of it (3)
12. Lay out clothes department with skill (7)
13. It helps clear the air in the section I service (7)
14. Go on and on about wages in recession (3)
15. Arm supporters to thwart raid on island (5)
17. Those who are chosen among the Israelites (5)
18. People in northern Iraq mentioned source of cheese (5)
20. Actors start to entertain class in India (5)
22. Laughed regularly for a long time (3)
24. Mythical beast's mad canter engaged Ulysses at first (7)
25. I'll go round to probe cipher to find clash (7)
26. Daniel avoids odd characters in trouble (3)
27. He's too self-absorbed, say, to sit elsewhere (7)
28. Bomb attack destroys 15 protecting gunners (3,4)
29. Aaron spells out what to install to save energy (5,6)

Down

1. I left rocky moon in outer space at the same time (15)
2. It's caught and cooked, but not in the same pot (7)
3. Incidentally, it doesn't include the minor road (5)
4. Old kinky film fellow collected – it's prohibited (3,6)
5. Madden foreign grandee (7)
6. Following row at home, a man is silly to keep large pets (8,7)
7. Corrupt son unwilling to work to earn euros (6)
8. EU's in reverse, taking wrong turn? Yes, it's wrong (6)
16. House-painter broke a record, investing turnover (9)
18. A former friend of Castro in court to win prestige (6)
19. Secretary brought in a list specially about room (7)
21. Extend general broadcast (7)
23. Edward's accepted crew changes (6)
25. She's caught by Brian, WI cricketer (5)

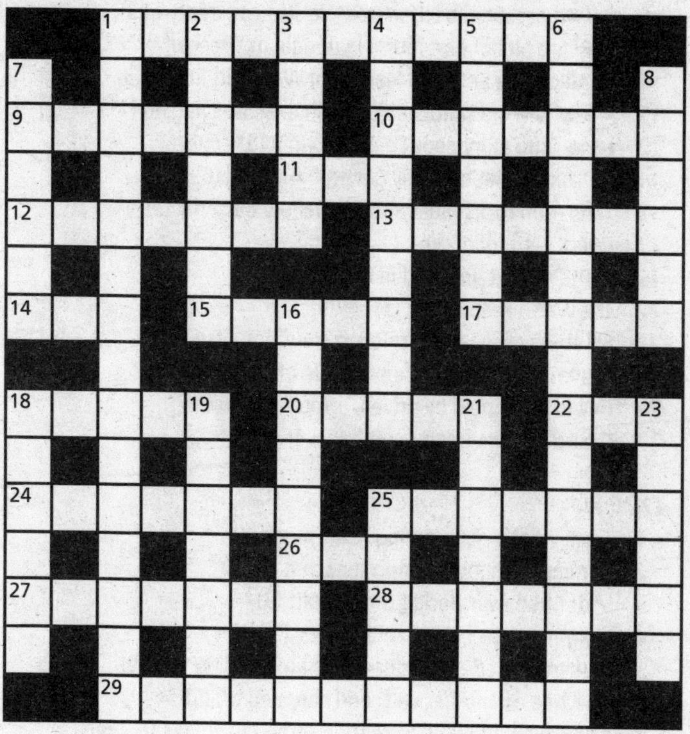

203

Across

1 PM took part, having admitted British difficulty (7)
5 Young reporter lives with East End artist (6)
9 Brown accepted best alternative security treaty (4,3)
10 Obscure bits of film found in middle of Greece (7)
11 Conflict, one between leaders of West and Russia (3)
12 A few rare old sailors enjoy posh exercises in gym (11)
13 Long, long story about earth's origin (5)
14 US soldier meets barmy general for drink (6,3)
16 Timber on rocks hides sulphur yellow butterfly (9)
17 Check car model (5)
19 Men Prescott annoyed in dispute (11)
22 The Welsh keep sheep (3)
23 Six shillings in poor wretched condition (7)
24 Leaves Lear's daughter in middle of wood (7)
26 Get to races held by drivers' group at home (6)
27 Castro follows trendy non-believer (7)

Down

1 Track what's gone wrong in earnings (7)
2 Comment on job location for scout (11,4)
3 Shot lifted over Becker at the start (3)
4 Long note can be read either way (5)
5 Alec organised and managed church closing sale (9)
6 One tree or another with end chopped off (5)
7 Andy dumped plans to change company drivers (6,3,6)
8 Franchisees sell up, squeezing tenant (6)
12 Soprano in America's hole in the head (5)
14 Doctor got shown round outback – nobody lives there (5,4)
15 College tests ten in the morning in French art (5)
16 British epics exaggerated beefcake features (6)
18 I wear fresh floret, typically shamrock (7)
20 Girl in film eats a yogurt dish (5)
21 New Zealanders wander round island (5)
25 Is he the Spanish leader of the fairies? (3)

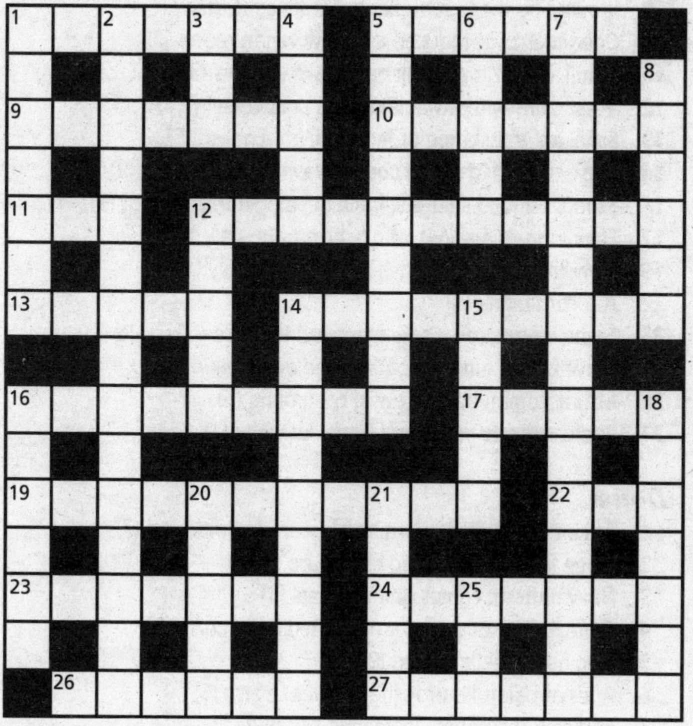

1
2
3
4
5
6
7
8
9
10
11
12
13
14
15
16
17
18
19
20
21
22
23
24
25
26
27

204

Across

1 4-0 in Cuba collapse? Rest up in this (7)
5 With training he could save litres in shower (6)
9 It could be the first of plants Auntie cultivated (7)
10 Condiment I introduced into new vegan recipe (7)
11 Either way, some bacilli may make you this (3)
12 Vessel, urn with a vile liquid – a vital vessel (7,4)
13 Subdued translation of Te Deum, not English (5)
14 Replace scuffed suede uppers, having scrubbed up (9)
16 Saw: Desmond sent one back to woodworker at first (9)
17 Fully mature and not wholly bad, ultimately (5)
19 How crook acquires dosh? In style, possibly (11)
22 A record high? (3)
23 Given instruction, Eddie managed to hire one female (7)
24 Tenor pulled out of Croatian medley for wind instrument (7)
26 Irish accommodate a few in compound (6)
27 Radio covered year in despotic authority (7)

Down

1 A gym is installed in British Museum for initiation (7)
2 Three figures describing one figure (5,10)
3 Navy uniform comes first in vessel (3)
4 Con/Lib new government recruited a big noise (5)
5 Film has to be unfolded (9)
6 A bit of painful narrowing of bone in arm (5)
7 In which the upper classes are 23? (6,9)
8 Charles makes an impression, I hear (6)
12 Hardy's obscure hero engaged German lawyer (5)
14 Hose supporter in communists' uprising about US writer (9)
15 Prepared cash (5)
16 Weird guest intermittently reveals clever device (6)
18 Old man hedges island in right-wing garden art (7)
20 This plus heroin produces morphine? Oui! (5)
21 Suspect salesman has recipe for fish (5)
25 He's said to be taking over broadcast (3)

1 Capital. 5 Sample. 9 Project. 10 Monocle. 11 End. 12
Constrained. 13 Sisal. 14 Universal. 16 Repenting. 17 Timid.
19 Blameworthy. 22 Nag. 23 Egotism. 24 Palette. 26 Skinny.
27 Secures.

Down
1 Cypress. 2 Proud as a peacock. 3 Tie. 4 Latin. 5 Something.
6 Mania. 7 Loch Ness monster. 8 Feudal. 12 Colon. 14
Uniformly. 15 Entry. 16 Rubber. 18 Digress. 20 Evian.
21 Tapes. 25 Lac.

Solutions

26

Across
1 Frankincense. 8 Evasion. 9 Bungled. 11 Matchmaker.
12 Half. 14 Furbelow. 16 Estate. 17 Oaf. 19 Frolic. 21
Rekindle. 24 Iota. 25 Descendant. 27 Edition. 28 Inertia. 29
Short-sighted.

Down
1 Flatter. 2 Arithmetic. 3 Kangaroo. 4 Nabbed. 5 Erne. 6
Sultana. 7 Term of office. 10 Differential. 13 Assignment. 15
War. 18 Fetching. 20 Ostrich. 22 Drafted. 23 Tennis. 26 Liar.

27

Across
6 Elizabethan age. 9 Stance. 10 Courting. 11 Carriage. 13
Hilary. 15 Ambush. 17 Israel. 19 Weasel. 20 Emission. 22
Hiawatha. 24 Onrush. 26 Tatterdemalion.

Down
1 Central America. 2 Finn. 3 Camera. 4 Thoughts. 5 Gnat. 7
Etched. 8 General consent. 12 Rebus. 14 Loads. 16 Solitary.
18 Legate. 21 Isobar. 23 Wits. 25 Ruin.

Solutions 1–4

1 *Across* **6** Whippersnapper. **9** Edible. **10** Soul mate.
11 Eminence. **13** Lethal. **15** Nimbus. **17** Oyster. **19** Mishit.
20 Epidemic. **22** Informed. **24** Denial. **26** Flight recorder.

Down **1** Two-dimensional. **2** Limb. **3** Spleen. **4** Annually.
5 Spam. **7** Russet. **8** Extraordinaire. **12** Nymph. **14** Title.
16 Ultimate. **18** Beadle. **21** Indoor. **23** Orgy. **25** Nude.

2 *Across* **1** Peer pressure. **8** Enclave. **9** Perturb.
11 Real estate. **12** Idea. **14** Layabout. **16** Candid. **17** Mad.
19 Gaiety. **21** Nebulous. **24** Cage. **25** Horror film. **27** Lookout.
28 Aeolian. **29** Spokesperson.

Down **1** Peccary. **2** Exacerbate. **3** Plectrum. **4** Expats.
5 Sore. **6** Rounded. **7** Neurological. **10** Blandishment.
13 Salubrious. **15** Tan. **18** Decrease. **20** In-group.
22 Opinion. **23** Foetus. **26** Hock.

3 *Across* **1** National debt. **8** Reuters. **9** Blossom.
11 Voiceprint. **12** Fair. **14** Agitated. **16** Bikini. **17** Run.
19 Intake. **21** Outgoing. **24** Iffy. **25** Gamekeeper. **27** Seeking.
28 Oarless. **29** Haberdashery.

Down **1** Nautili. **2** Theme parks. **3** Observer. **4** Albino.
5 Drop. **6** Basmati. **7** Trivialities. **10** Morning dress.
13 King George. **15** Duo. **18** Numerous. **20** Taffeta.
22 Impiety. **23** Ragged. **26** Fine.

4 *Across* **1** Ministry. **5** Kismet. **9** Youthful. **10** Narnia.
12 Last. **13** Adjudicate. **15** Sound judgment.
19 Norfolk Broads. **23** Daily bread. **25** Shoe. **28** Trilby.
29 Director. **30** Dry rot. **31** Smoothie.

Down **1** Mayfly. **2** Nouns. **3** Soho. **4** Rounded. **6** Iraqi.
7 Man-eaters. **8** Travesty. **11** Guru. **14** Euro. **15** Servility.
16 Jib. **17** Grab. **18** Unedited. **20** Kerb. **21** Realism. **22** George.
24 Yobbo. **26** Hutch. **27** Demo.

Solutions 5–8

5 *Across* **6** Weather station. **9** Advice. **10** Footpath.
11 Imminent. **13** In-offs. **15** Nought. **17** Wealth. **19** Cinema.
20 Overdose. **22** On the dot. **24** Custom. **26** Alphanumerical.

Down **1** Two-dimensional. **2** Saki. **3** Cheese. **4** Atropine.
5 Step. **7** Refute. **8** Out of this world. **12** In use. **14** Oiled.
16 Hoarding. **18** Bottom. **21** Encore. **23** Ha-ha. **25** Sick.

6 *Across* **6** Underdeveloped. **9** Stitch. **10** Redcoats.
11 Spectral. **13** Import. **15** In-laws. **17** Uglier. **19** Cannon.
20 Headrest. **22** Wingspan. **24** Frenzy. **26** Interpretation.

Down **1** Multiplication. **2** Edit. **3** Arthur. **4** Seedling.
5 Hobo. **7** Eerily. **8** Enterprise zone. **12** Colon. **14** Prior.
16 Windpipe. **18** Chance. **21** Affray. **23** Geek. **25** Exit.

7 *Across* **1** Penalty kick. **9** Excites. **10** Seminar. **11** Lot.
12 Ovulate. **13** Earthen. **14** Foe. **15** Field. **17** Evade. **18** Stoic.
20 Crypt. **22** Tag. **24** Astride. **25** Abridge. **26** QED. **27** Plateau.
28 Drawers. **29** Dead ringers.

Down **1** Picture postcard. **2** Not half. **3** Lisle. **4** Yesterday.
5 Immerse. **6** Kind-heartedness. **7** Tee off. **8** Bronze.
16 Exchequer. **18** Scampi. **19** Chimera. **21** Terrace. **23** Greasy.
25 Add-on.

8 *Across* **1** Sob story. **5** Make do. **9** Shake-ups. **10** Clause.
12 Ewer. **13** Jerry-built. **15** Impressionism. **19** Preoccupation.
23 Interferon. **25** Shun. **28** Nickel. **29** Commando. **30** Lilies.
31 Gymkhana.

Down **1** Sister. **2** Brave. **3** Trek. **4** Replete. **6** Ad lib.
7 Erudition. **8** Overtime. **11** Iris. **14** Epic. **15** Identical. **16** Sap.
17 Omit **18** Optional. **20** Used. **21** Apology. **22** Angora.
24 Reeve. **26** Henna. **27** Amok.

Solutions 9–12

9   *Across*   **1** Bayonets. **5** Skiers. **9** Old flame. **10** Mosque.
12 Silk. **13** Cartoonist. **15** Specification. **19** Spitting Image.
23 Usurpation. **25** Guru. **28** Iraqis. **29** Ricochet. **30** Geezer.
31 Sea horse.

Down   **1** Browse. **2** Yodel. **3** Null. **4** Timpani. **6** Kyoto.
7 Exquisite. **8** Sweating. **11** Etui. **14** Text. **15** Stimulate.
16 Fog. **17** Adam. **18** Assuming. **20** Note. **21** Idolise.
22 Auntie. **24** Poise. **26** Usher. **27** Tosh.

10   *Across*   **1** Bus stop. **5** Scribe. **9** Nuanced. **10** Autocue.
11 Odd. **12** Well dressed. **13** Ruffs. **14** Corollary. **16** Epidermis.
17 Giddy. **19** Aphrodisiac. **22** Ice. **23** Deepest. **24** Suspend.
26 Estate. **27** Elapsed.

Down   **1** Bonjour. **2** Standoffishness. **3** Tic. **4** Pedal.
5 Standards. **6** Retie. **7** Back-seat drivers. **8** Deadly. **12** Waste.
14 Committee. **15** Logic. **16** Elands. **18** Yielded. **20** Omega.
21 Issue. **25** Spa.

11   *Across*   **1** Jabberwocky. **9** Hamster. **10** Tribute. **11** Lac.
12 Weighty. **13** Heigh-ho. **14** Rug. **15** Pasha. **17** Elope.
18 Toffs. **20** Bless. **22** Tar. **24** Implant. **25** Measles. **26** Oca.
27 Tea room. **28** Godsend. **29** Efficacious.

Down   **1** Jumping-off place. **2** Botch-up. **3** Early.
4 Watchcase. **5** Cuisine. **6** Youth hostellers. **7** Shower.
8 Become. **16** Subatomic. **18** Thirty. **19** Slag off. **21** So-and-so.
23 Reside. **25** Magic.

12   *Across*   **1** Compost heap. **9** Annular. **10** Rostrum. **11** Ely.
12 Deejays. **13** Pie-eyed. **14** Lei. **15** Debar. **17** Drone.
18 Conga. **20** Style. **22** Fur. **24** Overarm. **25** Eardrum. **26** Eye.
27 Doormat. **28** Resents. **29** Decolletage.

Down   **1** Convenience food. **2** Mallard. **3** Ogres.
4 Tory party. **5** East End. **6** Party conference. **7** Sandal.
8 Smudge. **16** Base metal. **18** Cloudy. **19** Anaemic.
21 Eurasia. **23** Remiss. **25** Eerie.

Solutions 13–16

13 *Across* **1** Departmental. **8** Organic. **9** Phantom.
11 Strengthen. **12** Unit. **14** On the sly. **16** Eclair. **17** Set.
19 Cajole. **21** Signally. **24** Raja. **25** Sheet metal. **27** Set sail.
28 Orchids. **29** Out of the blue.

Down **1** Dogtrot. **2** Pine needle. **3** Recitals. **4** Muppet.
5 Near. **6** Antenna. **7** House of cards. **10** Motorcyclist.
13 Economical. **15** Yes. **18** Time zone. **20** Jujitsu. **22** Latrine.
23 Chalet. **26** Sago.

14 *Across* **1** Chassis. **5** Raceme. **9** Brazier. **10** Fair sex. **11** Lea.
12 Impermanent. **13** Ratel. **14** Neighbour. **16** Fort Worth.
17 Riser. **19** Coffee house. **22** Ill. **23** A la mode. **24** Baloney.
26 At rest. **27** Lip-read.

Down **1** Cobbler. **2** As a matter of fact. **3** Ski. **4** Strip.
5 Refurbish. **6** China. **7** Master of Science. **8** Exeter.
12 In-law. **14** Northwest. **15** Horse. **16** Facial. **18** Relayed.
20 Evoke. **21** Umbel. **25** Lap.

15 *Across* **1** Suspend. **5** Except. **9** Erasure. **10** Chemist.
11 Leo. **12** Armour plate. **13** Habit. **14** So to speak.
16 Bath chair. **17** Agree. **19** Cold storage. **22** Pub. **23** Exhaust.
24 Emperor. **26** Smelly. **27** Tally-ho.

Down **1** Stealth. **2** Star of Bethlehem. **3** Emu. **4** Dream.
5 Encounter. **6** Cheep. **7** Private property. **8** Streak. **12** Attic.
14 Seaworthy. **15** Stale. **16** Bucket. **18** Embargo. **20** Skull.
21 Agent. **25** Pal.

16 *Across* **6** Washing machine. **9** Proust. **10** Inscribe.
11 Espousal. **13** Lather. **15** Annual. **17** Afters. **19** Cleric.
20 Operator. **22** Swelling. **24** Result. **26** Cross-examining.

Down **1** Sword-swallower. **2** Esau. **3** Hiatus. **4** Bass clef.
5 Char. **7** Grille. **8** Noblesse oblige. **12** Owner. **14** Theta.
16 Archives. **18** Loggia. **21** Earwig. **23** Lush. **25** Soil.

Solutions 17–20

17 **Across** **1** Accidentally. **8** Animals. **9** Whisper.
11 Third class. **12** Poll. **14** Catalyse. **16** Groyne. **17** Eva.
19 Oyster. **21** Epistles. **24** Pâté. **25** Belladonna. **27** Idolise.
28 Gunfire. **29** Antimacassar.

Down **1** Animist. **2** Chandelier. **3** Disclose. **4** Newish.
5 Aria. **6** Leprosy. **7** Fait accompli. **10** Roller skater.
13 Presidents. **15** Eve. **18** Apologia. **20** Sit down. **22** Lankier.
23 Geneva. **26** Mini.

18 **Across** **1** Lobotomising. **8** Bandana. **9** Thermal.
11 Tourniquet. **12** Crow. **14** Caryatid. **16** Teller. **17** Lid.
19 Exhale. **21** Golf ball. **24** Awry. **25** Double beds. **27** Entails.
28 Oxidise. **29** Occasionally.

Down **1** Languor. **2** Biannually. **3** Tranquil. **4** Mitten.
5 Seen. **6** Numeral. **7** Obstacle race. **10** Lower classes.
13 Self-denial. **15** Dig. **18** Doubloon. **20** Heretic. **22** Amenity.
23 Bonsai. **26** Visa.

19 **Across** **1** Plankton. **5** Coffin. **9** Antelope. **10** Enjoin.
12 Earl. **13** Refinement. **15** Dressing table.
19 Broken-hearted. **23** T-bone steak. **25** Slur. **28** Uganda.
29 Emphasis. **30** Tutors. **31** Scenario.

Down **1** Peahen. **2** Alter. **3** Kilt. **4** Oppress. **6** Ounce.
7 Flowerbed. **8** Nineteen. **11** Kiln. **14** Cede. **15** Deodorant.
16 Ire. **17** Tata. **18** Obstruct. **20** Hats. **21** Anaemic. **22** Fresco.
24 Elder. **26** Loser. **27** Shin.

20 **Across** **6** Indecipherable. **9** Editor. **10** Chipmunk.
11 Logotype. **13** Duster. **15** Prince. **17** Octavo. **19** Asleep.
20 Rescript. **22** Last post. **24** Endure. **26** Venture capital.

Down **1** Birds of passage. **2** Adit. **3** Scurry. **4** Periodic.
5 Palm. **7** Pocket. **8** Lance corporals. **12** Ovine. **14** Stair.
16 Cupboard. **18** Critic. **21** Steppe. **23** Ta-ta. **25** Date.

Solutions 21–24

21   *Across*   **6** Alsace-Lorraine. **9** Stereo. **10** Describe.
11 Navy blue. **13** Midget. **15** Tomboy. **17** Angels. **19** Scanty.
20 Overlook. **22** Split pea. **24** Temple. **26** Central heating.

     Down   **1** Past participle. **2** User. **3** School. **4** Freshman.
5 Pair. **7** Ladder. **8** Noblesse oblige. **12** Yemen. **14** Dwell.
16 Olympian. **18** Potash. **21** Entrap. **23** Iota. **25** Main.

22   *Across*   **1** Intravenous. **9** Nosebag. **10** Offbeat. **11** Ulm.
12 Tickles. **13** Meat pie. **14** Her. **15** Refer. **17** Denim.
18 Cuppa. **20** Chess. **22** Pro. **24** Bellini. **25** Ego trip. **26** Ohm.
27 Lie-down. **28** Albania. **29** Trailblazer.

     Down   **1** Insect repellent. **2** Tubular. **3** Angus.
4 E-commerce. **5** Offhand. **6** Sleeping partner. **7** Snatch.
8 Stream. **16** Fictional. **18** Cobble. **19** Arizona. **21** Showbiz.
23 Orphan. **25** E-mail.

23   *Across*   **1** Woodcock. **5** Escudo. **9** Eligible. **10** Bridle.
12 Tier. **13** Dreamworld. **15** Guided missile.
19 Feeding bottle. **23** Interprets. **25** Isle. **28** Isobar.
29 Obdurate. **30** Latest. **31** Brake pad.

     Down   **1** Wreath. **2** Olive. **3** Coin. **4** Calorie. **6** Straw.
7 Undermine. **8** Overdoes. **11** Calm. **14** Kiwi. **15** Greatcoat.
16 Dab. **17** Site. **18** Official. **20** Germ. **21** October.
22 Behead. **24** Roads. **26** Sharp. **27** Duck.

24   *Across*   **1** Part-time. **5** Powwow. **9** Tapeworm. **10** Callus.
12 Nude. **13** Clothes peg. **15** Every which way.
19 Prime minister. **23** Spot checks. **25** Loch. **28** Dainty.
29 Slag heap. **30** Celery. **31** Staysail.

     Down   **1** Patent. **2** Rapid. **3** Town. **4** Morally. **6** Ovate.
7 Willpower. **8** Wise guys. **11** Etch. **14** Cede. **15** Editorial.
16 Won. **17** City. **18** Episodic. **20** Ibex. **21** Ink blot. **22** Chapel.
24 Cater. **26** Omega. **27** Ugly.

Solutions 25–28

25 *Across* **1** Towpath. **5** Evenly. **9** Own goal. **10** Earldom.
11 Gas. **12** Crystal sets. **13** Tired. **14** Atrophied. **16** Diesel oil.
17 Nawab. **19** Down-and-outs. **22** Ice. **23** Captain. **24** Falsify.
26 Breeze. **27** Tear gas.

Down **1** Thought. **2** Windscreen wiper. **3** Ado. **4** Holly.
5 Electoral. **6** Enrol. **7** Ladies-in-waiting. **8** Amused. **12** Cadge.
14 Avoidance. **15** Pants. **16** Deduce. **18** Bye-byes. **20** Awake.
21 Unfit. **25** Lea.

26 *Across* **1** Shaving foam. **9** Scenery. **10** Lounger. **11** Led.
12 Inkwell. **13** Elegist. **14** Elf. **15** Salsa. **17** Thyme. **18** Rehab.
20 Sieve. **22** Nay. **24** Pedants. **25** Illegal. **26** Tub. **27** Saviour.
28 Soprano. **29** Left-wingers.

Down **1** Speak of the devil. **2** Ageless. **3** Idyll. **4** Golden age.
5 Opulent. **6** Magnifying glass. **7** Aspire. **8** Writhe. **16** Last straw.
18 Repast. **19** Bunk off. **21** Ellipse. **23** Yellow. **25** Ibsen.

27 *Across* **1** Impedimenta. **9** Restate. **10** Rehears. **11** Sri.
12 Berates. **13** Hip bone. **14** Yam. **15** Media. **17** Reins.
18 Pence. **20** Stall. **22** Sac. **24** Pharaoh. **25** Sincere. **26** Ago.
27 Critter. **28** Network. **29** Nucleic acid.

Down **1** Instrumentation. **2** Phantom. **3** Dress.
4 Marihuana. **5** No-hoper. **6** Anabolic steroid. **7** Crabby.
8 Aspens. **16** Discharge. **18** Papacy. **19** Elastic. **21** Lunatic.
23 Checks. **25** Sonic.

28 *Across* **1** Rose-coloured. **8** Insular. **9** Therein.
11 Dendrology. **12** Stir. **14** Mesmeric. **16** Untrue. **17** Cop.
19 Aboard. **21** Demerara. **24** Otto. **25** Social work.
27 Re-elect. **28** Avignon. **29** Countersigns.

Down **1** Resents. **2** Solar years. **3** Cyrillic. **4** Let's go.
5 Used. **6** Elector. **7** Misdemeanour. **10** Nerve-racking.
13 Underlying. **15** Cod. **18** Pelicans. **20** On the go. **22** Anoints.
23 Jostle. **26** Vein.

Solutions 29–32

29 *Across* **1** Hostess. **5** Belt up. **9** Rancour. **10** Opposed.
11 One. **12** Chamber pots. **13** Nifty. **14** Orang-utan.
16 Racetrack. **17** Lemur. **19** Clay pigeons. **22** Nod.
23 Chimera. **24** Genuine. **26** Annexe. **27** New Year.

Down **1** Harpoon. **2** Sense of occasion. **3** Ego. **4** Syria.
5 Bootblack. **6** Leper. **7** Unsportsmanlike. **8** Edison. **12** Crypt.
14 Orangeade. **15** Gulls. **16** Rococo. **18** Red deer. **20** Peeve.
21 Organ. **25** Now.

30 *Across* **1** Arcades. **5** Legacy. **9** Hamster. **10** Grown-up.
11 Ski. **12** Magisterial. **13** Chart. **14** Twitchers. **16** Plimsolls.
17 Ducat. **19** Line printer. **22** Tad. **23** Prolong. **24** Glacial.
26 Skidoo. **27** Striker.

Down **1** Aphasic. **2** Combination lock. **3** Dot. **4** Shrug.
5 Logistics. **6** Glove. **7** Confidence trick. **8** Spells. **12** Maths.
14 Talking-to. **15** Cedar. **16** Polyps. **18** Tiddler. **20** Proud.
21 Tagus. **25** Air.

31 *Across* **6** Adult education. **9** Estate. **10** Sulphide.
11 Egg timer. **13** Lacuna. **15** Potato. **17** My dear. **19** Trumps.
20 Escapist. **22** Songster. **24** Caftan. **26** Prima ballerina.

Down **1** Massage parlour. **2** Pupa. **3** Stream. **4** Ice lolly.
5 Etch. **7** Disarm. **8** Ordinary seaman. **12** Totem. **14** Creep.
16 Test tube. **18** Neural. **21** Cachet. **23** Game. **25** Fail.

32 *Across* **1** Run-of-the-mill. **8** Aviator. **9** Kinetic.
11 Suspenders. **12** Viva. **14** Long jump. **16** Scampi.
17 Paw. **19** Relict. **21** Divorcee. **24** Numb. **25** Duffel coat.
27 Tear gas. **28** Loiters. **29** Morality play.

Down **1** Reins in. **2** Natterjack. **3** Firedamp. **4** Hikers.
5 Many. **6** Lithium. **7** Bass clarinet. **10** Clarinettist.
13 Schoolgirl. **15** Pad. **18** Wilfully. **20** Lumbago.
22 Cookery. **23** Muesli. **26** Agra.

Solutions 33–36

33 **Across** **1** Musicologist. **8** Tantara. **9** Upwards.
11 Face to face. **12** Sole. **14** Embolism. **16** Shut up. **17** Her.
19 Speech. **21** Telltale. **24** Idea. **25** Paintbrush. **27** Trochee.
28 Derides. **29** Weighs anchor.

Down **1** Minicab. **2** Smart aleck. **3** Crayfish. **4** Launch.
5 Gown. **6** Sort out. **7** Stuffed shirt. **10** Steeplechase.
13 Childbirth. **15** Met. **18** Reined in. **20** Eyesore. **22** Asunder.
23 Camels. **26** Thug.

34 **Across** **1** Aperture. **5** Across. **9** Negative. **10** Spread.
12 Nerd. **13** Rose window. **15** Physiotherapy.
19 Chimney breast. **23** Creditable. **25** Gaza. **28** Edible.
29 Dandruff. **30** Matron. **31** Et cetera.

Down **1** Awning. **2** Eager. **3** Tutu. **4** Ravioli. **6** Capri.
7 Overdraft. **8** Sideways. **11** Jest. **14** Hymn. **15** Price list.
16 Orb. **17** Edam. **18** Ice cream. **20** Year. **21** Reliant.
22 Raffia. **24** Igloo. **26** Acute. **27** Adze.

35 **Across** **6** Expense account. **9** Breeze. **10** Infantry.
11 Prisoner. **13** Loathe. **15** Toerag. **17** Isomer. **19** Wicket.
20 Ardently. **22** Skeleton. **24** Mirage. **26** Interdependent.

Down **1** Terror-stricken. **2** Apse. **3** Intern. **4** Scuffles. **5** Torn.
7 Emigré. **8** Northern lights. **12** Speck. **14** Adman. **16** Attitude.
18 Catnap. **21** Domino. **23** Lien. **25** Reef.

36 **Across** **6** Roaring Forties. **9** Odessa. **10** Unsteady.
11 Obliging. **13** Regard. **15** Lastly. **17** Ate out. **19** At rest.
20 Tinsmith. **22** Agnostic. **24** Racism. **26** Upwardly mobile.

Down **1** Credibility gap. **2** Lass. **3** Kigali. **4** Bowsprit. **5** Stye.
7 Grunge. **8** Elder statesmen. **12** Issue. **14** Gloom. **16** Latitude.
18 Stocky. **21** Narrow. **23** Oral. **25** Coif.

Solutions 37–40

37 *Across* **1** Compost heap. **9** Torture. **10** Loiters. **11** Yak. **12** Swindle. **13** In haste. **14** Sou. **15** Debug. **17** Trout. **18** Bruin. **20** Bloom. **22** Fat. **24** Dovecot. **25** Bizarre. **26** Oar. **27** Art deco. **28** Arrange. **29** Earthenware.

Down **1** Curriculum vitae. **2** Moulded. **3** Oxeye. **4** Talking-to. **5** Epithet. **6** Press conference. **7** Stasis. **8** Ascent. **16** Baby tooth. **18** Bedlam. **19** Nuclear. **21** Mazurka. **23** Tiered. **25** Brain.

38 *Across* **1** Nose dive. **5** Cosmos. **9** Resemble. **10** Abuser. **12** Ogle. **13** Underworld. **15** Tax-deductible. **19** Indeterminate. **23** Cow parsley. **25** Shoe. **28** Attack. **29** Disposal. **30** Merits. **31** Skin-deep.

Down **1** Narrow. **2** Sisal. **3** Damp. **4** Valance. **6** Oxbow. **7** Miserable. **8** Shredder. **11** Beau. **14** Exit. **15** Tidewater. **16** Dim. **17** Trap. **18** Disclaim. **20** Rest. **21** Ice-pick. **22** Dewlap. **24** Ascot. **26** Haste. **27** Spun.

39 *Across* **1** Phone box. **5** Harass. **9** Red Cross. **10** Dotted. **12** Lyre. **13** Bone marrow. **15** Self-evidently. **19** Interventions. **23** Deservedly. **25** Jude. **28** Overdo. **29** Catapult. **30** Take on. **31** Renegade.

Down **1** Parole. **2** Order. **3** Euro. **4** Onshore. **6** Aroma. **7** Arthritis. **8** Sideways. **11** Yeti. **14** Slur. **15** So to speak. **16** Van. **17** Eros. **18** Piedmont. **20** Ewes. **21** Tillage. **22** Kettle. **24** Radio. **26** Uvula. **27** Mate.

40 *Across* **1** Faffing. **5** Polish. **9** Eternal. **10** Basmati. **11** Zed. **12** Tchaikovsky. **13** Remit. **14** Written up. **16** Affiliate. **17** Upset. **19** Replacement. **22** Ray. **23** Cheerio. **24** Shampoo. **26** Whilst. **27** Liaised.

Down **1** Freezer. **2** Freedom of speech. **3** Inn. **4** Gulch. **5** Publicise. **6** Lasso. **7** Stars and Stripes. **8** Tidy up. **12** Total. **14** Whaleboat. **15** Trust. **16** Africa. **18** Thyroid. **20** April. **21** Easel. **25** Aga.

Solutions 41–44

41 *Across* **1** Romanticism. **9** Upfront. **10** Prairie. **11** Era.
12 Duelled. **13** Thither. **14** Ash. **15** Taste. **17** Eclat. **18** Shrew.
20 Altos. **22** Ill. **24** Blossom. **25** Upright. **26** Eel. **27** Aerator.
28 Tillage. **29** Embarrassed.

Down **1** Refresher course. **2** Moonlit. **3** Noted. **4** Impatient
5 Imagine. **6** Marshalling yard. **7** Tundra. **8** Secret.
16 Stammerer. **18** Subway. **19** Washtub. **21** Surplus.
23 Litter. **25** Ultra.

42 *Across* **1** Loudspeaker. **9** Cracker. **10** Geordie. **11** Ill.
12 Aqueous. **13** Episode. **14** Loo. **15** Nosey. **17** Globe.
18 Sunup. **20** Cadge. **22** Tom. **24** Titanic. **25** Heinous. **26** Leo.
27 Proviso. **28** Othello. **29** Soft-hearted.

Down **1** League of Nations. **2** Unknown. **3** Saris.
4 Eagle-eyed. **5** Knowing. **6** Radio-controlled. **7** Scrawl.
8 Recede. **16** Sackcloth. **18** Sit-ups. **19** Pontiff. **21** Epithet.
23 Mascot. **25** Hoo-ha.

43 *Across* **1** Last Judgment. **8** Adoring. **9** Bus stop.
11 Friendship. **12** Scot. **14** American. **16** On edge. **17** Vat.
19 Hubris. **21** Gavottes. **24** Ukes. **25** Wristwatch. **27** Extract.
28 Entente. **29** Half measures.

Down **1** Leonine. **2** Scientific. **3** Jugoslav. **4** Dublin.
5 Mask. **6** Noticed. **7** Halfway house. **10** Potter's wheel.
13 In hot water. **15** Nag. **18** Tapsters. **20** Beef tea. **22** Tetanus.
23 Writhe. **26** Waif.

44 *Across* **1** Adverse. **5** Splice. **9** Sandbag. **10** Orlando.
11 Nil. **12** Benefaction. **13** Lease. **14** Odourless.
16 Arc welder. **17** Macho. **19** Ticket agent. **22** Ton.
23 Unequal. **24** Vertigo. **26** Smithy. **27** Snorkel.

Down **1** Arsenal. **2** Vanilla ice cream. **3** Rob. **4** Egg on.
5 Shop floor. **6** Lilac. **7** Confidence trick. **8** Points. **12** Breve.
14 Old Bailey. **15** Remit. **16** Arthur. **18** Own goal. **20** Erupt.
21 Eaves. **25** Rio.

Solutions 45–48

45 **_Across_** **1** Rebirth. **5** ID card. **9** Nankeen. **10** Varnish. **11** Oaf. **12** Dress circle. **13** Ratty. **14** Arboretum. **16** Infuriate. **17** Weave. **19** Falling star. **22** Doc. **23** Surveys. **24** Tapioca. **26** Mystic. **27** Riposte.

Down **1** Rancour. **2** Benefit of clergy. **3** Rye. **4** Hinge. **5** Invisible. **6** Corgi. **7** Rain cats and dogs. **8** Phlegm. **12** Dryer. **14** Analgesic. **15** Rower. **16** Infuse. **18** Enclave. **20** Inert. **21** Tutor. **25** Pip.

46 **_Across_** **6** Vacuum cleaners. **9** Opener. **10** Molehill. **11** Drift net. **13** Tights. **15** Toledo. **17** Asimov. **19** Odious. **20** Practice. **22** Tiramisu. **24** Trojan. **26** Skirting boards.

Down **1** Evaporated milk. **2** Scan. **3** Fun run. **4** Depletes. **5** Inch. **7** Come to. **8** Relative clause. **12** Folio. **14** Gamut. **16** Dispirit. **18** Sprung. **21** Author. **23** Acre. **25** Ogre.

47 **_Across_** **1** Object lesson. **8** Holy man. **9** Rescind. **11** Take the rap. **12** Lass. **14** Concerto. **16** Milieu. **17** Ill. **19** Put out. **21** Denarius. **24** Emma. **25** Outpatient. **27** Sea salt. **28** Risotto. **29** Hidden agenda.

Down **1** Oilskin. **2** Jump the gun. **3** Confetti. **4** Larvae. **5** Sash. **6** Origami. **7** Photocopiers. **10** Disquisition. **13** Bipartisan. **15** Old. **18** Leapfrog. **20** Timpani. **22** Inertia. **23** Suntan. **26** Bard.

48 **_Across_** **1** Bulldog clips. **8** Perhaps. **9** Amorous. **11** Rolled over. **12** Zinc. **14** Portland. **16** Russia. **17** Tin. **19** Intent. **21** Milch cow. **24** Troy. **25** Page-turner. **27** Saddles. **28** Include. **29** Incandescent.

Down **1** Burglar. **2** Leave alone. **3** Discount. **4** Gravel. **5** Look. **6** Peonies. **7** Appropriates. **10** Social worker. **13** Dutch uncle. **15** Dim. **18** Ninepins. **20** Trodden. **22** Conduct. **23** Caused. **26** Alga.

Solutions 49–52

49 *Across* **1** Midships. **5** Fresco. **9** Funerary. **10** Satrap.
12 Lure. **13** Eucalyptus. **15** Electromagnet. **19** Rack-and-pinion.
23 Generation. **25** Afro. **28** Lariat. **29** Gambling. **30** Ducats.
31 Pendulum.

Down **1** Muffle. **2** Donor. **3** Here. **4** Pursuit. **6** Ready.
7 Serotonin. **8** Opposite. **11** Sago. **14** Feta. **15** Eccentric.
16 Rip. **17** Acid. **18** Wriggled. **20** Duty. **21** Iron age.
22 Dodgem. **24** Roast. **26** Frill. **27** Abed.

50 *Across* **6** Insulating tape. **9** Scarab. **10** Midships.
11 Amethyst. **13** Bedlam. **15** Thrush. **17** Remote. **19** Snooze.
20 Home page. **22** Singular. **24** Rustic. **26** Slaughterhouse.

Down **1** Circumstantial. **2** Tsar. **3** Old boy. **4** Inedible.
5 Etch. **7** Tomato. **8** Papua New Guinea. **12** Torso. **14** Droop.
16 Stealthy. **18** Charge. **21** Martha. **23** Glum. **25** Shut.

51 *Across* **6** Endocrine gland. **9** Advent. **10** Vertebra.
11 Unvoiced. **13** Sought. **15** Meekly. **17** Pseudo. **19** Screen.
20 Urbanity. **22** Air rifle. **24** Inbred. **26** Dental surgeons.

Down **1** Vending machine. **2** Adze. **3** Acetic. **4** Neurosis.
5 Aloe. **7** Invade. **8** North-northeast. **12** Obese. **14** U-turn.
16 Landfall. **18** Bureau. **21** Bridge. **23** Rite. **25** Book.

52 *Across* **1** Megalomania. **9** Upright. **10** Louvred. **11** Elk.
12 Edibles. **13** T-shirts. **14** Big. **15** Saddo. **17** Sofia. **18** Lying.
20 Sahib. **22** Cod. **24** Go-karts. **25** Ear drum. **26** Tar.
27 Maestro. **28** Atomise. **29** Steamroller.

Down **1** Morning sickness. **2** Goggles. **3** Lutes.
4 Milk tooth. **5** Noughts. **6** Aircraft carrier. **7** Superb. **8** Odessa.
16 Dust storm. **18** Legume. **19** Garotte. **21** Barn owl.
23 Dimmer. **25** Erato.

53 *Across* **1** Describe. **5** Sister. **9** Famously. **10** Galosh.
12 Coca. **13** Comic opera. **15** Greenhouse gas.
19 Self-propelled. **23** Upside down. **25** Saga. **28** Apiece.
29 Arrogate. **30** Exhort. **31** Islander.

Down **1** Deface. **2** Sumac. **3** Rout. **4** Balloon. **6** Idaho.
7 Two-legged. **8** Rehearse. **11** Silo. **14** Help. **15** Goldsmith.
16 Hop. **17** Silk. **18** Osculate. **20** Odds. **21** Ex-works.
22 Career. **24** Decor. **26** Award. **27** Soda.

54 *Across* **1** Town hall. **5** Cancel. **9** Unionism. **10** Catnap.
12 Loft. **13** Stealthily. **15** Hydroelectric. **19** Silver jubilee.
23 Logistical. **25** Acre. **28** Oracle. **29** Sun-dried. **30** Yellow.
31 Caseload.

Down **1** Tousle. **2** Whiff. **3** Hone. **4** Lesotho. **6** Adapt.
7 Concierge. **8** Lip-synch. **11** Bawl. **14** Edge. **15** Holy Grail.
16 Ecu. **17** Cult. **18** Psalmody. **20** Jail. **21** Bravura.
22 Weeded. **24** Salvo. **26** Cairo. **27** Idle.

55 *Across* **1** Dialect. **5** Navajo. **9** Coulomb. **10** Vesicle. **11** Due.
12 Smorgasbord. **13** Dread. **14** Fabricate. **16** Title role.
17 Atlas. **19** Irrefutable. **22** Ram. **23** Swahili. **24** Broaden.
26 Seance. **27** End-user.

Down **1** Decided. **2** Amusement arcade. **3** Ego. **4** Taboo.
5 Navigable. **6** Visas. **7** Jack of all trades. **8** Meddle. **12** Sidle.
14 Front line. **15** Irate. **16** Thirst. **18** Seminar. **20** Feign.
21 Bible. **25** Odd.

56 *Across* **1** Unrealistic. **9** Audible. **10** Cypress. **11** Ago.
12 Worsted. **13** Granite. **14** Yah. **15** Cacti. **17** Toast. **18** Uncle.
20 Odour. **22** Wow. **24** Mountie. **25** Liberty. **26** Coo.
27 Satsuma. **28** Toccata. **29** Rattlesnake.

Down **1** Under the counter. **2** Robotic. **3** Ahead. **4** Incognito.
5 Topmast. **6** Chemical warfare. **7** Galway. **8** Assent.
16 Close call. **18** Utmost. **19** Entrust. **21** Rebecca. **23** Waylay.
25 Lotus.

Solutions 57–60

57 ***Across*** **1** Chill factor. **9** Ennoble. **10** Blogger. **11** Gnu.
12 Execute. **13** Lightly. **14** Mop. **15** Drain. **17** Trove. **18** Lurid.
20 Omens. **22** Ova. **24** Vintner. **25** Decorum. **26** You.
27 Rooftop. **28** Grumble. **29** Sustainable.

Down **1** Contemporaneous. **2** Inbound. **3** Liège.
4 Ambulance. **5** Thought. **6** Right Honourable. **7** Te Deum.
8 Argyle. **16** Apocrypha. **18** Livery. **19** Denotes. **21** Succumb.
23 Armies. **25** Dug in.

58 ***Across*** **1** Self-delusion. **8** Overbuy. **9** Buffalo.
11 Masquerade. **12** Pony. **14** Tone-deaf. **16** En bloc. **17** Kip.
19 Embryo. **21** Novelist. **24** Mugs. **25** Encyclical.
27 No entry. **28** Aspirin. **29** Clothes horse.

Down **1** Stetson. **2** Labour Days. **3** Daybreak. **4** Libido.
5 Safe. **6** On a roll. **7** Committeeman. **10** Oxyacetylene.
13 Interloper. **15** Fin. **18** Polymath. **20** Big deal. **22** Incurve.
23 Enzyme. **26** Stet.

59 ***Across*** **1** Cobbler. **5** Betray. **9** Lily pad. **10** Thin air. **11** Mar.
12 Irreligious. **13** Ovoid. **14** Incursion. **16** Wednesday.
17 Laser. **19** Non-specific. **22** Elf. **23** Elision. **24** Diploma.
26 Agency. **27** Plaudit.

Down **1** Colombo. **2** Ballroom dancing. **3** Lop. **4** Radar.
5 Battle-cry. **6** Thing. **7** Anabolic steroid. **8** Prison. **12** Indie.
14 Indecency. **15** Relic. **16** Winter. **18** Refract. **20** Prion.
21 Fed up. **25** Pea.

60 ***Across*** **1** Sawdust. **5** Utmost. **9** Chimney. **10** Buckler.
11 Bat. **12** Trepidation. **13** Yield. **14** Knife-edge.
16 Petty cash. **17** Orlop. **19** Tape measure. **22** Erg. **23** Chortle.
24 Apostle. **26** Prefer. **27** Encrypt.

Down **1** Sick bay. **2** Whistle-stop tour. **3** Urn. **4** Thyme.
5 Un-British. **6** Mecca. **7** Self-indulgently. **8** Orange. **12** Toddy.
14 Koala bear. **15** Evoke. **16** Putsch. **18** Pigment. **20** Motif.
21 Usage. **25** Orc.

Solutions 61–64

61 *Across* **6** Orthodox Church. **9** Scampi. **10** Polygamy.
11 Reckless. **13** Exotic. **15** Embody. **17** Cygnet. **19** Kitbag.
20 Internet. **22** Gemstone. **24** Ornate. **26** Asset-stripping.

Down **1** Concrete mixers. **2** Item. **3** Iodine. **4** Scullery.
5 Bung. **7** Oppose. **8** Committee stage. **12** Kebab. **14** Owner.
16 Doghouse. **18** Linear. **21** Troops. **23** Stem. **25** Nail.

62 *Across* **1** Presbyterian. **8** Sloe gin. **9** Ominous.
11 Chain-smoke. **12** Pass. **14** Ice cream. **16** Bogota. **17** Lad.
19 Tiptoe. **21** Majestic. **24** Ibex. **25** Sleigh ride. **27** Torrent.
28 Cadenza. **29** Staying power.

Down **1** Probate. **2** Engine room. **3** Bone meal. **4** Troika.
5 Rail. **6** Avocado. **7** Psychiatrist. **10** Saskatchewan.
13 Foreshadow. **15** Mam. **18** Davis Cup. **20** Pierrot.
22 Thinner. **23** Gluten. **26** Levy.

63 *Across* **1** Mademoiselle. **8** Uprisen. **9** Granges.
11 Colour-fast. **12** Acne. **14** Amortise. **16** Dewlap. **17** Ham.
19 Casino. **21** Room-mate. **24** Inky. **25** Altar cloth. **27** Naivety.
28 Sallies. **29** Embarrassing.

Down **1** Morello. **2** Disgusting. **3** Monkfish. **4** Ingest.
5 Exam. **6** Logical. **7** Dutch auction. **10** Steeplechase.
13 Vermicelli. **15** Ear. **18** Molasses. **20** Sikhism. **22** Adoring.
23 Player. **26** Beta.

64 *Across* **1** Fail-safe. **5** Warm-up. **9** Moisture. **10** Horror.
12 Name. **13** Kick around. **15** Mouth-watering.
19 Table football. **23** Relentless. **25** Thus. **28** Insert.
29 Abortive. **30** Yes-men. **31** Animated.

Down **1** Foment. **2** Idiom. **3** Site. **4** Furnish. **6** Amour.
7 Mercurial. **8** Paradigm. **11** Okra. **14** June. **15** Mobilises.
16 Woo. **17** Elan. **18** Eternity. **20** Ogle. **21** Test ban.
22 Ascend. **24** Nerve. **26** Hoist. **27** Gram.

Solutions 65–68

65 ***Across*** **6** Reception rooms. **9** Scheme. **10** Deadline. **11** Volcanic. **13** Ladder. **15** Salary. **17** Cobweb. **19** Atonal. **20** Equalise. **22** In-flight. **24** Tubing. **26** Psychoanalysis.

Down **1** Precious stones. **2** Acne. **3** Spleen. **4** Intaglio. **5** Tool. **7** Induce. **8** Monkey business. **12** Colon. **14** Dowel. **16** Religion. **18** Pectin. **21** Untold. **23** Lock. **25** Bask.

66 ***Across*** **6** Law of the jungle. **9** Usable. **10** Inkstand. **11** Scariest. **13** Renown. **15** Nation. **17** Barman. **19** Scroll. **20** Big wheel. **22** Dog-lover. **24** Novena. **26** Psychoanalysis.

Down **1** Class-conscious. **2** Swab. **3** Effete. **4** Djakarta. **5** Gnat. **7** Hoists. **8** Long-windedness. **12** Ratio. **14** Nymph. **16** Oblivion. **18** Oberon. **21** Gentle. **23** Lick. **25** Vest.

67 ***Across*** **1** Point of view. **9** Carry-on. **10** Oversee. **11** Eat. **12** Moonlit. **13** Briefly. **14** Sea. **15** Cubit. **17** Nylon. **18** Rhino. **20** Laser. **22** Had. **24** Cryptic. **25** Envenom. **26** Lea. **27** Prussia. **28** Growing. **29** Threatening.

Down **1** Personality cult. **2** Idyllic. **3** Tenet. **4** Footbaths. **5** Iberian. **6** Wishful thinking. **7** Scamps. **8** Kenyan. **16** Balaclava. **18** Recipe. **19** Obtuser. **21** Ravioli. **23** Damage. **25** Eagle.

68 ***Across*** **1** Dyestuff. **5** Cancel. **9** Gourmand. **10** Bureau. **12** Even. **13** Illiterate. **15** Establishment. **19** Weather-beaten. **23** Faithfully. **25** Beef. **28** Clammy. **29** Open fire. **30** Dressy. **31** Deserted.

Down **1** Digger. **2** Exude. **3** Tomb. **4** Fan club. **6** Acute. **7** Caesarean. **8** Laureate. **11** Nisi. **14** Itch. **15** Eradicate. **16** Lab. **17** Hate. **18** Two-faced. **20** Roué. **21** Eclipse. **22** Offend. **24** Humus. **26** Edict. **27** Knee.

Solutions 69–72

69 *Across* **1** Positive. **5** Abbess. **9** Filament. **10** Siesta. **12** Iota. **13** Assignment. **15** Financial year. **19** Stage-managing. **23** Lobster pot. **25** Over. **28** Tie-ups. **29** Nicotine. **30** Dotard. **31** Pharmacy.

Down **1** Puffin. **2** Split. **3** Tome. **4** Venison. **6** Bairn. **7** Easter egg. **8** Slattern. **11** Kiwi. **14** Anne. **15** Flabbiest. **16** Can. **17** Lair. **18** Isolated. **20** Acre. **21** Abolish. **22** Freely. **24** Taper. **26** Voila. **27** Hour.

70 *Across* **1** Cowslip. **5** Inhale. **9** Skipper. **10** Younger. **11** Out. **12** Lie detector. **13** Knelt. **14** Sugar beet. **16** Saturnine. **17** Older. **19** Repetitious. **22** Dim. **23** Choc ice. **24** Colleen. **26** Briefs. **27** Riposte.

Down **1** Cassock. **2** Whistle-stop tour. **3** Lop. **4** Purse. **5** Ivy League. **6** House. **7** Light-headedness. **8** Dry rot. **12** Later. **14** Shiftless. **15** Roots. **16** Struck. **18** Romance. **20** Twine. **21** Oscar. **25** Lap.

71 *Across* **1** Standoffish. **9** Playpen. **10** Apparel. **11** Cos. **12** Episode. **13** Halfway. **14** Doh. **15** Adieu. **17** Error. **18** Admit. **20** Robot. **22** Hoe. **24** Earplug. **25** Semi-pro. **26** Una. **27** Uncivil. **28** Leasing. **29** Never-ending.

Down **1** Spanish-American. **2** Amphora. **3** Dance. **4** Flashbulb. **5** Impulse. **6** Hero-worshipping. **7** Append. **8** Player. **16** Irregular. **18** Avenue. **19** Tel Aviv. **21** Timpani. **23** Enough. **25** Salon.

72 *Across* **1** Talent scout. **9** Milkman. **10** Gulf War. **11** Nag. **12** Topiary. **13** Eyebrow. **14** Coo. **15** Onset. **17** Lifer. **18** Bleep. **20** Radar. **22** Tar. **24** Neutron. **25** Duchess. **26** Gee. **27** Subsume. **28** Plunger. **29** Rabbit hutch.

Down **1** Telephone number. **2** Lumbago. **3** Nanny. **4** Suggested. **5** Oil well. **6** Tower of strength. **7** Emetic. **8** Grower. **16** Serengeti. **18** Banish. **19** Perturb. **21** Recruit. **23** Resort. **25** Depth.

73 *Across* **1** Chief of staff. **8** Accuser. **9** Mastiff. **11** Third class. **12** Tuna. **14** High jump. **16** Kopeck. **17** Bat. **19** Amoeba. **21** Marzipan. **24** Ivan. **25** Ginger wine. **27** Globule. **28** Balkans. **29** Hydrotherapy.

Down **1** Cycling. **2** Inside jobs. **3** Forelimb. **4** Famish. **5** Task. **6** Failure. **7** Faith healing. **10** Frankincense. **13** Mozzarella. **15** Pam. **18** Tangible. **20** Oratory. **22** Privacy. **23** Silent. **26** Purr.

74 *Across* **1** Ancient. **5** Drogue. **9** Alleged. **10** Speckle. **11** You. **12** Wisdom tooth. **13** Tibia. **14** Virulence. **16** Reinforce. **17** Souse. **19** Bodybuilder. **22** Nib. **23** Elector. **24** Brazier. **26** Ushers. **27** Tally-ho.

Down **1** Analyst. **2** Colour blindness. **3** Egg. **4** Tides. **5** Discourse. **6** Overt. **7** Unknown quantity. **8** Tee-hee. **12** Wharf. **14** Verdigris. **15** Loser. **16** Rabies. **18** Embargo. **20** Bathe. **21** Debut. **25** Awl.

75 *Across* **1** Cyclist. **5** Seesaw. **9** Defence. **10** Debacle. **11** Ice. **12** Little Women. **13** Motet. **14** Funicular. **16** Tableland. **17** Bosom. **19** Overprecise. **22** Mud. **23** Know-all. **24** Tidings. **26** Eke out. **27** Oversee.

Down **1** Cadmium. **2** Coffee-table book. **3** Inn. **4** Tweet. **5** Sidelined. **6** Elbow. **7** Accomplishments. **8** Tenner. **12** Lathe. **14** Flageolet. **15** Cable. **16** Troika. **18** Medusae. **20** Piano. **21** Intro. **25** Doe.

76 *Across* **6** Ornithologists. **9** Advice. **10** Describe. **11** Polka dot. **13** Answer. **15** Rarity. **17** Gazump. **19** Bosnia. **20** Crackpot. **22** Esoteric. **24** Pouffe. **26** As clear as a bell.

Down **1** Hold your horses. **2** Anti. **3** Attend. **4** Moussaka. **5** Pier. **7** Oddity. **8** Tablespoonfuls. **12** Koran. **14** Stuck. **16** Tea break. **18** Acacia. **21** Appeal. **23** Talc. **25** Uses.

77 *Across* **1** Sneak preview. **8** Usurper. **9** Dictate.
11 Sisterhood. **12** Diet. **14** Tungsten. **16** Manege. **17** Fin.
19 Mellow. **21** Larkspur. **24** Tame. **25** Precaution.
27 Sea legs. **28** Tableau. **29** House of cards.

Down **1** Shuts in. **2** Expression. **3** Kerchief. **4** Red-hot.
5 Vice. **6** Examine. **7** Guesstimates. **10** Entrepreneur.
13 Back number. **15** Nil. **18** Narcotic. **20** Lumbago. **22** Primers.
23 Fresco. **26** Fees.

78 *Across* **1** Frankincense. **8** Own goal. **9** Tapioca.
11 Greensward. **12** Fast. **14** Tinsmith. **16** Lethal. **17** Tor.
19 Engine. **21** Throttle. **24** Oars. **25** Malt whisky. **27** Snaffle.
28 Ribcage. **29** Idiosyncrasy.

Down **1** Fonteyn. **2** Anointment. **3** Kilowatt. **4** Notary.
5 Expo. **6** Stomach. **7** Forget-me-nots. **10** Artillerymen.
13 Xenophobia. **15** Hot. **18** Rhetoric. **20** Garland.
22 Tuscany. **23** Lately. **26** Afro.

79 *Across* **1** Violence. **5** Pompom. **9** Place mat. **10** Consul.
12 Rare. **13** Blood donor. **15** Transatlantic. **19** Environmental.
23 Shrink wrap. **25** Stir. **28** Ageism. **29** Ointment. **30** Easily.
31 In a hurry.

Down **1** Vipers. **2** On air. **3** Eden. **4** Chablis. **6** Ovoid.
7 Postnatal. **8** Mill race. **11** Port. **14** Pair. **15** Taverners.
16 Arm. **17** Arts. **18** Persuade. **20** News. **21** Elation. **22** Grotty.
24 Nasal. **26** Their. **27** Etch.

80 *Across* **6** Crème de la crème. **9** Foul up. **10** Creature.
11 Blowpipe. **13** Laughs. **15** Heresy. **17** Domain. **19** Blotto.
20 Hedgehog. **22** Granddad. **24** Arcade. **26** Unknown Soldier.

Down **1** Schoolchildren. **2** Bell. **3** Delphi. **4** Waterloo. **5** Fret.
7 Etcher. **8** Marching orders. **12** Worst. **14** Usage.
16 Slow down. **18** Shades. **21** Deadly. **23** Nana. **25** Coin.

Solutions 81–84

81 *Across* **6** Across the board. **9** Skewer. **10** Roughage.
11 Atlantic. **13** Impish. **15** Earthy. **17** Brogue. **19** Geodes.
20 Internet. **22** Breather. **24** Unripe. **26** Photosynthesis.

Down **1** Market research. **2** Prow. **3** Esprit. **4** Peculiar.
5 Loch. **7** Thrice. **8** Registered post. **12** Aired. **14** Pager.
16 Hush-hush. **18** Micron. **21** Touchy. **23** Arts. **25** Rasp.

82 *Across* **1** Air terminal. **9** Rate-cap. **10** Spinner. **11** Ass.
12 Defrost. **13** Moorhen. **14** Sac. **15** Naiad. **17** Elope.
18 Osaka. **20** Piano. **22** Vet. **24** Scherzo. **25** Avenues. **26** Mad.
27 Flare-up. **28** Dolphin. **29** Tissue paper.

Down **1** Artificial heart. **2** Raccoon. **3** Expat.
4 Mass media. **5** Noisome. **6** Luncheon voucher. **7** Grades.
8 Orange. **16** Impromptu. **18** Ossify. **19** Airless. **21** Overlap.
23 Tisane. **25** Add up.

83 *Across* **1** Brandish. **5** Clinic. **9** Rainfall. **10** Cartel. **12** Item.
13 Population. **15** Fruit machines. **19** Country dances.
23 Articulate. **25** Hero. **28** Iraqis. **29** Sinister. **30** Needle.
31 Old flame.

Down **1** Birdie. **2** Agile. **3** Defy. **4** Sell-out. **6** Llama.
7 Nutrients. **8** Colonist. **11** Tuba. **14** Bust. **15** Frustrate.
16 Mad. **17** Hock **18** Occasion. **20** Yelp. **21** Anthill. **22** Soirée.
24 Chill. **26** Extra. **27** Fief.

84 *Across* **1** Test tube. **5** Plaque. **9** Clangour. **10** Mosaic.
12 Item. **13** Immaterial. **15** Projectionist. **19** Broken-hearted.
23 Eye contact. **25** Opal. **28** Attain. **29** Colossus. **30** Earner.
31 Symphony.

Down **1** Tocsin. **2** Spade. **3** Toga. **4** Brummie. **6** Loose.
7 Qualified. **8** Escalate. **11** Mast. **14** Sore. **15** Protector.
16 Cue. **17** Otto. **18** Abnegate. **20** Hate. **21** Anchovy.
22 Classy. **24** On ice. **26** Pesto. **27** Coop.

Solutions 85–88

85   *Across*   **1** Thin air. **5** Thumbs. **9** Butcher. **10** Crusade. **11** Ear. **12** Linen basket. **13** Usher. **14** Sycophant. **16** Municipal. **17** Pikes. **19** Dreadnought. **22** Tie. **23** Subvert. **24** Overeat. **26** Censor. **27** Malmsey.

Down   **1** Tableau. **2** Interchangeable. **3** Ash. **4** Rerun. **5** Technical. **6** Uvula. **7** Black marketeers. **8** Beat it. **12** Lyric. **14** Supporter. **15** Pipit. **16** Modest. **18** Sweetly. **20** Dress. **21** Gloom. **25** Eel.

86   *Across*   **1** Word for word. **9** Rosette. **10** Pleased. **11** Ear. **12** Slip-ups. **13** Old rope. **14** Nag. **15** Hyena. **17** Yacht. **18** Alpha. **20** Cleft. **22** Roc. **24** Stirrup. **25** Amenity. **26** Tad. **27** Tsunami. **28** Insight. **29** Delinquency.

Down   **1** Washing-up liquid. **2** Retouch. **3** Frees. **4** Reprobate. **5** Open day. **6** Disconcertingly. **7** Prison. **8** Advent. **16** Exception. **18** Assets. **19** Airmail. **21** Treason. **23** Coyote. **25** Adieu.

87   *Across*   **1** Pussy willow. **9** Mollusc. **10** Babysit. **11** Coe. **12** Cochlea. **13** Traffic. **14** Sac. **15** Dowse. **17** Sally. **18** Henna. **20** Tango. **22** Hop. **24** Not fair. **25** Science. **26** Flu. **27** Subsoil. **28** Meaning. **29** Eye-catching.

Down   **1** Police constable. **2** Squalid. **3** Yucca. **4** In between. **5** Libyans. **6** Wishful thinking. **7** Smacks. **8** Sticky. **16** Water flea. **18** Honest. **19** Abalone. **21** Origami. **23** Pledge. **25** Sumac.

88   *Across*   **1** Swimming pool. **8** Attacks. **9** Bath tub. **11** Stronghold. **12** Peel. **14** Theories. **16** Bonsai. **17** Fie. **19** Equity. **21** Rush hour. **24** Oust. **25** Out on a limb. **27** Freshly. **28** Turmoil. **29** Stock markets.

Down   **1** Set free. **2** Incinerate. **3** Mischief. **4** Nebula. **5** Pith. **6** Outlets. **7** Raise the roof. **10** Billiard ball. **13** Joshua tree. **15** Sir. **18** Eurostar. **20** Upswept. **22** Ominous. **23** Yum-Yum. **26** Chic.

Solutions 89–92

89 **Across** **1** Cologne. **5** Trauma. **9** Avenger. **10** Epsilon.
11 Tea. **12** Self-seeking. **13** Lives. **14** Very light.
16 Fly-tipper. **17** See 15. **19** Discourtesy. **22** Hag. **23** Italics.
24 Begonia. **26** Addled. **27** Demesne.

Down **1** Chattel. **2** Lee Harvey Oswald. **3** Gig. **4** Enrol.
5 Treasurer. **6** Aisle. **7** Milking machines. **8** Knight. **12** Sushi.
14 Vaporised. **15/17** Lucky charm. **16** Fade-in. **18** Migrate.
20 Oriel. **21** Embed. **25** Gum.

90 **Across** **1** Cockpit. **5** Sedate. **9** Sangria. **10** Colleen.
11 Oar. **12** Slave labour. **13** Katie. **14** Wisecrack. **16** Tall order.
17 Lower. **19** Orthopaedic. **22** Dog. **23** Good egg. **24** William.
26 Estate. **27** Sloe gin.

Down **1** Cassock. **2** Congratulations. **3** Par. **4** Tiara.
5 Successor. **6** Delta. **7** The royal wedding. **8** Anorak. **12** Steno.
14 Wide-angle. **15** Colic. **16** Trough. **18** Regimen. **20** Omega.
21 Downs. **25** Loo.

91 **Across** **6** Elder statesman. **9** Beryls. **10** Vertebra.
11 Daughter. **13** Immune. **15** Impact. **17** Myopic. **19** Canyon.
20 Contempt. **22** Literati. **24** Potion. **26** Unaccounted for.

Down **1** Generalisation. **2** Eddy. **3** Preset. **4** Eternity. **5** Isle.
7 Tavern. **8** Airing cupboard. **12** Guppy. **14** Maple.
16 Cinnamon. **18** Action. **21** Nipper. **23** Each. **25** Tiff.

92 **Across** **1** Benefactress. **8** Plateau. **9** Undying.
11 Third class. **12** Idea. **14** Forswear. **16** Breeds. **17** Fan.
19 Limply. **21** Muckrake. **24** Euro. **25** Mechanical. **27** Sultana.
28 Trodden. **29** Vote of thanks.

Down **1** Brazier. **2** Ne'er-do-well. **3** Four-leaf. **4** Course.
5 Rude. **6** Swindle. **7** Spitefulness. **10** Glass ceiling.
13 Broken down. **15** Ram. **18** Nuthatch. **20** Morello.
22 Accedes. **23** Behalf. **26** Kale.

Solutions 93–96

93 **_Across_** **1** Mountain lion. **8** Refrain. **9** Fig leaf. **11** Villainous.
12 Fair. **14** Cartload. **16** One-off. **17** Wet. **19** Unkind.
21 Bumbling. **24** Chip. **25** Incoherent. **27** Lateral. **28** Integer.
29 Critical mass.

Down **1** Muffler. **2** Unavailing. **3** Tenon saw. **4** Influx.
5 Logo. **6** Oregano. **7** Privy Council. **10** Firefighters.
13 In absentia. **15** Deb. **18** Tutorial. **20** Knitter. **22** Ice ages.
23 En bloc. **26** Trot.

94 **_Across_** **1** Underage. **5** Crafts. **9** Ukuleles. **10** Flinch.
12 Even. **13** Bleary-eyed. **15** Ground control.
19 Rateable value. **23** Dehumanise. **25** Step. **28** Crunch.
29 Bulkhead. **30** Rhesus. **31** Metaphor.

Down **1** Usurer. **2** Deuce. **3** Reed. **4** Gremlin. **6** Rally.
7 Fancy-free. **8** Schedule. **11** Laic. **14** Nova. **15** Gatehouse.
16 Die. **17** Nile. **18** Producer. **20** Lane. **21** Vesture.
22 Spider. **24** Macau. **26** Teeth. **27** Okra.

95 **_Across_** **6** All-in wrestling. **9** Trench. **10** Aperture.
11 Age limit. **13** Tetchy. **15** Bisque. **17** Pseudo. **19** Pliers.
20 Entreaty. **22** Moussaka. **24** Widows. **26** Interest groups.

Down **1** Barrage balloon. **2** Plan. **3** Anthem. **4** Asbestos.
5 Plot. **7** Rialto. **8** North-northwest. **12** Lisle. **14** Taupe.
16 Unshaven. **18** Pedant. **21** Thwart. **23** Seep. **25** Drum.

96 **_Across_** **6** Identification. **9** Eclair. **10** Serenade. **11** Broccoli.
13 Except. **15** Onrush. **17** Debris. **19** Get off. **20** Incision.
22 Seafarer. **24** Abrupt. **26** Strong language.

Down **1** Pincer movement. **2** Feta. **3** Stereo. **4** Scorsese.
5 Stun. **7** Fossil. **8** Oedipus complex. **12** Cargo. **14** Corps.
16 Suffrage. **18** Sierra. **21** Change. **23** Frog. **25** Rear.

Solutions 97–100

97 *Across* **1** Dive bombers. **9** Apparel. **10** No-hoper. **11** Guy.
12 Trounce. **13** Sunburn. **14** Pea. **15** Award. **17** Eagle.
18 Climb. **20** Add-on. **22** Nap. **24** Backlog. **25** Pit prop.
26 Eye. **27** Enrages. **28** Welfare. **29** Stalactites.

Down **1** Diplomatic corps. **2** Veranda. **3** Bulge.
4 Many-sided. **5** Enhance. **6** Septuagenarians. **7** Gas tap.
8 Grange. **16** Analgesia. **18** Cobweb. **19** Bologna.
21 Notelet. **23** Puppet. **25** Pewit.

98 *Across* **1** Wardrobe. **5** Lessee. **9** Migraine. **10** Decamp.
12 Lays. **13** Chain store. **15** Stiletto heels. **19** Catchment area.
23 Well-wisher. **25** Afro. **28** Icicle. **29** Arterial. **30** Gneiss.
31 Smoulder.

Down **1** Wimple. **2** Rugby. **3** Rear. **4** Banshee. **6** Evens.
7 Soap opera. **8** Espresso. **11** Rift. **14** Dish. **15** Satellite.
16 Ten. **17** Hero. **18** Scowling. **20** East. **21** Theorem. **22** Boiler.
24 Welds. **26** Fried. **27** Beau.

99 *Across* **1** Hard copy. **5** Barber. **9** Navy blue. **10** Ragtag.
12 Role. **13** Mechanical. **15** Search warrant. **19** Fighter-bomber.
23 Large-scale. **25** Dice. **28** Equity. **29** Dejected. **30** Topple.
31 Illusory.

Down **1** Hungry. **2** Revel. **3** Cube. **4** Poulenc. **6** Again.
7 Bath chair. **8** Regulate. **11** Show. **14** Wait. **15** Sugar lump.
16 Hub. **17** Robe. **18** Affluent. **20** Rock. **21** Oil well.
22 Deadly. **24** Extol. **26** Intro. **27** Peru.

100 *Across* **1** Absence. **5** Marshy. **9** Railway. **10** Summits.
11 Bum. **12** Eating apple. **13** Tinge. **14** Broad bean.
16 Pachyderm. **17** Ovule. **19** Dispensable. **22** Pay. **23** Ululate.
24 Martini. **26** Bedeck. **27** Sunbeam.

Down **1** Acrobat. **2** Swimming costume. **3** Now. **4** Egypt.
5 Misinform. **6** Rumba. **7** Heir presumptive. **8** Astern. **12** Elegy.
14 Beefsteak. **15** Drove. **16** Podium. **18** Elysium. **20** Evade.
21 Bumps. **25** Run.

Solutions 101–104

101 *Across* **1** Persian Gulf. **9** Mailbag. **10** Grown-up. **11** Ooh. **12** Rat-a-tat. **13** Twinset. **14** Ash. **15** Corgi. **17** Noisy. **18** Motif. **20** Green. **22** God. **24** Cowgirl. **25** Article. **26** Awn. **27** Warrant. **28** Tearoom. **29** Disgraceful.

Down **1** Paint the town red. **2** Robotic. **3** Ingot. **4** Night-time. **5** Utopian. **6** Finishing school. **7** Umbria. **8** Apathy. **16** Regulator. **18** Macaws. **19** Fridays. **21** Not half. **23** Dreamy. **25** Antic.

102 *Across* **1** Theoretical. **9** Puritan. **10** Enhance. **11** Car. **12** Towpath. **13** Earthly. **14** Yen. **15** Syrup. **17** Dross. **18** Usher. **20** Sonic. **22** Via. **24** Satanic. **25** No-trump. **26** UFO. **27** Low gear. **28** Blather. **29** Loudspeaker.

Down **1** Throw in the towel. **2** Entraps. **3** Ranch. **4** Thereupon. **5** Cohered. **6** Luncheon voucher. **7** Spotty. **8** Beryls. **16** Rest cures. **18** Unsold. **19** Rondeau. **21** Cut back. **23** Aspire. **25** Noble.

103 *Across* **1** Creepy-crawly. **8** Episode. **9** Wolf cub. **11** Sunglasses. **12** Fair. **14** Guide dog. **16** Retell. **17** Web. **19** Assets. **21** Lawmaker. **24** Ugly. **25** Sepulchral. **27** Exalted. **28** Holster. **29** Fermentation.

Down **1** Chianti. **2** Emollients. **3** Peep show. **4** Cowper. **5** Axle. **6** Lactate. **7** Key signature. **10** Burglar alarm. **13** Vermicelli. **15** Gel. **18** Babushka. **20** Selvage. **22** Keratin. **23** Tendon. **26** Atom.

104 *Across* **1** Package. **5** Proust. **9** Awfully. **10** Refrain. **11** Ice. **12** Catastrophe. **13** Gutsy. **14** Nutrition. **16** Subatomic. **17** Total. **19** Green pepper. **22** Dig. **23** Amongst. **24** Low gear. **26** Ski run. **27** Treason.

Down **1** Peaking. **2** Coffee-table book. **3** All. **4** Egypt. **5** Parasitic. **6** Offer. **7** Sharp-wittedness. **8** Unseen. **12** Crypt. **14** Number Ten. **15** Inter. **16** Signal. **18** Leg iron. **20** Niger. **21** Pilot. **25** Woe.

Solutions 105–108

105 *Across* **1** Reprove. **5** Rip-off. **9** Needful. **10** Shallot.
11 Was. **12** Sitting room. **13** Loony. **14** Charlatan.
16 Suffocate. **17** Brawl. **19** Ports of call. **22** Eat. **23** Ennoble.
24 Prowler. **26** Terror. **27** Natural.

Down **1** Renewal. **2** Press conference. **3** Off. **4** Eclat.
5 Rusticate. **6** Prang. **7** Fellow traveller. **8** Stamen.
12 Say-so. **14** Chauffeur. **15** Libel. **16** Supper. **18** Literal.
20 Sober. **21** Aspen. **25** Opt.

106 *Across* **6** Nuclear physics. **9** Formal. **10** Decisive.
11 Omelette. **13** Eerily. **15** Norman. **17** Craven. **19** Gusher.
20 Unafraid. **22** Panpipes. **24** Yawned. **26** Demisemiquaver.

Down **1** Incommensurate. **2** Scam. **3** Pellet. **4** Thick ear.
5 Isis. **7** Rudder. **8** Civil engineers. **12** Lurch. **14** Rover.
16 Air speed. **18** Muesli. **21** Asylum. **23** Prim. **25** Wavy.

107 *Across* **1** Tuberculosis. **8** Left off. **9** Light up.
11 Steam irons. **12** Drab. **14** Blast off. **16** Mammal. **17** Fog.
19 Object. **21** Brake pad. **24** Earl. **25** Godfathers. **27** Seclude.
28 Imagine. **29** Mothers-in-law.

Down **1** Taffeta. **2** Broomstick. **3** Riffraff. **4** Upland.
5 Orgy. **6** Interim. **7** Glass-blowers. **10** Pebble-dashed.
13 Basketball. **15** Fob. **18** Graffiti. **20** Jericho. **22** Preview.
23 Poseur. **26** Mush.

108 *Across* **1** Bouncy castle. **8** On trial. **9** Rhombus.
11 Quarter day. **12** Slur. **14** Inspects. **16** Panama. **17** Yak.
19 Tropic. **21** Yearbook. **24** Date. **25** Worshipful. **27** Reading.
28 Old rope. **29** Well-attended.

Down **1** Betrays. **2** Up in the air. **3** Celerity. **4** Corral.
5 Smog. **6** Lobelia. **7** Conquistador. **10** Serial killer.
13 Fair-minded. **15** Say. **18** Keystone. **20** Oatcake.
22 Offload. **23** Nougat. **26** Sill.

Solutions 109–112

109 *Across* **1** Ethereal. **5** Uses up. **9** Pavilion. **10** Prayer.
12 Sort. **13** Typing pool. **15** No great shakes.
19 Treasure chest. **23** Nasturtium. **25** Over. **28** Iguana.
29 Buzz word. **30** Setter. **31** February.

Down **1** Expose. **2** Hover. **3** Roll. **4** Anodyne. **6** Sprig.
7 Skyrocket. **8** Paralyse. **11** Pint. **14** Ages. **15** Needs must.
16 Awe. **17** Heed. **18** Stand-ins. **20** Rite. **21** Couture.
22 Friday. **24** Ulnae. **26** Viola. **27** Czar.

110 *Across* **6** Inappositeness. **9** Safari. **10** Ballyhoo.
11 Après-ski. **13** Tights. **15** Impute. **17** Acumen. **19** Stylus.
20 In a sense. **22** Belittle. **24** Weepie. **26** Strawberry mark.

Down **1** Disappointment. **2** Saga. **3** Optics. **4** Athletic.
5 Envy. **7** Submit. **8** Shooting sticks. **12** Expel. **14** Gimme.
16 Test tube. **18** Linear. **21** Always. **23** Imam. **25** Edam.

111 *Across* **6** Massage parlour. **9** Trudge. **10** Eminence.
11 Estrange. **13** Awning. **15** Iodine. **17** Oeuvre. **19** Angora.
20 Undulate. **22** Obedient. **24** Bottom. **26** Senile dementia.

Down **1** Impressionable. **2** Used. **3** Tavern. **4** Badinage.
5 Sloe. **7** Eleven. **8** Unconventional. **12** Rodeo. **14** Novel.
16 Neatened. **18** Hustle. **21** Dubbed. **23** Dais. **25** Tote.

112 *Across* **1** Stone's throw. **9** Enclave. **10** Medulla. **11** Cue.
12 Verdict. **13** Leanest. **14** Set. **15** Aesop. **17** Dated. **18** Tacit.
20 Omega. **22** Bob. **24** Maudlin. **25** Hatpins. **26** Doe.
27 Recover. **28** Alcohol. **29** Level-headed.

Down **1** Security Council. **2** Ocarina. **3** Erect. **4** Time-lapse.
5 Red card. **6** Well-established. **7** Leaves. **8** Matted.
16 Scoundrel. **18** Timbre. **19** Tel Aviv. **21** Antacid.
23 Basalt. **25** Heave.

Solutions 113–116

113 *Across* **1** Hot flush. **5** Pathos. **9** Sedative. **10** Cicero.
12 Able. **13** Snail's pace. **15** Lackadaisical. **19** Spinning jenny.
23 Acceptance. **25** T-bar. **28** Blotch. **29** Episodic. **30** Lahore.
31 Starters.

Down **1** Hussar. **2** Tidal. **3** Loth. **4** Savanna. **6** Amiss.
7 Hierarchy. **8** Slovenly. **11** Pisa. **14** Scan. **15** Loincloth.
16 Dog. **17** Sunk. **18** Istanbul. **20** Near. **21** Jackpot. **22** Braces.
24 Pacer. **26** Badge. **27** Tsar.

114 *Across* **1** Bulldoze. **5** Ambush. **9** Soya bean. **10** Window.
12 Calm. **13** Rotisserie. **15** Treasure-trove. **19** Emulsion paint.
23 Take the rap. **25** Shot. **28** Exotic. **29** Corundum. **30** Tiddly.
31 Off-piste.

Down **1** Bisect. **2** Loyal. **3** Debt. **4** Zealous. **6** Mains.
7 Undercoat. **8** Hawk-eyed. **11** Liar. **14** Fees. **15** Trunk road.
16 Urn. **17** Toil. **18** Sentient. **20** Omen. **21** Play-off.
22 Stymie. **24** Twill. **26** Hides. **27** Pump.

115 *Across* **1** Dresser. **5** Haunch. **9** Archive. **10** Pianist. **11** Ova.
12 Pussy willow. **13** Drama. **14** Hook-nosed. **16** Spin-dryer.
17 Iowan. **19** Innumerable. **22** Nun. **23** Teacups. **24** Diocese.
26 Skidoo. **27** Treason.

Down **1** Diamond. **2** Exclamation mark. **3** Ski. **4** Reeks.
5 Happy hour. **6** Umami. **7** Chinless wonders. **8** Stowed.
12 Plaid. **14** Hey presto. **15** Noise. **16** Shirty. **18** Nankeen.
20 Mound. **21** Bidet. **25** One.

116 *Across* **1** Bright spark. **9** Needful. **10** Relieve. **11** Lee.
12 Archery. **13** Nureyev. **14** Ski. **15** Title. **17** Nouns.
18 Digit. **20** O-ring. **22** Sod. **24** Footway. **25** Glorify. **26** Flu.
27 Undergo. **28** Ascetic. **29** Reservation.

Down **1** Bleaching powder. **2** Inflect. **3** Holly. **4** Serengeti.
5 Aileron. **6** Keep your shirt on. **7** Annals. **8** Leaves.
16 Two-by-four. **18** Duff up. **19** Towards. **21** Gnocchi.
23 Dry ice. **25** Guava.

Solutions 117–120

117 *Across* 1 Gatecrasher. 9 Emotion. 10 Ransack. 11 Oaf.
12 Outside. 13 Illegal. 14 Elf. 15 Nobel. 17 Roams. 18 Truer.
20 Sisal. 22 Due. 24 Idiotic. 25 Scarcer. 26 Aye. 27 Eternal.
28 Ice rink. 29 Silly season.

Down 1 Go out of business. 2 Tuition. 3 Canoe. 4 Airfields.
5 Handler. 6 Rearguard action. 7 Genome. 8 Skills. 16 Basically.
18 Tribes. 19 Retinol. 21 Loafers. 23 Eureka. 25 Seine.

118 *Across* 1 Town planners. 8 Immense. 9 Spin-off.
11 Hollow-eyed. 12 Silo. 14 Yugoslav. 16 Kismet. 17 Nit.
19 Tackle. 21 Zimbabwe. 24 Ufos. 25 Rebellious. 27 G-string.
28 Excrete. 29 Waldorf salad.

Down 1 Time-lag. 2 Windowsill. 3 Plebeian. 4 Answer.
5 Nail. 6 Rhodium. 7 Highly strung. 10 Frontiersmen.
13 Diabolical. 15 Viz. 18 Tireless. 20 Croatia. 22 Book end.
23 Verger. 26 Wind.

119 *Across* 1 Ecstasy. 5 Cleave. 9 Loosely. 10 Rotorua. 11 Vet.
12 Observation. 13 Neigh. 14 Induction. 16 Secretive.
17 Occur. 19 Waiting game. 22 Etc. 23 Ali Baba. 24 Olympia.
26 Egress. 27 Diagram.

Down 1 Enliven. 2 Short-circuiting. 3 Ate. 4 Yo-yos.
5 Cartridge. 6 Extra. 7 Virginia creeper. 8 Cannon. 12 Ochre.
14 Isinglass. 15 Clone. 16 So what. 18 Reclaim. 20 Image.
21 Avoid. 25 Yea.

120 *Across* 1 Back out. 5 Valise. 9 Road tax. 10 Salvage.
11 Log. 12 Restructure. 13 Radio. 14 Commodore.
16 Safety pin. 17 Tulip. 19 Inadvertent. 22 Bra. 23 Firedog.
24 Engorge. 26 Escort. 27 Tally-ho.

Down 1 Burglar. 2 Chargé d'affaires. 3 Opt. 4 Taxis.
5 Vestryman. 6 Lilac. 7 Statue of Liberty. 8 Renege. 12 Roost.
14 Copyright. 15 Octet. 16 Sniffy. 18 Placebo. 20 Video.
21 Event. 25 Gel.

Solutions 121–124

121 *Across* **6** Tongue-twisters. **9** Invent. **10** Obstruct.
11 Off and on. **13** Viewer. **15** Rococo. **17** Travel. **19** Affair.
20 Intrigue. **22** Air miles. **24** Eunuch. **26** Devil's advocate.

Down **1** Stand for office. **2** Knee. **3** Suited. **4** Dissever.
5 Star. **7** Thorny. **8** Rocket launcher. **12** Accra. **14** Envoi.
16 Careless. **18** Biased. **21** Tremor. **23** Mail. **25** Neat.

122 *Across* **1** Hypochondria. **8** Relabel. **9** Parvenu.
11 Interacted. **12** Find. **14** Werewolf. **16** Veneer. **17** Lab.
19 System. **21** Doughnut. **24** Itch. **25** Jack-the-lad. **27** Glorify.
28 One-time. **29** Trigonometry.

Down **1** Holster. **2** Pub-crawler. **3** Cold call. **4** Osprey.
5 Dire. **6** Itemise. **7** Brainwashing. **10** Understudies.
13 Lengthiest. **15** Fad. **18** Bookworm. **20** Succour. **22** Nullify.
23 Canyon. **26** Wing.

123 *Across* **1** Carte blanche. **8** Spindle. **9** Disturb.
11 Woodcutter. **12** Ta-ta. **14** Dry-clean. **16** Impend. **17** Lek.
19 Exodus. **21** Telethon. **24** Deed. **25** Watchstrap. **27** Yiddish.
28 Igneous. **29** Feature films.

Down **1** Chicory. **2** Ridiculous. **3** Eventual. **4** Ladies.
5 Nosh. **6** Haulage. **7** Ash Wednesday. **10** Boarding pass.
13 Impersonal. **15** Net. **18** Kerchief. **20** Overdue. **22** Harlots.
23 Lather. **26** Wilt.

124 *Across* **1** Pastiche. **5** Cosmos. **9** Verbiage. **10** Bistro.
12 Note. **13** Casual work. **15** Flesh and blood.
19 Black and white. **23** Democratic. **25** Rage. **28** Embark.
29 Espresso. **30** Twenty. **31** Unearned.

Down **1** Paving. **2** Strut. **3** Iris. **4** Hogwash. **6** Oriel.
7 Metronome. **8** Stockade. **11** Burn. **14** Meek.
15 Flammable. **16** Add. **17** Brim. **18** Obedient. **20** Near.
21 Whitsun. **22** Behold. **24** Carat. **26** Arson. **27** Area.

125 *Across* **6** Orthodox Church. **9** Tether. **10** Heraldry.
11 Binaural. **13** Dim sum. **15** Gringo. **17** Attain. **19** Ceased.
20 Long wave. **22** Starkers. **24** Virago. **26** Gregorian chant.

Down **1** Covering letter. **2** Etch. **3** Poorer. **4** Accredit. **5** Dull.
7 On hold. **8** Circumnavigate. **12** Adios. **14** Miaow.
16 Gadgetry. **18** Plasma. **21** Novice. **23** Rags. **25** Roam.

126 *Across* **6** Washing machine. **9** Amused. **10** Nest eggs.
11 Civil war. **13** Wraith. **15** Galley. **17** Symbol. **19** Gratis.
20 Claimant. **22** Informed. **24** Mutiny. **26** Assault courses.

Down **1** Swimming trunks. **2** As is. **3** Mildew.
4 Causeway. **5** Shoe. **7** Gentry. **8** Night blindness. **12** Inlet.
14 Album. **16** Ensemble. **18** Acidic. **21** Armour. **23** Okay.
25 Tosh.

127 *Across* **1** Forthcoming. **9** Slender. **10** Galleon. **11** Sea.
12 Indulge. **13** Necktie. **14** Elm. **15** Gecko. **17** Tahoe.
18 Refer. **20** Extol. **22** Tom. **24** Hyped up. **25** Digests. **26** Ado.
27 Element. **28** Mob caps. **29** Hide-and-seek.

Down **1** Freedom of speech. **2** Red flag. **3** Horse.
4 Organ loft. **5** Illicit. **6** Great white shark. **7** Aspire.
8 Annexe. **16** Cleopatra. **18** Reheel. **19** Redhead. **21** Legible.
23 Misuse. **25** Domed.

128 *Across* **1** Cut-price. **5** Pathos. **9** Thespian. **10** Pogrom.
12 Undo. **13** Penicillin. **15** Vacuum cleaner.
19 Spiny anteater. **23** Unequalled. **25** Alto. **28** Goatee.
29 Drop kick. **30** Delude. **31** Twilight.

Down **1** Citrus. **2** Trend. **3** Ripe. **4** Chateau. **6** Aioli.
7 Hardliner. **8** Seminary. **11** Disc. **14** Icky. **15** Voicemail.
16 Met. **17** Eats. **18** Assuaged. **20** Nile. **21** Eyebrow.
22 Socket. **24** Upend. **26** Lying. **27** Opal.

Solutions 129–132

129 *Across* **1** Idolatry. **5** Loggia. **9** Forename. **10** Stinko.
12 Rosy. **13** Prep school. **15** Value-added tax.
19 Confabulation. **23** Arithmetic. **25** Over. **28** Beat it.
29 Payphone. **30** Eyeful. **31** Penchant.

Down **1** Infirm. **2** Ogres. **3** Acne. **4** Remorse. **6** Optic.
7 Guncotton. **8** Apoplexy. **11** Sped. **14** Plea. **15** Vindicate.
16 Awl. **17** Emir. **18** Scramble. **20** Urea. **21** Agitate.
22 Orient. **24** Haiku. **26** Viola. **27** Epic.

130 *Across* **1** Somehow. **5** Parish. **9** Ennoble. **10** Sidecar.
11 Lac. **12** Intentional. **13** Hyena. **14** Retaliate. **16** Sorrowful.
17 Style. **19** Mischievous. **22** Off. **23** Origami. **24** Oil well.
26 Techie. **27** Endings.

Down **1** Stealth. **2** Manic-depressive. **3** Hob. **4** Wrest.
5 Postnatal. **6** Radii. **7** Secondary modern. **8** Grilse. **12** Idaho.
14 Reflexive. **15** Lists. **16** Samson. **18** Enfolds. **20** Heath.
21 Ozone. **25** Lid.

131 *Across* **1** Unchristian. **9** Arsenic. **10** Thermal. **11** Alf.
12 Booze-up. **13** Illness. **14** Yet. **15** Ensue. **17** Yacht.
18 Demur. **20** Aroma. **22** Use. **24** Sunlamp. **25** Hellcat. **26** Era.
27 Unified. **28** Bugbear. **29** Emendations.

Down **1** Unsportsmanlike. **2** Convene. **3** Recap. **4** Set fire to.
5 Ideally. **6** Number crunchers. **7** Carboy. **8** Closet.
16 Stampeded. **18** Dust-up. **19** Realise. **21** Allegro. **23** Entire.
25 Habit.

132 *Across* **1** Baker's dozen. **9** Alumnus. **10** Scooter. **11** Pop.
12 Resides. **13** Ego trip. **14** Nil. **15** Malta. **17** Yelps. **18** Fused.
20 Boers. **22** Cud. **24** Coroner. **25** Paupers. **26** Ice. **27** Neutron.
28 Tobacco. **29** Smithereens.

Down **1** Brussels sprouts. **2** Kingdom. **3** Rasps. **4** Desperate.
5 Zoology. **6** Natural sciences. **7** Barren. **8** Grapes. **16** Labyrinth.
18 Facing. **19** Denarii. **21** Stumble. **23** Despot. **25** Peter.

Solutions 133–136

133 *Across* **1** Apprehensive. **8** Airdrop. **9** Prosaic.
11 Flashpoint. **12** Guru. **14** Artistes. **16** Little. **17** Rub.
19 Coping. **21** Elegance. **24** Sure. **25** Exactitude. **27** Overage.
28 Orderer. **29** Supernatural.

Down **1** Abreast. **2** Purchasing. **3** Employer. **4** Expand.
5 Swot. **6** Viaduct. **7** San Francisco. **10** Cause celebre.
13 Ring binder. **15** Sue. **18** Blackout. **20** Parvenu.
22 Neutral. **23** Extern. **26** Vale.

134 *Across* **1** Suss out. **5** Ossify. **9** Loosely. **10** Tank top.
11 Irk. **12** Inefficient. **13** Hence. **14** Toothache. **16** Gift token.
17 Verse. **19** Cold weather. **22** Sea. **23** Oceania.
24 Pre-empt. **26** Assets. **27** Yolk sac.

Down **1** Selfish. **2** Stocking fillers. **3** Ore. **4** Thyme.
5 Out of town. **6** Sonic. **7** Father Christmas. **8** Spathe. **12** Inert.
14 Takeaways. **15** Haver. **16** Geckos. **18** Elastic. **20** Happy.
21 Wince. **25** Eel.

135 *Across* **1** Paddock. **5** Tattoo. **9** E number. **10** Element.
11 Eel. **12** Dental plate. **13** Tabby. **14** Yardstick.
16 Hard disks. **17** Regal. **19** Great-nephew. **22** You.
23 Related. **24** Vacated. **26** Oddity. **27** Scrumpy.

Down **1** Pretext. **2** Double-barrelled. **3** Orb. **4** Koran.
5 Thesaurus. **6** Twerp. **7** Operating system. **8** Streak. **12** Dryad.
14 Yesterday. **15** Shrew. **16** Hegira. **18** Laundry. **20** Tutsi.
21 Hives. **25** Cur.

136 *Across* **6** Impressionable. **9** Phylum. **10** Misplace.
11 Doggerel. **13** Enable. **15** Merlin. **17** Sudoku. **19** Ischia.
20 Sunbathe. **22** Airbrush. **24** Votary. **26** Universal joint.

Down **1** High Commission. **2** Opal. **3** Reamer. **4** Rousseau.
5 Tail. **7** Simile. **8** Local authority. **12** Girth. **14** Aroma.
16 In a hurry. **18** Asthma. **21** Navajo. **23** Bevy. **25** Twin.

Solutions 137–140

137 *Across* **1** Self-destruct. **8** Marital. **9** Nothing.
11 Locker room. **12** Menu. **14** Atom bomb. **16** Harass.
17 Saw. **19** Assume. **21** Dark room. **24** Inch. **25** Annexation.
27 Neutral. **28** Sedates. **29** Absent-minded.

Down **1** Sirocco. **2** Letter bomb. **3** Doldrums. **4** Sun-god.
5 Rite. **6** Chimera. **7** Amalgamation. **10** Gruesomeness.
13 Backhanded. **15** Bad. **18** Water-ski. **20** Succumb.
22 Omitted. **23** Anklet. **26** True.

138 *Across* **1** Wolf whistles. **8** Resents. **9** Drastic.
11 Starry-eyed. **12** Fees. **14** Colloquy. **16** Grater. **17** Lei.
19 Thirty. **21** Smashing. **24** Iffy. **25** Power bases. **27** Granule.
28 Ice floe. **29** Pecking order.

Down **1** Wassail. **2** Lunar month. **3** Wasteful. **4** Indeed.
5 Thaw. **6** Entreat. **7** Press cutting. **10** Cash register.
13 Crossbreed. **15** Yes. **18** Impetigo. **20** Inflame. **22** Insular.
23 Solemn. **26** Buck.

139 *Across* **1** Press-ups. **5** Eighth. **9** Monogamy. **10** Florin.
12 Chef. **13** Understudy. **15** Periodic table. **19** Identity cards.
23 Aquamarine. **25** Oral. **28** Instep. **29** Semantic. **30** Thrust.
31 Sensuous.

Down **1** Pumice. **2** Ernie. **3** Sage. **4** Pimento. **6** Idles.
7 Harquebus. **8** Honey bee. **11** Yeti. **14** Tort. **15** Precursor.
16 Dry. **17** Turn. **18** Finalist. **20** Turf. **21** Convene. **22** Slices.
24 Meets. **26** Retro. **27** Bars.

140 *Across* **6** Committee stage. **9** Tender. **10** Bonemeal.
11 Acid rain. **13** Grumpy. **15** Facial. **17** Wraith. **19** Ocelot.
20 All-in-one. **22** Wisteria. **24** Demote. **26** Pneumatic drill.

Down **1** Science fiction. **2** Amid. **3** Sierra. **4** Teenager.
5 Item. **7** Tubing. **8** Grasp the nettle. **12** Ducal. **14** Union.
16 After tax. **18** Malawi. **21** La-di-da. **23** Thug. **25** Mail.

Solutions 141–144

141 *Across* 6 Hypersensitive. 9 Demean. 10 Prophesy.
11 Headgear. 13 Instep. 15 Ebbing. 17 Chilli. 19 Kung fu.
20 Nauseate. 22 Victoria. 24 Remark. 26 Tercentenaries.

Down 1 Chief executive. 2 Apse. 3 Orange. 4 Astonish.
5 Etch. 7 Expert. 8 Vested interest. 12 Debug. 14 Solve.
16 Neutrino. 18 Inmate. 21 Unread. 23 Tact. 25 Mail.

142 *Across* 1 Nursing home. 9 Stencil. 10 Naughty. 11 Asp.
12 Tolstoy. 13 Opinion. 14 Era. 15 Lucid. 17 Tacit. 18 Indic.
20 Shrug. 22 Elk. 24 Scherzo. 25 Grown-up. 26 Ria.
27 Tremolo. 28 Machine. 29 Dry-cleaning.

Down 1 Needle and thread. 2 Recital. 3 Inlay.
4 Gunpowder. 5 Oculist. 6 Ethnic cleansing. 7 Tsetse.
8 Cygnet. 16 Castor oil. 18 In situ. 19 Cursory. 21 Gnocchi.
23 Kipper. 25 Gamma.

143 *Across* 1 Sciatica. 5 Hairdo. 9 Saturate. 10 Dollop.
12 Moon. 13 Belongings. 15 Gynaecologist.
19 Soul-searching. 23 Assortment. 25 Emir. 28 Thrace.
29 Motor car. 30 Reward. 31 Aeronaut.

Down 1 Sesame. 2 Intro. 3 Tyre. 4 Cat's-eye. 6 Along.
7 Relenting. 8 Opposite. 11 Soho. 14 Onus. 15 Grub screw.
16 Cur. 17 Odin. 18 Ask after. 20 Army. 21 Connote.
22 Dry rot. 24 Recur. 26 Mecca. 27 Polo.

144 *Across* 1 Diatribe. 5 Thesis. 9 Festival. 10 Beacon.
12 Meet. 13 Malefactor. 15 Fallopian tube. 19 Nativity plays.
23 Schismatic. 25 Viva. 28 Arnica. 29 Oak apple. 30 Dressy.
31 Syphilis.

Down 1 Defame. 2 Aisle. 3 Rain. 4 Bravado. 6 Hyena.
7 Secateurs. 8 Sundries. 11 Semi. 14 Slav. 15 Fat chance.
16 Pay. 17 Noah. 18 Inkstand. 20 Tram. 21 Primary.
22 Caress. 24 Sacks. 26 Impel. 27 Sash.

Solutions 145–148

145 *Across* **1** Reverse. **5** Lyceum. **9** Drummer. **10** Mindset.
11 Ash. **12** Petrodollar. **13** Tunes. **14** Monocycle.
16 Whipround. **17** Dante. **19** Obligations. **22** Cop. **23** Elastic.
24 Tapioca. **26** Ashore. **27** Treason.

Down **1** Radiant. **2** Vaughan Williams. **3** Rum. **4** Egret.
5 Lampooned. **6** Canto. **7** Unselfconscious. **8** Starve. **12** Poser.
14 Moustache. **15** Cedes. **16** Wooden. **18** Explain. **20** Get to.
21 Octet. **25** Pie.

146 *Across* **1** Orange juice. **9** Machete. **10** Tallest. **11** Bye.
12 Thimble. **13** Necktie. **14** Spa. **15** Corgi. **17** Trout. **18** Islam.
20 Dream. **22** Air. **24** Chekhov. **25** Sidings. **26** Ecu. **27** Stoical.
28 Moisten. **29** Non-specific.

Down **1** Once in a blue moon. **2** Alembic. **3** Grebe.
4 Jet engine. **5** Illicit. **6** Electromagnetic. **7** Smites. **8** Street.
16 Redevelop. **18** In case. **19** Mohican. **21** Midriff. **23** Resent.
25 Sumac.

147 *Across* **1** Advertising. **9** Art deco. **10** Brocade. **11** Tie.
12 Y-fronts. **13** Teashop. **14** Roe. **15** Maize. **17** Emcee.
18 Doggo. **20** Gunge. **22** Elm. **24** Lantern. **25** Ovation. **26** Inn.
27 Tornado. **28** Antenna. **29** Lord's Prayer.

Down **1** Attorney general. **2** Vietnam. **3** Roots.
4 In between. **5** Isolate. **6** Graphic designer. **7** Lawyer.
8 Temple. **16** Ingenious. **18** Delete. **19** Open air. **21** Exactly.
23 Maniac. **25** On air.

148 *Across* **1** Postgraduate. **8** Utopian. **9** Hotline.
11 Evangelise. **12** Stir. **14** Sickroom. **16** Entrap. **17** Nab.
19 Inland. **21** Teriyaki. **24** Ibex. **25** Sweetheart. **27** Niobium.
28 Insulin. **29** Interspersed.

Down **1** Prosaic. **2** Sniggering. **3** Ganglion. **4** Aghast.
5 Up to. **6** Twister. **7** Superstition. **10** Ear-splitting.
13 Antithesis. **15** Mat. **18** Benefice. **20** Lie down. **22** Availed.
23 Swamps. **26** Bike.

Solutions 149–152

149 *Across* **1** Sucrose. **5** Enigma. **9** Impetus. **10** Exordia.
11 Mat. **12** Army officer. **13** Ruler. **14** Rekindles.
16 Scapegoat. **17** Toxic. **19** Considerate. **22** Mum. **23** Outrage.
24 Gehenna. **26** Extent. **27** Ordered.

Down **1** Shimmer. **2** Capital gains tax. **3** Opt. **4** Epsom.
5 Eye socket. **6** In-off. **7** Medical examiner. **8** Walrus. **12** Agree.
14 Roosevelt. **15** Nitre. **16** Sector. **18** Command. **20** Image.
21 Aggro. **25** Hod.

150 *Across* **1** Couplet. **5** Haggle. **9** Ladette. **10** Voluble. **11** Mar.
12 Sitting duck. **13** Ochre. **14** Isolation. **16** Powerboat.
17 Otter. **19** Practically. **22** Net. **23** Ethical. **24** Respite.
26 Crates. **27** Consent.

Down **1** Colombo. **2** Under the weather. **3** Lit. **4** Tweet.
5 Have it out. **6** Gulag. **7** Labour-intensive. **8** Weaken.
12 Smear. **14** Isosceles. **15** Agony. **16** Puppet. **18** Retreat.
20 Tacit. **21** Lyric. **25** Son.

151 *Across* **6** Banner headline. **9** Nausea. **10** Alienate.
11 Painters. **13** Neo-con. **15** Locate. **17** Retina. **19** Angela.
20 Underpay. **22** Colossus. **24** Shorts. **26** Enterprise zone.

Down **1** Abraham Lincoln. **2** Onus. **3** Female. **4** Patience.
5 Clan. **7** Hoarse. **8** National anthem. **12** Nacre. **14** Osier.
16 Transept. **18** Muesli. **21** Dashed. **23** Over. **25** Oboe.

152 *Across* **1** Hard shoulder. **8** Huddled. **9** Declaim.
11 Melanesian. **12** Fiat. **14** Toodle-oo. **16** Tannin. **17** Who.
19 Eldest. **21** Misplace. **24** Alga. **25** Persecuted.
27 Year-end. **28** Initial. **29** Dessert spoon.

Down **1** Hidalgo. **2** Relentless. **3** Sideshow. **4** Ordeal.
5 Luck. **6** Elation. **7** Chemotherapy. **10** Matinee idols.
13 Cappuccino. **15** Ohm. **18** Oilskins. **20** Degrade.
22 Antlion. **23** Vendor. **26** Keys.

Solutions 153–156

153 *Across* **1** Chamber music. **8** Otalgia. **9** Milldam.
11 Networking. **12** Taps. **14** Flywheel. **16** Poland. **17** Gem.
19 Lonely. **21** Divorcee. **24** Note. **25** Parliament. **27** Yardarm.
28 Boudoir. **29** All-important.

Down **1** Chantry. **2** Anglophile. **3** Blackleg. **4** Remand.
5 Ugly. **6** Indiana. **7** Horn of plenty. **10** Misadventure.
13 Coloratura. **15** Led. **18** Millibar. **20** Natural. **22** Cheroot.
23 Warm up. **26** Saki.

154 *Across* **1** Fishcake. **5** Strait. **9** Mind's eye. **10** Raffia.
12 Lees. **13** Nom de plume. **15** Diesel engines.
19 Pitched battle. **23** Dung beetle. **25** Stow. **28** Mutton.
29 Age limit. **30** Corona. **31** Admonish.

Down **1** Family. **2** Singe. **3** Cusp. **4** Keyhole. **6** Tramp.
7 Affluence. **8** Traverse. **11** Edge. **14** Mesh. **15** Detonator.
16 Lob. **17** Gate. **18** Epidemic. **20** Diet. **21** Alleged. **22** Switch.
24 Brown. **26** Tempi. **27** Alto.

155 *Across* **6** Hot-water bottle. **9** Gerbil. **10** Worrying.
11 Splinter. **13** Impair. **15** Infest. **17** Jet lag. **19** Starve.
20 Coat-tail. **22** Bull's-eye. **24** Paltry. **26** Unaccounted for.

Down **1** Three-point turn. **2** Stab. **3** Wallet. **4** Abortive.
5 Stay. **7** Edward. **8** Lending library. **12** Infer. **14** Pilot.
16 Skeleton. **18** Screen. **21** Apples. **23** Lock. **25** Lift.

156 *Across* **6** Administration. **9** Dry rot. **10** Messmate.
11 Snitcher. **13** Adrift. **15** Orator. **17** Relish. **19** Effete.
20 Suspense. **22** Scot-free. **24** Big top. **26** Transcendental.

Down **1** Warrant officer. **2** Omar. **3** Snatch. **4** Arms race.
5 Atom. **7** Sombre. **8** Out of this world. **12** Trace. **14** Raise.
16 One-track. **18** Astern. **21** Subset. **23** Tiny. **25** Gate.

Solutions 157–160

157 *Across* **1** Out of bounds. **9** Redwood. **10** Lens cap. **11** Gap. **12** Ingenue. **13** Also-ran. **14** Map. **15** Elfin. **17** Rotor. **18** Dense. **20** Resit. **22** Cap. **24** Naivety. **25** Parquet. **26** Tea. **27** Mannish. **28** Crew cut. **29** Rock and roll.

Down **1** Old age pensioner. **2** Trounce. **3** Fudge. **4** Oil paints. **5** Non-user. **6** Security Council. **7** Truism. **8** Opener. **16** Forsythia. **18** Dynamo. **19** Elegiac. **21** Torpedo. **23** Potato. **25** Paced.

158 *Across* **1** Dispatch. **5** Savant. **9** Arum lily. **10** Ordain. **12** Espy. **13** Ophthalmic. **15** Pronouncement. **19** Queen's Counsel. **23** Adam's apple. **25** Oboe. **28** Isobel. **29** Scorpion. **30** Easter. **31** Eyeliner.

Down **1** Deaden. **2** Slump. **3** Axle. **4** Calypso. **6** Aorta. **7** Alarm bell. **8** Tenacity. **11** Stun. **14** Down. **15** Predators. **16** Ufo. **17** Easy. **18** Equalise. **20** Cape. **21** Unlucky. **22** Tenner. **24** Sieve. **26** Bairn. **27** Oral.

159 *Across* **1** Spinster. **5** Scrawl. **9** Cream tea. **10** Beaver. **12** Rely. **13** Main course. **15** Elephant grass. **19** Approximately. **23** Flashlight. **25** Emma. **28** Rwanda. **29** Militant. **30** Reefer. **31** Embolism.

Down **1** Secure. **2** Ideal. **3** Sump. **4** Eyewash. **6** Credo. **7** Adversary. **8** Largesse. **11** Anon. **14** Hero. **15** Esplanade. **16** Aim. **17** Grey. **18** Wayfarer. **20** Iris. **21** Atheism. **22** Bantam. **24** Hedge. **26** Miami. **27** Kilo.

160 *Across* **1** Paisley. **5** Allows. **9** Summery. **10** Tartlet. **11** War. **12** Restructure. **13** Reign. **14** Swordsman. **16** Kinswoman. **17** Of use. **19** Enemy action. **22** Tug. **23** Enthral. **24** Logical. **26** Orison. **27** Witness.

Down **1** Post-war. **2** Immersion heater. **3** Lie. **4** Yo-yos. **5** Afternoon. **6** Lyric. **7** Walrus moustache. **8** Strewn. **12** Renew. **14** Semicolon. **15** Drown. **16** Keeper. **18** Engulfs. **20** Yards. **21** In-law. **25** Got.

Solutions 161–164

161 *Across* **1** Sympathetic. **9** Reliant. **10** Lanolin. **11** Lay.
12 Presley. **13** Girding. **14** Lea. **15** Sofia. **17** Moist. **18** Rhino.
20 Rolls. **22** Nod. **24** Academy. **25** Pompous. **26** Fro.
27 Origami. **28** Palermo. **29** Number plate.

Down **1** Self-examination. **2** Measles. **3** Aptly.
4 Holy Grail. **5** Tantrum. **6** Collision course. **7** Propel. **8** Knight.
16 Forty-five. **18** Reason. **19** Overarm. **21** Somalia. **23** Despot.
25 Pop-up.

162 *Across* **1** Colonialism. **9** Outswim. **10** Topknot. **11** Ago.
12 Deaf aid. **13** Pale ale. **14** One. **15** Ducal. **17** Evict.
18 Bonus. **20** Noted. **22** Cop. **24** Aquiver. **25** Suffice. **26** Ado.
27 Lateral. **28** Unclear. **29** Yellowstone.

Down **1** Cottage industry. **2** Lowland. **3** Nomad. **4** Autopilot.
5 Impulse. **6** Mandarin Chinese. **7** Voodoo. **8** At rest.
16 Contralto. **18** Beadle. **19** Several. **21** De facto. **23** Poetry.
25 Souls.

163 *Across* **1** Motorcyclist. **8** Erratic. **9** Antwerp. **11** Peccadillo.
12 Boot. **14** Close-set. **16** Sledge. **17** RAF. **19** Forces.
21 Tactless. **24** Lift. **25** Nettle rash. **27** Yoghurt. **28** Avarice.
29 Self-catering.

Down **1** Morocco. **2** Tetrameter. **3** Receiver. **4** Yearly. **5** Lots.
6 Steroid. **7** Respectfully. **10** Potter's wheel. **13** Glitterati. **15** Tat.
18 Fast lane. **20** Refugee. **22** Erasing. **23** Bertha. **26** Puff.

164 *Across* **1** Far East. **5** Earthy. **9** Noonday. **10** Payback.
11 Rat. **12** Water closet. **13** Lemur. **14** Hackneyed.
16 Treadmill. **17** Given. **19** Charge sheet. **22** Doc.
23 E number. **24** Cleanse. **26** Remedy. **27** Liqueur.

Down **1** Funeral. **2** Room temperature. **3** Aid. **4** Tryst.
5 Empirical. **6** Royal. **7** Hearsay evidence. **8** Skated. **12** Wired.
14 Hairspray. **15** Night. **16** Ticket. **18** Nuclear. **20** Gable.
21 Excel. **25** Esq.

Solutions 165–168

165 *Across* **1** Postern. **5** Tramps. **9** Re-elect. **10** Slobber.
11 Wok. **12** Columbarium. **13** Gaffe. **14** Outskirts.
16 Maharajah. **17** Lilac. **19** Middle-class. **22** Too. **23** Ravioli.
24 Pinhole. **26** Allege. **27** Amnesia.

Down **1** Periwig. **2** Speak of the devil. **3** Eve. **4** Natal.
5 Test match. **6** Aroma. **7** Public relations. **8** Crumbs. **12** Cheer.
14 Objective. **15** Kilts. **16** Memory. **18** Cholera. **20** Loose.
21 Alpha. **25** Nun.

166 *Across* **6** Inverted commas. **9** Scores. **10** Sturgeon.
11 Lifelong. **13** Inbred. **15** Insure. **17** Myrtle. **19** Barley.
20 Eternity. **22** No-frills. **24** Ramrod. **26** Hypersensitive.

Down **1** Discriminatory. **2** Aver. **3** Fresco. **4** Scrutiny.
5 Smug. **7** Ensign. **8** Aforementioned. **12** Easel. **14** Baton.
16 Royalist. **18** Season. **21** Earwig. **23** Reek. **25** Main.

167 *Across* **1** Home counties. **8** Abandon. **9** Wetland.
11 Battledore. **12** Lieu. **14** Tenon saw. **16** Funnel. **17** Nil.
19 At home. **21** Ginger up. **24** Rule. **25** Water-skier. **27** Nigella.
28 Oxidise. **29** Snap fastener.

Down **1** Hearten. **2** Middle name. **3** Canadian. **4** Upward.
5 Ta-ta. **6** Evasion. **7** Rabbit warren. **10** Double-parked.
13 Suggestion. **15** Wig. **18** Lifeboat. **20** Halogen. **22** Rainier.
23 Sahara. **26** Blip.

168 *Across* **1** Life sentence. **8** Outsell. **9** Cockpit.
11 Hard-boiled. **12** Nine. **14** Roll over. **16** Direct. **17** Sub.
19 Oyster. **21** Tollgate. **24** Gape. **25** Multimedia. **27** Example.
28 Oatmeal. **29** Morning dress.

Down **1** Literal. **2** Freebooter. **3** Saltires. **4** Nickel. **5** Etch.
6 Caprice. **7** Mother tongue. **10** Trestle table. **13** Millimetre.
15 Rut. **18** Boatload. **20** Soprano. **22** Address. **23** Tureen.
26 Spin.

Solutions 169–172

169 *Across*   **1** On demand. **5** Atomic. **9** Musketry. **10** Stanza.
12 Lays. **13** Vampire bat. **15** Once and for all.
19 Opportunistic. **23** Strategist. **25** Adze. **28** Exodus.
29 Lemonade. **30** Deepen. **31** Adroitly.

Down   **1** Ormolu. **2** Dusty. **3** Meet. **4** Nirvana. **6** Tutor.
7 Mont Blanc. **8** Chattels. **11** Sped. **14** Scar. **15** On purpose.
16 Nun. **17** Oath. **18** Loose end. **20** Urge. **21** Instead.
22 Celery. **24** Truce. **26** Dealt. **27** Polo.

170 *Across*   **6** Robin redbreast. **9** Ascend. **10** Two-timer.
11 Quotient. **13** Usable. **15** Enmesh. **17** Detain. **19** Fourth.
20 Booze-ups. **22** Skiplane. **24** Tyrant. **26** Cross-pollinate.

Down   **1** Pressure cooker. **2** Able. **3** On edge. **4** Absolute.
5 Yeti. **7** Entity. **8** Shetland ponies. **12** Timer. **14** Agave.
16 Schnapps. **18** Abseil. **21** Outfit. **23** Push. **25** Read.

171 *Across*   **6** Holding company. **9** France. **10** Falsetto.
11 Conserve. **13** Wintry. **15** Dreamy. **17** Frugal. **19** Boards.
20 Ponytail. **22** Gendarme. **24** Coyote. **26** Standard-bearer.

Down   **1** Sherwood Forest. **2** Clan. **3** Linear. **4** World War.
5 Apse. **7** Gifted. **8** Natural history. **12** Smear. **14** Night.
16 Mistreat. **18** Spread. **21** Nuclei. **23** Dent. **25** York.

172 *Across*   **1** Missing link. **9** Malaise. **10** Liven up. **11** Pod.
12 Account. **13** Flighty. **14** Tea. **15** Eyrie. **17** Hoard. **18** Rover.
20 Dodgy. **22** Tar. **24** Canasta. **25** Dukedom. **26** Roe.
27 Desktop. **28** Violent. **29** Spontaneous.

Down   **1** Male chauvinists. **2** Seizure. **3** Inept. **4** Goldfield.
5 Inveigh. **6** Kind-heartedness. **7** Umlaut. **8** Spayed.
16 Red carpet. **18** Recede. **19** Risotto. **21** Yoko Ono.
23 Remote. **25** Devon.

Solutions 173–176

173 *Across* **1** Transept. **5** Techie. **9** Pharisee. **10** Hang up.
12 Shed. **13** Unfaithful. **15** Telegraph pole. **19** Field of vision.
23 Postscript. **25** Redo. **28** Sorrow. **29** Notional. **30** Enrich.
31 Peroxide.

Down **1** Typist. **2** Awake. **3** Soil. **4** Pfennig. **6** Exact.
7 High-flown. **8** Espalier. **11** Data. **14** Sled. **15** Treasurer.
16 Rev. **17** Hail. **18** Off-piste. **20** Fern. **21** Implore. **22** Collie.
24 Stoic. **26** Ennui. **27** Silo.

174 *Across* **1** Deadlock. **5** Turban. **9** Cylinder. **10** Kuwait.
12 Onyx. **13** Order paper. **15** Funny business.
19 Spitting image. **23** Inhabitant. **25** Swam. **28** Affair.
29 Observer. **30** Tiller. **31** Restores.

Down **1** Doctor. **2** Alloy. **3** Link. **4** Clearly. **6** Usurp.
7 Blaspheme. **8** Notarise. **11** Beau. **14** Gnat. **15** Frightful.
16 Big. **17** Iran. **18** Aspirant. **20** Note. **21** Ignoble. **22** Smirks.
24 Bribe. **26** Waver. **27** Pest.

175 *Across* **1** Deserts. **5** Iodide. **9** Secrete. **10** Nemesis.
11 Awn. **12** Impecunious. **13** Drill. **14** Dunce's cap.
16 Doctorate. **17** Carer. **19** Commutation. **22** Ill. **23** Chapati.
24 Insight. **26** Adhere. **27** Moneyed.

Down **1** Disband. **2** Second in command. **3** Rye. **4** Sleep.
5 Innocence. **6** Demon. **7** Disconcertingly. **8** Uses up. **12** Igloo.
14 Dramatise. **15** Ex-con. **16** Decoct. **18** Related. **20** Usage.
21 Idiom. **25** Son.

176 *Across* **1** Imperialism. **9** Utterly. **10** Transit. **11** Moo.
12 En route. **13** Pep talk. **14** Ash. **15** Yodel. **17** Trews.
18 Genie. **20** Aitch. **22** Arm. **24** Lie down. **25** Saveloy. **26** Obi.
27 Embarks. **28** Gradual. **29** Expeditious.

Down **1** Interchangeable. **2** Perjury. **3** Rhyme. **4** Autopilot.
5 In a spot. **6** Massage parlours. **7** Eureka. **8** Stakes.
16 Diagnosed. **18** Galley. **19** Ego trip. **21** Have a go.
23 Mayfly. **25** Sight.

Solutions 177–180

177 *Across* **1** Compost heap. **9** Couples. **10** Reasons. **11** Isa.
12 Decades. **13** Noisome. **14** Coo. **15** Corfu. **17** Edict.
18 Whelk. **20** Dwarf. **22** Rod. **24** Ingrown. **25** Mr Right.
26 Due. **27** Drachma. **28** Toecaps. **29** Down-to-earth.

Down **1** Church of England. **2** Melodic. **3** Oasis.
4 Tarantula. **5** Evasive. **6** Photomicrograph. **7** Acidic.
8 Ascent. **16** Redundant. **18** Weirdo. **19** Know-how.
21 Forbear. **23** Detest. **25** Metre.

178 *Across* **1** Unemployment. **8** Excited. **9** Disowns.
11 Chromosome. **12** Derv. **14** Caseload. **16** Damson. **17** Lee.
19 Mirage. **21** Wantonly. **24** Espy. **25** Vermicelli. **27** Stipend.
28 Foppish. **29** Haberdashery.

Down **1** Uncorks. **2** Entomology. **3** Pedestal. **4** Oedema.
5 Musk. **6** Newness. **7** Beachcombers. **10** Seventy-eight.
13 Participle. **15** Dew. **18** Earmuffs. **20** Replica. **22** Nullify.
23 Wedded. **26** Hebe.

179 *Across* **1** Satanic. **5** Legacy. **9** Elastic. **10** Chamber.
11 Tea. **12** Flashpoints. **13** Dogma. **14** Fire-eater. **16** Directors.
17 Opine. **19** Inquisitive. **22** Ice. **23** Playful. **24** In vitro.
26 Debris. **27** Tax-free.

Down **1** Scented. **2** Trafalgar Square. **3** Nut. **4** Cocoa.
5 Lock horns. **6** Guano. **7** Cabinet minister. **8** Eraser. **12** Franc.
14 Flotillas. **15** Erode. **16** Drippy. **18** Eyesore. **20** Infer.
21 Idiot. **25** Vex.

180 *Across* **1** Geckoes. **5** Second. **9** Almoner. **10** Exalted.
11 Gad. **12** Crystallise. **13** Woozy. **14** Panama hat.
16 Rum-runner. **17** Attic. **19** Contact lens. **22** Nil. **23** Premier.
24 Bowling. **26** Ascend. **27** Renegue.

Down **1** Glasgow. **2** Comedy of manners. **3** Own. **4** Surly.
5 Sweetener. **6** Crawl. **7** Notwithstanding. **8** Advent.
12 Coypu. **14** Punctured. **15** Means. **16** Recipe. **18** Cologne.
20 Alive. **21** Ember. **25** Win.

Solutions 181–184

181 *Across* **6** Open University. **9** Scream. **10** Superman. **11** Esoteric. **13** Teller. **15** Elbows. **17** Thanks. **19** Astral. **20** Underact. **22** Quibbled. **24** Novena. **26** Penny-farthings.

Down **1** Worcester sauce. **2** Mere. **3** Murmur. **4** Despatch. **5** Tsar. **7** Insect. **8** Travel sickness. **12** Tabor. **14** Loner. **16** Wildlife. **18** Sunder. **21** Dinghy. **23** Bony. **25** Vent.

182 *Across* **1** Mouth-to-mouth. **8** Ailment. **9** Dervish. **11** Horsepower. **12** Purr. **14** Nineteen. **16** Breeze. **17** Sip. **19** Clam up. **21** Pleiades. **24** Rare. **25** Baby-minder. **27** Yobbish. **28** Old-time. **29** Stage manager.

Down **1** Milk run. **2** Uneventful. **3** Hatboxes. **4** Oodles. **5** Ours. **6** Tribute. **7** Cash-and-carry. **10** Harley Street. **13** Prairie dog. **15** Nip. **18** Play down. **20** Acrobat. **22** Dodgier. **23** Fathom. **26** King.

183 *Across* **1** Habit-forming. **8** Home run. **9** Chattel. **11** Linseed oil. **12** View. **14** Sum total. **16** Hunger. **17** Far. **19** Pantry. **21** Dovetail. **24** Idol. **25** Great Danes. **27** Endwise. **28** Impasse. **29** Hypochondria.

Down **1** Homonym. **2** Bargeboard. **3** Tone-deaf. **4** Orchid. **5** Mean. **6** Nothing. **7** Philosophise. **10** Lower classes. **13** Super-duper. **15** Lad. **18** Rogation. **20** Noonday. **22** Amnesia. **23** Breech. **26** Lido.

184 *Across* **1** Stockade. **5** Cymbal. **9** Chastise. **10** Gallon. **12** Even. **13** Mechanical. **15** Skirting board. **19** Encyclopaedia. **23** Guidelines. **25** Roam. **28** Titbit. **29** Pole Star. **30** Ninety. **31** Terminal.

Down **1** Sacred. **2** Osage. **3** Kite. **4** Dissent. **6** Yearn. **7** Balaclava. **8** Landlady. **11** Shin. **14** Zinc. **15** Sacristan. **16** Imp. **17** Bide. **18** Heighten. **20** Ovid. **21** Acetone. **22** Amoral. **24** Eliot. **26** Often. **27** Beam.

Solutions 185–188

185 *Across* **6** Indestructible. **9** Jetsam. **10** Wardrobe. **11** Trial run. **13** Icarus. **15** Solver. **17** Unwise. **19** Edible. **20** Rollneck. **22** Undertow. **24** Vernal. **26** Pyramid selling.

Down **1** Vice presidency. **2** Odds. **3** Isomer. **4** Scorpion. **5** Liar. **7** Rewind. **8** Labour exchange. **12** Ad lib. **14** Align. **16** Electric. **18** Prawns. **21** Lively. **23** Esau. **25** Rein.

186 *Across* **6** Out of this world. **9** Player. **10** Identify. **11** Unswayed. **13** Orache. **15** Sloppy. **17** Adjoin. **19** Gallop. **20** Tethered. **22** Vindaloo. **24** Rotund. **26** Inverted commas.

Down **1** Polling station. **2** Stay. **3** Affray. **4** Asteroid. **5** Tout. **7** Hairdo. **8** Left-handedness. **12** Whorl. **14** Alone. **16** Populate. **18** Stroud. **21** Turbot. **23** Diet. **25** Tomb.

187 *Across* **1** Poltergeist. **9** Renames. **10** Abstain. **11** Ear. **12** Britain. **13** Workshy. **14** Yes. **15** Ochre. **17** Raise. **18** Cramp. **20** Ruler. **22** End. **24** Amphora. **25** Deviant. **26** Foe. **27** Convent. **28** Leonine. **29** Reservation.

Down **1** Pencil sharpener. **2** Lumbago. **3** Essen. **4** Gearwheel. **5** Insurer. **6** Transliteration. **7** Grubby. **8** Enzyme. **16** Hereafter. **18** Chance. **19** Prowess. **21** Ravioli. **23** Dither. **25** Delta.

188 *Across* **1** Commando. **5** Oblige. **9** Orthodox. **10** Muscle. **12** Aide. **13** Beach buggy. **15** Commemoration. **19** Incommunicado. **23** Greedy guts. **25** Ugly. **28** Leaves. **29** Engineer. **30** Rehash. **31** Deformed.

Down **1** Choral. **2** Muted. **3** Atom. **4** Diocese. **6** Blurb. **7** Incognito. **8** Everyone. **11** Echo. **14** Imam. **15** Cycle path. **16** Men. **17** Arab. **18** Singular. **20** Urge. **21** Intense. **22** Hybrid. **24** Dregs. **26** Gleam. **27** Biro.

Solutions 189–192

189 *Across* **1** Casement. **5** Corpus. **9** Clear-cut. **10** Linnet.
12 Oath. **13** Dismembers. **15** Flesh and blood.
19 Pinking shears. **23** Excellence. **25** Four. **28** Calves.
29 Sapphire. **30** Target. **31** New World.

Down **1** Cuckoo. **2** Sheet. **3** Mare. **4** Nourish. **6** Odium.
7 Ponderous. **8** Set-aside. **11** Omen. **14** Deli. **15** Funicular.
16 Ass. **17** Boar. **18** Uppercut. **20** Grew. **21** Hectare. **22** Friend.
24 Liege. **26** Osier. **27** Spew.

190 *Across* **1** Bombast. **5** Secede. **9** Oilskin. **10** Nureyev.
11 Hit. **12** Undignified. **13** Rival. **14** Anguished. **16** Prostrate.
17 Arrow. **19** Take-home pay. **22** Bye. **23** Shackle. **24** Athlete.
26 Floral. **27** Annoyed.

Down **1** Brother. **2** Molotov cocktail. **3** Auk. **4** Tuned.
5 Synagogue. **6** Corgi. **7** Daylight robbery. **8** Evaded. **12** Unlit.
14 Alarm bell. **15** Italy. **16** Potash. **18** Weekend. **20** Hiker.
21 Plaza. **25** Hun.

191 *Across* **1** South Africa. **9** Enables. **10** Runners. **11** Toe.
12 Endgame. **13** Babysit. **14** Ken. **15** Haifa. **17** Elope.
18 Aloof. **20** Nadir. **22** Tub. **24** Trailer. **25** Protest. **26** Coo.
27 Nairobi. **28** Welfare. **29** Nitty-gritty.

Down **1** Standing ovation. **2** Unleash. **3** Haste. **4** Firebrand.
5 Ignoble. **6** Aversion therapy. **7** Bedeck. **8** Tsetse. **16** Inner city.
18 Attune. **19** Fall out. **21** Rootlet. **23** Butter. **25** Power.

192 *Across* **1** Utilitarian. **9** Fuchsia. **10** Bouquet. **11** Gee.
12 Immerse. **13** Raiment. **14** You. **15** Riser. **17** Gulch. **18** Skier.
20 Asset. **22** Cap. **24** Bravura. **25** Esquire. **26** Fit. **27** Abigail.
28 Hailing. **29** Elbow grease.

Down **1** Uncommunicative. **2** Insurer. **3** Image.
4 Ambergris. **5** Inuring. **6** Nouvelle cuisine. **7** Effigy. **8** Stitch.
16 Scapa Flow. **18** Subway. **19** Rhubarb. **21** Tequila.
23 Pledge. **25** Ether.

193 *Across* **1** Mailbag. **5** Truism. **9** Rickets. **10** Oatcake. **11** Urn.
12 Inopportune. **13** Sleek. **14** Behaviour. **16** Round trip.
17 Lilac. **19** Synchronise. **22** Boa. **23** Griddle. **24** Admirer.
26 Pliers. **27** Carry on.

Down **1** Marquis. **2** Inconsequential. **3** Bee. **4** Gusto.
5 Troopship. **6** Utter. **7** Statue of Liberty. **8** Meteor. **12** Irked.
14 Borrowers. **15** Value. **16** Resign. **18** Chagrin. **20** Hedge.
21 Isaac. **25** Mar.

194 *Across* **1** Cochlea. **5** Poplar. **9** Orinoco. **10** Examine. **11** Eel.
12 Transparent. **13** Tasty. **14** Sea change. **16** Unwitting.
17 Naked. **19** Constantine. **22** Cue. **23** Ice-cold. **24** Obtains.
26 Asleep. **27** Snagged.

Down **1** Closest. **2** Chinless wonders. **3** Loo. **4** Aroma.
5 Press-gang. **6** Plaza. **7** Alive and kicking. **8** Beetle. **12** Tryst.
14 Skinny-dip. **15** Hinge. **16** Urchin. **18** Dressed. **20** T-bone.
21 Irons. **25** Tea.

195 *Across* **1** Nail scissors. **8** Outwear. **9** Fiancée.
11 Clay pigeon. **12** Over. **14** Riffraff. **16** Satrap. **17** Fop.
19 Paddle. **21** Graffiti. **24** Tuff. **25** Chimney pot. **27** Hectare.
28 Sustain. **29** Monkey wrench.

Down **1** Not half. **2** Inexpertly. **3** Shrug off. **4** Inflow. **5** Scan.
6 Recover. **7** Concert pitch. **10** Ear-splitting. **13** Half-nelson.
15 Fog. **18** Promiser. **20** De facto. **22** Impeach. **23** Cheery.
26 Hawk.

196 *Across* **1** Two-way mirror. **8** Amputee. **9** Million.
11 Dependable. **12** Tier. **14** Fanciful. **16** Gringo. **17** Mat.
19 Occult. **21** Ballroom. **24** Oval. **25** East Berlin. **27** Roe deer.
28 Cabbage. **29** Tuberculosis.

Down **1** Topspin. **2** Ostensibly. **3** Ageratum. **4** Mumble.
5 Roll. **6** Opinion. **7** Maid of honour. **10** Narrow-minded.
13 Trolleybus. **15** Lab. **18** Tactical. **20** Chateau. **22** Oilcans.
23 Fabric. **26** Seve.

Solutions 197–200

197 *Across* **6** Ancient history. **9** Asleep. **10** Toll gate. **11** Original. **13** Gummed. **15** Drover. **17** Prefab. **19** Acumen. **20** Premiere. **22** Zimbabwe. **24** Campus. **26** Indirect speech.

Down **1** Mass production. **2** Acme. **3** Tenpin. **4** Villager. **5** Stag. **7** Tittle. **8** Rotten boroughs. **12** Groom. **14** Mufti. **16** Ennobled. **18** Upbeat. **21** Escape. **23** Bail. **25** Meet.

198 *Across* **6** News conference. **9** Meagre. **10** Salutary. **11** Snowfall. **13** Oldish. **15** Uganda. **17** Bonsai. **19** Riddle. **20** Everyone. **22** Thickset. **24** Thread. **26** Administrative.

Down **1** Undernourished. **2** Swag. **3** Eczema. **4** Well-to-do. **5** Heat. **7** Nestle. **8** Christian names. **12** Weald. **14** Dusty. **16** Deerskin. **18** Sextet. **21** Entrap. **23** Chic. **25** Rain.

199 *Across* **1** Home page. **5** Indigo. **9** Tail coat. **10** Scythe. **12** Even. **13** Cattle grid. **15** Money-spinners. **19** Vote of censure. **23** Apothecary. **25** Lira. **28** Idiots. **29** Kerosene. **30** Needle. **31** Sympathy.

Down **1** Hotbed. **2** Maize. **3** Pack. **4** Granary. **6** Niche. **7** Interfere. **8** Overdose. **11** Step. **14** Undo. **15** Meteorite. **16** Sue. **17** Nous. **18** Aviation. **20** Cock. **21** Nursery. **22** Bakery. **24** Hotel. **26** Inept. **27** Romp.

200 *Across* **1** Warranty. **5** Cooper. **9** Caffeine. **10** Sleepy. **12** Even. **13** Periodical. **15** Telephoto lens. **19** Effectiveness. **23** Vermicelli. **25** Stet. **28** Raised. **29** Operator. **30** Easily. **31** Re-employ.

Down **1** Wicked. **2** Rifle. **3** Apex. **4** Tense up. **6** Oiled. **7** Preachers. **8** Royalist. **11** Silo. **14** Alec. **15** Taffrails. **16** HIV. **17** Over. **18** Perverse. **20** Ibex. **21** Eclipse. **22** Stormy. **24** Ideal. **26** Total. **27** Gram.

Solutions 201–204

201 *Across* **1** Direct debit. **9** Refutes. **10** Setback. **11** Tip.
12 Unnerve. **13** En masse. **14** Eat. **15** Pipit. **17** Trios. **18** Chair.
20 Recto. **22** End. **24** Lithium. **25** Vagrant. **26** Axe. **27** Lectern.
28 Railing. **29** Extra virgin.

Down **1** Definite article. **2** Rat-trap. **3** Caste. **4** Dyspeptic.
5 Bath mat. **6** Transliteration. **7** Grouse. **8** Skiers.
16 Pyromania. **18** Calmly. **19** Raiment. **21** Ongoing.
23 Dotage. **25** Verdi.

202 *Across* **1** Cold-blooded. **9** Longbow. **10** Foreman. **11** Awl.
12 Adeptly. **13** Ioniser. **14** Yap. **15** Radii. **17** Elite. **18** Curds.
20 Caste. **22** Age **24** Centaur. **25** Collide. **26** Ail. **27** Egotist.
28 Air raid. **29** Solar panels.

Down **1** Contemporaneous. **2** Lobster. **3** Byway.
4 Off limits. **5** Derange. **6** Domestic animals. **7** Sleazy.
8 Untrue. **16** Decorator. **18** Cachet. **19** Spatial. **21** Enlarge.
23 Emends. **25** Clara.

203 *Across* **1** Problem. **5** Cubist. **9** Test ban. **10** Eclipse.
11 War. **12** Somersaults. **13** Yearn. **14** Ginger ale.
16 Brimstone. **17** Audit. **19** Contretemps. **22** Ewe. **23** Proviso.
24 Oregano. **26** Attain. **27** Infidel.

Down **1** Pathway. **2** Observation post. **3** Lob. **4** Minim.
5 Clearance. **6** Balsa. **7** Supply and demand. **8** Lessee.
12 Sinus. **14** Ghost town. **15** Exams. **16** Biceps. **18** Trefoil.
20 Raita. **21** Maori. **25** Elf.

204 *Across* **1** Bivouac. **5** Douche. **9** Petunia. **10** Vinegar. **11** Ill.
12 Jugular vein. **13** Muted. **14** Supersede. **16** Witnessed.
17 Adult. **19** Dishonestly. **22** Alp. **23** Edified. **24** Ocarina.
26 Isomer. **27** Tyranny.

Down **1** Baptism. **2** Vital statistics. **3** Urn. **4** Clang.
5 Developed. **6** Ulnar. **7** Higher education. **8** Prince. **12** Judge.
14 Suspender. **15** Ready. **16** Widget. **18** Topiary. **20** Opium.
21 Trout. **25** Air.

Also available from Hamlyn

Pitcherwits
£8.99
Volume 5: 978-0-600-63622-9

Daily Mail Quick Crosswords
£6.99
Volume 1: 978-0-600-63623-6
Volume 2: 978-0-600-63624-3

Daily Mail Cryptic Crosswords
£6.99
Volume 1: 978-0-600-63626-7
Volume 2: 978-0-600-63627-4

Daily Mail Big Book of Cryptic Crosswords
£7.99
Volume 1: 978-0-600-63630-4
Volume 2: 978-0-600-63631-1

Daily Mail Big Book of Quick Crosswords
£7.99
Volume 1: 978-0-600-63628-1
Volume 2: 978-0-600-63629-8